# SOURCE BOOK IN GEOLOGY
## 1900–1950

# SOURCE BOOKS IN THE HISTORY OF THE SCIENCES
Edward H. Madden  ·  General Editor

SOURCE BOOK IN ASTRONOMY, 1900–1950

Harlow Shapley  ·  Harvard University

A SOURCE BOOK IN GREEK SCIENCE

Morris R. Cohen  ·  College of the City of New York and University of Chicago AND I. E. Drabkin  ·  College of the City of New York

A SOURCE BOOK IN ANIMAL BIOLOGY

Thomas S. Hall  ·  Washington University

A SOURCE BOOK IN CHEMISTRY

Henry M. Leicester  ·  San Francisco College of Medicine and Surgery AND Herbert M. Klickstein  ·  Edgar Fahs Smith Library in the History of Chemistry, University of Pennsylvania

A SOURCE BOOK IN PHYSICS

William Francis Magie  ·  Late Professor of Physics, Princeton University

A SOURCE BOOK IN THE HISTORY OF PSYCHOLOGY

Richard J. Herrnstein and Edwin G. Boring  ·  Harvard University

# SOURCE BOOK IN GEOLOGY

## 1900–1950

*Edited by Kirtley F. Mather*

HARVARD UNIVERSITY PRESS

CAMBRIDGE, MASSACHUSETTS    1967

# GENERAL EDITOR'S PREFACE

The Source Books in this series are collections of classical papers that have shaped the structures of the various sciences. Some of these classics are not readily available and many of them have never been translated into English, thus being lost to the general reader and frequently to the scientist himself. The point of this series is to make these texts readily accessible and to provide good translations of the ones that either have not been translated at all or have been translated only poorly.

The series was planned originally to include volumes in all the major sciences from the Renaissance through the nineteenth century. It has been extended to include ancient and medieval Western science and the development of the sciences in the first half of the present century. Many of these books have been published already and several more are in various stages of preparation.

The Carnegie Corporation originally financed the series by a grant to the American Philosophical Association. The History of Science Society and the American Association for the Advancement of Science have approved the project and are represented on the Editorial Advisory Board. This Board at present consists of the following members.

Marshall Clagett, History of Science, University of Wisconsin
I. Bernard Cohen, History of Science, Harvard University
C. J. Ducasse, Philosophy, Brown University
Ernst Mayr, Zoology, Harvard University
Ernest A. Moody, Philosophy, University of California at Los Angeles
Ernest Nagel, Philosophy, Columbia University
Harlow Shapley, Astronomy, Harvard University
Harry Woolf, History of Science, Johns Hopkins University

The series was begun and sustained by the devoted labors of Gregory D. Walcott and Everett W. Hall, the first two General Editors. I am indebted to them, to the members of the Advisory Board, and to Joseph D. Elder, Science Editor of Harvard University Press, for their indispensable aid in guiding the course of the Source Books.

Edward H. Madden

GENERAL EDITOR

Department of Philosophy
State University of New York at Buffalo
Buffalo, New York

# PREFACE

This is a sequel to the Mather and Mason Source Book in Geology published in 1939 by McGraw-Hill and reprinted in 1964 by Stechert-Hafner. That book contained representative selections from geological literature originating prior to 1900; this one deals similarly with contributions to geological science made during the first half of the twentieth century.

It is organized according to the same pattern as that designed for its predecessor. The excerpts from original writings are presented in the chronologic order of the dates of birth of their authors. For ready reference, a Guide to Subject Matter is provided, in which the articles dealing with more than a score of the major concerns of the geologist are listed in the order of the dates of publication. The brief biographical notes do little more than identify the time, country, and major activities of the authors. Only occasionally, and never for a living geologist, has any attempt been made to evaluate their work, although the mere fact of inclusion in this compilation indicates the belief that each of them has made a significant contribution to the development of the science.

In each instance the style of the original article has been retained, even though frequent inconsistencies in punctuation, abbreviation, and spelling have resulted. Footnotes, unless otherwise indicated, are from the original publications. My comments, whether in the text or in footnotes, are enclosed in square brackets. A few of the titles given for the articles are mine, not those of the original authors.

The number of pages of geological lore printed between 1900 and 1950 is several times that published in all the preceding four hundred years. Much of it consists of reports of field studies carried on in previously unknown or inadequately known regions. This was the half-century during which geologists roamed the earth as never before, in response to the awakening desire to use mineral resources for human welfare or for private profit or to increase military strength. It was also a time when the importance of basic research as a prerequisite to the practical application of scientific knowledge in human affairs began to be widely recognized. By mid-twentieth-century it became apparent that the distinction between "science as a quest for knowledge" and "science as a servant of mankind" had blurred almost to disappearance.

Most important in the present context is the fact that this half-century was a time of increasingly intense specialization on the part of those concerned with widely ramifying science of the earth. Not even the most industrious of general geologists of the old school could keep himself informed in more than a superficial way about all the new developments along the rapidly expanding frontiers of such specialties as paleomagnetism, tectonophysics, geochemistry, x-ray crystallography, geochronology, petroleum geology, sedimentation, and oceanography. I therefore appealed to upwards of a hundred geologists in various countries and with diverse specialties for assistance in identifying the contributions that should be included in this compilation. Two criteria were suggested as loosely defined guidelines: writings in which new concepts or techniques were presented or new directions opened for research, and articles describing the status of theory and practice in a specialized area as it appeared to be in the latter part of the half-century under scrutiny.

The response to my appeal was most gratifying and I take this opportunity to thank the many colleagues who contributed much more than they realize to the completion of my difficult task. Among those who were especially helpful in one way or another are Francis Birch, Carleton A. Chapman, Charles A. Cotton, Allan V. Cox, David B. Ericson, Maurice Ewing, Clifford Frondel, Benjamin F. Howell, C. S. Hurlbut, Jr., David R. Inglis, Philip H. Kuenen, L. Don Leet, Wilbur A. Nelson, Thomas B. Nolan, William T. Pecora, James E. Richey, Robert P. Sharp, Glenn L. Shepherd, Edward M. Spieker, George A. Thiel, J. H. F. Umbgrove, and Horace Winchell.

It should be noted, however, that the final responsibility for selecting or rejecting articles under consideration is mine, regardless of the advice received from others. I am sure that many of my colleagues who see this book will wonder why certain names and articles, enshrined in their personal pantheons, are missing from its assemblage. The only response I can make is to say that I, too, have a list of honored names and favored writings that I regretfully omitted because of the drastic limitations of space available in a book of reasonable size. In certain instances where other considerations were nearly equal, preference was given to publications that are likely to be least accessible for the majority of geologists because of the limitations of many libraries.

Following that train of thought with its implied desire to make this book as useful as possible for students and professional geologists alike, I have included translations of several articles originally published in foreign languages and not previously available in English. For this translating I am indebted to Judith Frondel (Mrs. Clifford Frondel) and Robert G. Wertheimer, from German, and John B. Southard, from Russian. Each translator is credited at the appropriate place in the following pages.

There are several persons here in Cambridge to whom I am deeply grateful for services rendered with regard to the innumerable details involved in locating references, securing biographical data, and readying the manuscript for the press. Foremost in this group is Elbert A. King, Jr., who worked on the project on a part-time basis while studying for his Ph. D. degree in geology at Harvard, thanks to a subsidy provided by the American Philosophical Association's Committee on Source Books in the History of the Sciences, through the courtesy of the committee's general editor, Edward H. Madden. Next are the librarians upon whom I relentlessly imposed my needs; among those whose assistance is most deeply appreciated are Tomislav Munetic, Marjorie Ainsworth, and Karen Dooks, of the Museum of Comparative Zoology, and Maureen Murphy, Ida Lewis, and Jean M. Shreve, of Harvard University's Department of Geological Sciences. Here, too, are Cynthia Hunt, secretary of that department, and my wife, Marie Porter Mather, who has been my invaluable aid in manifold ways for more than fifty-four years.

I am also grateful for permission freely given by the following editors and publishers to reprint material from their journals and books: John Rodgers, Editor, *American Journal of Science;* E. Wm. Heinrich, Editor, *The American Mineralogist;* Arthur A. Meyerhoff, Managing Editor, *Bulletin of the American Association of Petroleum Geologists;* Martin Russell, Managing Editor, *Bulletin of the Geological Society of America;* Karl V. Steinbrugge, Secretary, *Bulletin of the Seismological Society of America;* O. M. B. Bulman, Sedgwick Museum, Cambridge, England, *Geological Magazine;* University of Chicago Press, *Journal of Geology;* Madaleine A. Fritz, Editor, *Proceedings of the Geological Association of Canada;* Publications Committee, *Quarterly Journal of the Geological Society of London;* Royal Geographical Society, *Research Series;* Waldo E. Smith, Executive Secretary, American Geophysical Union, *Transac-*

*tions of the A. G. U.* and *Journal of Geophysical Research;* R. William Taylor, Executive Director, *Transactions of the American Institute of Mining Engineers;* Charles Scribner's Sons, *Radioactive Transformations,* by Ernest Rutherford. Specific references for the excerpts from these publications, as well as for those from other sources, are given in connection with each article in the following pages.

Kirtley F. Mather

Cambridge, Massachusetts
15 June 1966

# CONTENTS

# CONTENTS

# CONTENTS

# SOURCE BOOK IN GEOLOGY
## 1900–1950

# EMMONS

EMMONS Samuel Franklin Emmons (1841–1911), American economic geologist, graduated from Harvard College in 1861, studied in Paris and Freiburg, and in 1867 joined the staff of Clarence King for the Geological Exploration of the Fortieth Parallel. When the U. S. Geological Survey was established in 1879, he was appointed Geologist in Charge of the Rocky Mountain Division and for the next thirty years he continued his distinguished career in the U. S. G. S., serving part of that time as Geologist in Charge of the Division of Economic Geology. His monograph on the geology and mining industry of Leadville, Colorado, won for geology a place in the American mining industry that has never since been denied. His paper on secondary enrichment, excerpted here, bears witness to his wide knowledge of the geology of mining districts as well as his scientific acumen.

## SECONDARY ENRICHMENT OF ORE DEPOSITS*

From the foregoing geological evidence, which could be doubtless very much enlarged, it appears to be fairly well established:

1. That descending waters not only cause migrations, or transference and reconcentration, of the alteration products of the original vein-materials in oxidized form, producing in one place an enrichment, and in another possibly an impoverishment, of the original deposit, but that in their further downward course the oxidized forms are frequently reduced and redeposited as sulphides, thereby producing a sulphide enrichment of the original vein-materials.

2. That this secondary enrichment of sulphides is not necessarily a reduction in the presence of organic matter, but is frequent where no organic matter can be supposed to be present; it occurs mainly in contact with the original sulphides of the deposits, and is, presumably, a result of chemical reaction between these sulphides and the materials brought down in solution by the descending waters.

3. That while this re-deposition of sulphides in many cases appears to commence at or near the groundwater-level, it does not appear to have a necessary connection with that level, and may under favorable conditions extend below that level for a distance as yet undetermined, the most important favoring conditions appearing to be recent or post-

*From *American Institute of Mining Engineers, Transactions 30* (1901), 177–207.

mineral fractures, which have admitted a relatively free and uninter-rupted descent of these waters.

In endeavoring to trace back the processes by which the results have been brought about, it is important to bear in mind the physical changes that may be assumed to have taken place during the time that has elapsed since a given ore-deposit was originally formed and before it reached the condition in which it is found at the present day. These changes necessarily vary with each mining region or district, being in some cases very considerable, in others relatively slight. They may be classed under two general categories:

*First,* the rock shatterings resulting from dynamic force connected with earth-movements or eruptive action. These have opened channels for the entrance of surface-waters within the rock-mass and thereby extended the areas to which the chemical actions produced by the lat-ter may have extended.

*Second,* the erosion or denudation to which the region has been sub-jected, and which has gradually worn down the original surface to its present configuration. As a result of this wearing down the lower parts of an ore-deposit have been continually approaching the surface, and in no case, probably, is what was originally the superficial portion of an ore-deposit still in existence. The amount of the wearing away is not always determinable, but it may have been very large; thus, at Leadville, I estimated that in round numbers a thickness of about 10,000 feet of rocks had been worn away in order to bring the ore-bodies at present exposed to the surface.

In the Butte district, where there are no stratified rocks, there exists no criterion by which to estimate accurately the amount of denudation, but the readily disintegrable character of the granite country-rock and the faulting to which I have already alluded show that it must have been very considerable. There the ore-deposits occurring along nearly vertical fissures, and the later shattering having produced extraordinar-ily abundant secondary fissures nearly coincident with the earlier ones, the conditions were unusually favorable for an abundant leaching down of the material taken up in solution by the surface-waters. As the sur-face gradually lowered we may conceive that the insoluble materials were carried off mechanically; of the soluble minerals, however, but a relatively small proportion would have been removed by the actual surface run-off. The greater portion would have been carried back to lower levels before they came near enough to the actual surface to be taken up in the run-off.

It will aid our conception to divide the veins theoretically into three horizontal zones. The upper-, or surface-zone, that which immediately adjoins the present surface, is necessarily the zone of highest and most recent oxidation. Any sulphides found in it will simply be residual masses which, for some reason, the oxidation has not completely penetrated. The changes which have taken place in this zone will have been mainly of removal, rarely of addition, and any enrichment that will have come about in this zone will have been, as a rule, differential, resulting from the greater proportion of valueless or base metals removed.

The second, or intermediate-zone may be called the zone of oxide-enrichment. In this, the less soluble or more readily precipitable metals which have been brought down from the zone above, are found as carbonates or oxides, or in some cases as native-metals.

The third zone may be called the zone of sulphide-enrichment, in which the materials brought down in solution, and not deposited in the zone next above, are deposited as sulphides (also as sulph-arsenides and sulph-antimonides) or in some cases as native-metals in contact with the original sulphides of the deposit.

The presence of organic matter would hasten the reduction to sulphide, and might cause the deposition of the latter, under favorable conditions, even at the surface, but it should be considered as an accidental, rather than an essential occurrence.

These zones are, as has been said, a theoretical conception; in practice they are rarely well-defined, and in many cases one or more may be wanting. One will run into the other, and, as denudation progresses, a lower zone is slowly changing to the one next above it; thus, as time goes on, it will be a constantly richer zone that rises to the surface to be oxidized, and has part of its oxidation products carried back and re-deposited either as oxides or sulphides. Hence, other things being equal, the longer a deposit has been subjected to denudation the greater will be the enrichment below the surface-zone. The rate of denudation may also have influence upon the amount of enrichment, for it can be conceived that the surface-rocks may be so readily disintegrable and the rate of erosion under favoring climatic conditions may be so rapid, that the surface-removal of the oxidized material, both mechanical and chemical, may proceed so much faster than the downward seepage along the plane of the ore-deposit, that little or no enrichment of the interior portion of the deposit may have taken place.

Such a rapid denudation may be conceived to have taken place on exposed points during the ice-invasion of the glacial period, at which time, moreover, under the low surface-temperatures chemical decomposition would have been relatively sluggish. In arid regions, on the other hand, where the great heat would render chemical decomposition more energetic, and where there has been not only no ice-action, but also comparatively little erosion by water to wear down the surface, we should expect the zone of oxide-enrichment to extend down to great depths, but if the aridity were so great that there was very little water percolating through the rocks in depth, there might be but little sulphide-enrichment.

*Chemical Processes Involved*—I do not feel prepared to discuss in detail the chemical processes that are involved in the changes which are shown to have taken place by the above quoted observations. They necessarily vary from one deposit to another under the varying mineralogical and physical conditions that prevail in each place. Moreover, the chemical reactions that are suggested by previous investigations should be tested experimentally before any one can state with any degree of confidence what the succession of chemical processes in a given case has been; for these investigations have generally been conducted with another object in view, or with a different conception of the actual conditions in nature . . .

The most common sulphide-minerals in original ore-deposits are the iron sulphides, pyrite, marcasite, pyrrhotite, chalcopyrite and arsenopyrite; and next to these, galena, zinc-blende and various copper sulphides. While there is a great variety of other metallic compounds in ore-deposits, yet in most deposits the greater bulk is so far formed by one or more of the above minerals that the chemical changes will be largely governed by the reactions to which these appear to be subject. Of these sulphides marcasite is the most readily decomposed, while pyrite, if occurring by itself in pure crystals, often proves very resistant to alteration. Where there are mixed sulphides, however, the oxidation is observed to proceed more rapidly and all are readily attacked.

The actual changes observed by me in a great body of pyrite carrying galena in a limestone country-rock, which had undergone partial decomposition from the periphery inwards, are as follows: The original fresh pyrite or marcasite crystals are first disintegrated and slightly pitted on the surface, then changed to melanterite or hydrated ferrous sulphate and the galena becomes anglesite. In the outer or more fully oxidized zone the iron-vitriol has changed in part to yellow basic sulphate; in part to limonite with a separation of native sulphur.

The theoretical changes that are assumed to take place by the action of waters carrying oxygen or oxidizing agents are: first, an alteration of the iron sulphide to ferrous sulphate with the formation of sulphuretted hydrogen and sulphur which may have oxidized to sulphuric or sulphurous acid. By further oxidation the ferrous sulphate will become, in part at least, ferric sulphate, and this in its turn will react upon the remaining ferrous sulphate, or upon the sulphides, and form more ferrous sulphate or sulphates of the other metals which are present. By this cycle of reactions a supply of both ferric and ferrous sulphates would seem to be provided in the oxidized zone, but the extending downwards of the ferric salts would decrease as the supply of oxygen in the waters became less abundant.

It may be assumed that the sulphates of the metals thus formed would be transported for greater or less distances, generally in proportion to their solubility, the iron sulphates being the most soluble; next, those of copper and zinc; silver sulphate is less soluble and also more readily decomposed, while lead sulphate is extremely insoluble.

This accords with the facts generally observed in nature. Thus, from the gossan, which is generally a porous siliceous mass stained by the limonite or hematite resulting from the decomposition of part of the iron sulphate, the copper- and zinc-salts may have been more or less completely removed or transformed to less soluble carbonates and silicates. Where galena has been present in considerable amount the sulphate (anglesite) is generally found quite near the surface or forming a coating around residual masses of galena which some think it has protected from oxidation. Where carbonate of lime is present, as in limestone deposits, it is transformed to the carbonate (cerussite) which is more soluble, especially in the presence of an excess of carbonic acid, and may be transported from its original location and concentrated in bonanzas of more or less crystalline mineral. The silver sulphate formed near the surface is generally transformed to the chloride, but is not infrequently reduced to the native state. Gold probably does not form a sulphate, but when combined, as in the form of the telluride, is directly reduced to the metallic state. It is, however, to a certain extent soluble in ferric sulphide, and would in part be transported by this solution until it is precipitated by the reduction of the ferric to the ferrous condition which may occur in contact with the sulphide or with ferrous salts.

Under certain conditions ferric sulphate will decompose the metallic sulphides with the formation of ferrous salts and sulphates of the metals; possibly also with a solution of part as sulphides. Actual test has shown that it acts with great readiness on the iron sulphides, but much more slowly on silver sulphides. The action of copper sulphide has not been tested, but is probably intermediate between the two. . . .

# CHAMBERLIN

**CHAMBERLIN** Thomas Crowder Chamberlin (1843–1928), American geologist and cosmologist, resigned from the presidency of the University of Wisconsin in 1892 to become the first head of the Department of Geology in the new University of Chicago, a position which he occupied until his retirement in 1918. As geologist of the United States Geological Survey, his most notable work dealt with the Pleistocene glacial phenomena of the Mississippi Valley. During the last third of his life, his research was directed more generally toward cosmogony and the geological problems that can be solved only by knowledge of the deeper structure of the earth. As a teacher of geology, he exerted a profound influence upon many of the individuals responsible for the advancement of that science during the earlier decades of the twentieth century.

## DIASTROPHISM AS THE ULTIMATE BASIS OF CORRELATION*

There are many and diverse views relative to the nature and the causes of diastrophic movements. To keep as largely as may be on common ground, most of these divergencies of view may be set aside as immaterial to our present purpose. . . .

No doubt we can easily agree on the present great working factors: (1) abysmal basins occupying about two-thirds of the earth's surface, bordered by terrace faces rising at angles of 2° to 5° for, say, 12,000 feet to a quite definite terrace-angle about 100 fathoms below the sea-level; (2) continental platforms whose upper faces slope gently up from this angle to the coast-line and thence ascend into the various reliefs of the land. If we thus agree that the upper face of the continental platform is bounded by the edge of the continental shelf, and that this edge is equally the boundary of the abysmal basins, whether the waters overlap the edge or not, we may also agree that the edge of the oceanic waters, whether they agree with the edge of the abysmal basins or not, form the chief line of demarkation between the great erosions and the great depositions the world over. It is not the only line of such demarkation, to be sure, for degradation gives place to aggradation at many other local horizons, but in this discussion let us agree to deal only with factors of the larger order and to neglect incidentals; let us deal with body deformation, rather than local or provincial warpings. We all recognize further that the sea-level is not only a dividing plane between two great divisions of physical agencies, but between two great biological divisions.

To this list of agreements there are two other propositions which we cannot add quite so unhesitatingly, because we need to weigh them

*From *Journal of Geology 17* (1909), 685–693.

well, and if we cannot all agree respecting them, we must agree to differ, for they are fundamental to the further discussion. These relate to the effects of body deformation on the relations of land and sea.

If deformation were confined to the abysmal bottoms and were compensatory, no effect would be felt on the relations of land and sea. If deformation were confined wholly to the interior of the continents, it would be similarly ineffectual. Deformations so limited are, however, likely to be only provincial, and fall outside our discussion.

There remain two conceptions of general or body deformation between which choice must be made. In the one, the deformations are supposed to be indifferent to their predecessors, and to disregard the configurations produced by previous deformations. Their successive effects upon continental outlines and basin capacities are thus heterogeneous and the combined results irregular and uncertain. It is not clear to me how they can be made a very trustworthy basis of systematic correlation. The submergent phase of one continent or fraction of a continent may, in this case, be contemporaneous with the emergent phase of another continent or fraction of a continent, and the progress of events on one continent is as likely to be contrasted with those of another continent as to fall in with them co-ordinately.

According to the other view, deformations are inheritances, one of which follows another in due dynamical kinship. The succession is therefore homogeneous and the results co-ordinate. If, for example, the first depression of the abysmal basins was due to the superior specific gravity of the basin-bottoms, this specific gravity remained and participated in the next deformation. If the continental masses, at the outset of continental formation, were relatively low in specific gravity, this low specific gravity was handed down to later periods and helped to renew deformation of the same phases in the same regions. Under this view, ocean basins and continental elevations tended toward self-perpetuation. It is not assumed that this prevented shell crumplings, provincial warpings, or block movements of diverse phases within the continental or the abysmal areas, for these might obviously be necessary effects of the general deformative movements, or at least inevitable incidents connected with the dynamics lying back of them.

A choice between these two conceptions is imperative to this discussion, as they lie at the parting of the ways in the interpretation of the larger events of geologic history. I accept the second view with much confidence. It should be more fully qualified respecting the incidental accompaniments just mentioned, but time does not permit. . . .

It is important that we should agree, or agree to disagree, on one further point. Have diastrophic movements been in progress constantly, or at intervals only, with quiescent periods between? Are they perpetual or periodic? The latter view prevails, I think, among American geologists. This view has acquired especial claims since base-leveling has come to play so large a part in our science, for it is clear that the doctrine of base-leveling is specifically inconsistent with the doctrine of perpetual deformation, for the very conditions prerequisite to the accomplishment of base-leveling involve a high degree of stability through a long period. The great base-levelings, and the great sea-transgressions, which I think are little more than alternative expressions for the same thing, have, as their fundamental assumption, a sufficient stability of the surface to permit base-leveling to accomplish its ends. Shall we not therefore agree that there has been periodicity in the world-warping deformations? . . .

If we are agreed on the periodicity of great deformations, it clearly follows that in a quiescent state the base-leveling of the land means contemporaneous filling of the sea basins by transferred matter, and hence a slowly advancing sea-edge which is thus brought into active function as a base-leveling agent. This water movement is essentially contemporaneous the world over, and is thus a basis for correlation. *The base-leveling process implies a homologous series of deposits the world over.* . . .

Correlation by base-levels is one of the triumphs of American geology; correlation by its complement, transgressive deposits on a base-level, may easily be added, and perhaps on quite as firm or even firmer physical grounds. If we add the biological element the case is immeasurably strengthened, for correlation by cosmopolitan faunas, the very best of faunas for the purpose, is added to the physical correlation. Migration at the climax of base-leveling and sea-transgression is freer and more prompt than at other times. Correlation to the foot, as by an unconformity, may not be practicable, but the precision of correlation by unconformities has more apparent than real value, for the different parts of the same unconformity vary much in time. All distant correlations involve some measure of inexactness, and the more frankly it is made obvious, the less its liability to mislead.

Correlation by general diastrophic movements takes cognizance of four stages: (1) the stages of climacteric base-leveling and sea-transgression, (2) the stages of retreat which are the first stages of diastrophic movement after the quiescent period, (3) the stages of climacteric diastrophism and of greatest sea-retreat, and (4) the stages of early quiescence, progressive degradation, and sea-advance.

(1) The characteristics of the climacteric stage of base-leveling and sea-transgression need little further characterization here, for the func-

tion of base-levels is known to all American geologists and the function of great sea-transgression to every stratigrapher and paleontologist. We have in base-leveling conjoined with sea-transgression, just that combination of agencies which is competent to develop the broad epicontinental seas of nearly uniform depth requisite for an expansional evolution of shallow-water life. At the same time, it furnishes broad pathways around and across the continental surfaces for wide migrations and the comminglings that lead to cosmopolitan faunas of the shallow-water type.

(2) The stages of initial diastrophism and sea-retreat find their criteria in the deposits that spring from an increased erosion of the deep soil-mantles accumulated in the base-level period, in the effects of increasing turbidity, in the lessening areas suitable for the shallow-water life, and in the limitation of migration.

(3) The climacteric stages of diastrophism are marked by the stress of restrictional evolution among the shallow-water species; by increased clastic deposition in land basins, on low slopes, and on sea borders, by great land extension, but often, perhaps dominantly, by diversity of land surface and by liability to climatic severities and diversification. Areally, land life is favored, but it is hampered by the climatic and topographic diversities, and these may prove graver obstacles to migration and intermingling than even the tongues of sea that previously traversed the land surface. Correlation by glaciation in these stages is likely to prove a valuable adjunct, but we must first test our criterion, for we are not as yet quite sure that contemporaneity of glaciation is inferred on reliable grounds. The shallow-water life of the diastrophic stages is driven into narrow border tracts and into local embayments, and is thus forced into special adaptations and into narrowly provincial aspects.

(4) The early stages of quiescence and of base-leveling, with advancing seas, are peculiarly fruitful in biological criteria, for they are marked by re-expansions of the narrowly provincial shallow-water faunas of the previous stages. The progressive development of these provincial faunas and their successive unions with the faunas of neighboring provinces, as these come to coalesce by means of the progressive sea-advances, form one of the most fascinating chapters in life evolution, and give some of the most delicate of criteria for correlation. . . .

We are accustomed to look to the life record as our chief means of correlation. Its very high utility is quite beyond discussion. Thoughtful students, however, recognize that the paleontological record is based, in an essential way, on stratigraphy and that it is corrected and authenticated by the precise place the life is found to occupy in the stratigraphical succession. Stratigraphy and paleontology thus go hand in hand, each sanctioning the other. *Diastrophism lies back of both and furnishes the conditions on which they depend.* . . .

Diastrophism thus seems to me fundamental both to stratigraphic development and life development. Diastrophic action seems to be the forerunner of both these standard means of correlation. It therefore seems to be the ultimate basis of correlation. The criteria of this correlation include at once its own specific criteria, the criteria of stratigraphy as dependent on diastrophism, and the criteria of paleontology as modified by the direct and indirect effects of diastrophism.

# DAVIS William Morris Davis (1850–1934), American geomorphologist, was a member of the faculty of Harvard University throughout the greater part of his long life, serving as Sturgis-Hooper Professor of Geology from 1898 to 1912. As the great systematizer of the science of physical geography, he developed the concept of the fluvial cycle of erosion during the last two decades of the nineteenth century. In the first of the two articles excerpted here, he focused his analytical mind upon the problem of glacial erosion in mountains and presented his ideas with the assistance of his skillful draftsmanship. In the second, he proposed a two-cycle theory for the origin of most of the caves in limestone regions, an explanation of such caves that has subsequently been widely accepted.

## THE SCULPTURE OF MOUNTAINS BY GLACIERS *

*The present condition of the problem of glacial erosion*—The problem of glacial erosion in mountains has in recent years been carried many steps towards its solution by means of a series of studies in which the forms of formerly glaciated and of never glaciated mountains have been systematically compared. It has thus come to be believed by a number of observers that the glacial erosion of piedmont lake basins must be extended to the over-deepening of the main mountain valleys far upstream from the lakes, and that the retrogressive glacial erosion of cirques carries with it the sapping and sharpening of the culminating ridges and peaks. The last-named effect is truly not the direct work of ice, but it is so closely dependent upon glacial erosion that it should be included in any discussion of the sculpture of mountains by glacial agencies; just as the wearing of slopes and ridges by the weather goes with the erosion of valley bottoms by rivers. . . .

*The forms of normally sculptured mountains*—The forms of non-

*From *Scottish Geographical Magazine* 22 (1906), 76–89.

glaciated, normally sculptured mountains are well known to exemplify Playfair's law as to the accordant junction of lateral and main streams and valleys. In mountains which have reached a submature or a mature stage of normal carving, and in which lakes are therefore drained away and waterfalls are worn down to grade, except in small headwater streams, the law of decreasing slope from stream head to stream mouth will also obtain; and then the accordance that has been earlier developed at the junctions of main and side streams will be found to prevail even at the junctions of the innumerable headwater branches into which river systems are divided; and as each little headstream is followed up to its source, its steepening slope will be prolonged up the still steeper waste-covered slopes in the head and sides of the ravines which ascend to the mountain crests; but over the crests themselves there will be a decreasing convex slope. Examples of these normal forms which have come under my own observation are parts of the Apennines in northern Italy, the Cevennes in south-eastern France, the Black mountains of North Carolina, some of the lower ranges in the Rocky mountains and farther west, and certain non-glaciated members of the Tian Shan system: to these might be added the outer ranges of the Himalayas at Simla, and certain ranges in the Argentine Republic, except that, when these examples were seen, my attention had not been especially awakened to the points here considered. The perfection of stream organisation thus exhibited, with its delicate interdependence of parts, should be regarded as one of the strongest witnesses to the truth of the principles of rational uniformitarianism.

An important extension of Playfair's law concerns the relation of stream channels to each other and to the valleys in whose floors they are eroded. The channels occupy a very small part of the cross-section of the valleys, because water is a nimble fluid and its streams flow quickly in comparatively slender courses: furthermore, the very fact that the stream surfaces and the valley floors that border them meet in accordant level at the points of stream and valley junction necessitates the discordant junction of the channel beds whenever the confluent streams are of different size. The discordant junction of channel beds is not a conspicuous fact, because the streams in the comfortable climates of the older civilised countries usually fill their channels and hide their beds from immediate observations; but it is nevertheless a well-assured fact and a very important element in the present discussion.

*Deductions from theories*—Now if glaciers have no erosive power, then maturely dissected mountains that have been glaciated should present no features significantly unlike those above described for mature non-glaciated mountains. But if glaciers have strong erosive power, special and significant features should be found in mountains where glaciers have had time enough to do their work. The most notable features of this kind that one would expect to find may be stated as follows:—A large part of the cross-section of a glaciated valley would be included in the trough-like channel that was scoured out and occupied by the heavy, sluggish glacier; the bed of such a trough would have rock steps and rock basins similar to those in the bed of a river channel, but appropriately of much greater size; the sides or walls of such a trough would be comparatively even and parallel, like the sides or banks of a river channel; the troughs of small side glaciers would necessarily be of much less depth than the troughs of large trunk glaciers, and hence the bed of a side trough would hang hundreds of feet over the bed of the trunk trough; the valley sides above the trough would, in mountains of mature sculpture, be less steep than the trough walls themselves; the heads of the glacial beds would be broad-floored cirques, because the heads of glaciers are broad and leaf-like instead of being divided minutely like the headwater streams of rivers; the summits and ridges between cirques which head near each other would be sharpened into peaks and arêtes by atmospheric weathering, induced by the retrogressive glacial erosion of the ice in the cirques, and by the glacial widening of the troughs. Other features might be named, appropriate to glaciers of large or small size, or of short or long duration; but those here set forth are sufficient for a brief exposition.

*Graphic illustrations of glacial sculpture*—The attempt is made in Figs. 1, 2, and 3 to present examples of the unlike features just described. The figures make no pretence of being drawn from actual mountains; but they are in a way made up from various observations, sketches, and photographs, and in this respect correspond to the "deduced consequences" of the hypothesis that glaciers can erode, as announced in the preceding paragraph; for the consequences are not simply abstract deductions; they have been tested at nearly every step by observation. The figures undoubtedly need many amendments; they are hard and crude; yet they have some value in making the preceding paragraph clearer than it would be without them. Moreover, the figures ambitiously attempt to exhibit the changes that a given mountain mass would suffer from a preglacial time of normal sculpture, through a pronounced glacial period, to a postglacial time in which the work of the glacial period has as yet been but little affected by the return of normal conditions: in this respect they are necessarily only ideal examples.

Figure 1 shows the rounded, dome-like forms of a subdued moun-

Fig. 1. A normally eroded mountain mass, not affected by glacial erosion.

tain mass. The cliffs and ledges of an earlier stage of normal erosion have been worn away, and the waste cover has been very generally extended over the graded slopes that now reach from valley bottom to mountain top. This stage of mountain sculpture was chosen because it is so well represented in the Sawatch range of the Rocky mountains in Colorado in association with glacially sculptured forms, such as are illustrated in the later figures. Normally sculptured mountains of sharper form, like those of southern California, might have been taken had I seen them otherwise than in photographs. The main valley is widely opened; its floor is well graded to a continuous slope; its stream has no lakes or falls, but swings smoothly along a somewhat sinuous course between the spurs that come down with moderate slope from the higher ridges. The side valleys branch in a delicate fashion upwards, splitting the spurs into many spurlets; but all the streams and valley floors unite in accordant fashion at their many points of junction. The spurs are round-shouldered forms, exhibiting very few outlines by which their elusive curves may be represented; indeed, as here drawn, they have an undue resemblance to the sprawling feet of some huge pachyderm. I believe that, if mountains of this kind had been more familiar to those who have discussed the question of glacial sculpture in the Alps, a closer approach to agreement on the question of glacial erosion might have been reached ere now.

Figure 2 is intended to represent the accomplished work of a heavy glacial system on the mountain mass of Fig. 1. The main glacier has gained room for its broad current by wearing off the ends of the spurs that formerly entered the main valley from either side; and it has gained room for its heavy and deep ice body by excavating the valley floor to a greater depth than it had in preglacial time. The side glacier which enters from the upper left corner of the figure is manifestly less deep than the main glacier; hence, while the ice surfaces of the main and side ice-streams unite at accordant grade, the beds of their troughs or channels cannot unite in that even fashion; for when the troughs are once scoured out to a satisfactory depth for the two unequal ice streams, further change of trough depth will be small. The smaller branch glaciers in the main mountain mass have enlarged the branch valleys that they occupy, and retrogressive erosion at the heads of these glaciers has transformed the tapering valley heads of preglacial time into blunt-headed cirques. The slopes of the spurs and summits have

Fig. 2. The same mountain mass as in Fig. 1, strongly affected by glaciers which still occupy its valleys.

been greatly steepened and the ridges and peaks greatly sharpened by the active weathering resulting from glacial undercutting in the branch troughs and cirques. On the extreme right another mountain is shown in which two cirques have been excavated, not of sufficient size to transform the preglacial dome into a sharpened peak, yet large enough to have encroached on the spur that separated them, and thus to have transformed part of it into a serrate ridge. Mount Elbert, the highest summit of the Rocky mountains within the United States, presents just this sort of a contrast to its slightly lower neighbour, La Plata peak, whose summit has been sharpened into Alpine form. If the glacial conditions here pictured should last long enough, it is not to be doubted that the mountains would be in time reduced to lower and gentler forms than are here presented in the toothed peaks and serrated spurs of the central mass; and eventually they might be worn down so low that the glaciers would slowly and spontaneously disappear in consequence of the increasing mildness of climate thus produced—such being Tyndall's suggestion for the Alps; but the very fact that strongly glaciated forms, with the associated peaks and arêtes, now characterise the ranges that were heavily glaciated in Pleistocene time, suffices to prove that the glaciers did not disappear because of their own action in wearing down the mountains, but because of some external control of climatic change.

Figure 3 illustrates the appearance of the mountains and valleys after the glaciers of Fig. 2 have melted away. Now there is a superabundance of detail; the difficulty in drawing is to select the most significant outlines and to omit the rest. The forms that rose above the ice streams in Fig. 2 are here reproduced without essential change. The spurs on the left are unaltered in form, but are somewhat worn down from their appearance in Fig. 1. The forms that were buried under the ice streams of Fig. 2 are here disclosed to the light of day. The troughs of the smaller branch glaciers have ungraded floors, on which rock basins and rock steps alternate. The troughs of the large side glacier and of the main glacier are better smoothed. Alluvial fans are already accumulating on their sides, just as they are in the Alps and in other glaciated ranges. The fact of such accumulation suffices to prove a strong change from the conditions under which the troughs were excavated to the conditions in which they are now being filled up. The truncated spur-ends now continue downwards in the over-steepened trough sides, and curve at the base into the U-shaped trough floor. The junctions of the various glacial troughs—to which the name of valleys is of course ordinarily applied—are essentially discordant. The trough of the large side glacier hangs high above the floor of the main

Fig. 3. The same mountain mass as in Fig. 2, shortly after the glaciers have melted from its valleys.

glacier trough; the troughs of the smaller branch glaciers hang over the trough of the large side glacier. If the main trough could be followed down to its end, a large basin should be shown, occupied by a lake, and enclosed by morainic walls. As time progresses, all these peculiar features will be changed to normal features: a beginning of such changes is seen in the little slits by which the mouths of the hanging valleys are already beginning to be cut down; in the filling of the lakelets in the rock basins of the smaller branch troughs; and in the rapid wasting of the sharpened ridges and peaks, by which they will be in time rounded again; but the small amount of work thus far accomplished proves that the time since the evacuation of the district by its glaciers is comparatively short.

It is manifest that if a vigorous glacial system should soon again come to occupy the mountainous area of Fig. 3, it would produce relatively small changes compared to those by which the forms of Fig. 1 have been altered to those of Figs. 2 and 3; for the glacier system of the second epoch would find the valley-troughs so well adapted to its needs that there would be relatively small necessity of modifying them. The amount of sculpture effected in a first glacial epoch may therefore be reasonably estimated as of much greater volume than in a second glacial epoch.

*Consequences of theories confronted with facts*—When glaciated mountains are visited with the unlike consequences of the contrasted supposition above stated in mind, there can be little doubt whether glaciers are effective eroding agents or not. As far as the glaciated mountains of the world have been explored, it is found that they possess a large number of peculiar forms, which differ most strikingly from the forms due to the normal processes of erosion; it is further found that these peculiar forms are distributed with respect to one another in a most systematic and significant manner; and it is finally perceived that the peculiar forms are essentially similar to those above described and figured as producible by glaciers, under the supposition that glaciers have effective erosive power and that they have had time to use it. Thus the efficiency of glaciers in carving glaciated mountains is demonstrated by essentially the same method that has so thoroughly demonstrated the efficiency of the normal erosive agencies in carving nonglaciated mountains. . . .

It is thus both along direct and indirect lines of evidence that many observers have been led in recent years away from the supposition that glaciers cannot erode, and toward the supposition that glaciers can erode, even though the methods of glacial erosion are not yet fully understood. The sculpture of mountains by glaciers is indeed now proved by so many facts, widely and yet systematically distributed, that it savours of extreme conservatism any longer to deny the efficacy of glacial erosion.

## ORIGIN OF LIMESTONE CAVERNS *

### RELATION OF GROUND-WATER SOLUTION TO STAGES OF THE EROSION CYCLE

The solutional action of ground water beneath a dense limestone upland appears to be differently conditioned during successive stages of a cycle of combined subaerial and subterranean erosion. In an early stage of the cycle vadose water becomes carbonated as it sinks through the surface soil and applies its solvent power to the solution of limestones on the narrow joints and partings through which it slowly descends. Any of it that then sinks to ground-water level can perform

* From *Geological Society of America Bulletin 41* (1930), 475–628.

little solution; but whatever solution it does perform will be in the way of initiating a network of slender, interconnecting shafts and galleries.

At a more mature stage, when sinkholes, shafts and galleries above the water table are so well opened that descending vadose water runs rapidly through them, it is imperfectly carbonated, and once underground it runs so nimbly that much of it may succeed in reaching the open air again in valley-wide springs at gallery ends without allowing more than a small share of its volume to sink to deep-lying, ground-water levels. The little that does sink there, not being well carbonated, is a poor dissolver; but if it has a long-lasting underground course it may become saturated with calcite on the way to its ascending emergence in valley floor springs; and it will therefore continue the development of inter-connecting shafts and galleries, enlarging those already opened and opening new ones.

As the late stage of peneplanation of a limestone district is entered upon, a decidedly larger share of rain water than before sinks slowly into the gently sloping ground instead of running rapidly down steep-sided sinkholes or along active surface streams; and thus, although the direct runoff of the peneplain may make but small contribution to the subsurface water, a good share of the rainfall soaks into the interstream areas and there becomes well carbonated on its way to the ground water. Indeed, we here find the surface of low relief which some authors have regarded as essential for cavern-making, although they took the cavern-making agent to be vadose or water-table streams instead of deep-lying ground water.

Moreover, inasmuch as the water table lies but little below the worn-down surface of a peneplain the solvent power of the insoaking carbonated water may not be satisfied during its short descent to the water table, and may therefore still be in good part available at greater depths. Furthermore, if the region remains long undisturbed, the stage of peneplanation will endure much longer than the short stage of surface youth, when the main valleys were actively excavated by the larger surface streams; longer also than the stage of surface maturity when the enlargement of underground galleries by corrading subsurface streams was chiefly accomplished. Hence the solutional enlargement of a deep-lying network of interconnecting shafts and galleries by ground water, even to the point of widening the galleries irregularly into great chambers in the most soluble layers, may during this long-lasting stage of the erosion cycle come to be of large importance. It is possible that some corrasional enlargement also may then take place when vadose streams descend below the earlier level of the water table. Moreover, besides the three unlike conditions stated above, under which ground water acts as a dissolving agent below the water table during the earlier, medial and later stages of a cycle of erosion, there are two other factors which must be considered. These are, first, concentration of flow through galleries, and, second, solutional convection, which will shortly be taken up.

· · · · ·

### Concentration of Movement through Galleries

There is a significant difference between the movement of subsurface water through sandstone and through limestone. Sandstone, being porous, restricts the passage of water to its minute interstices; and the passage of water through such interstices is so much impeded that it is thought five years may be needed for it to advance a mile. Furthermore, sandstone being essentially insoluble, the passage of subsurface water through it is not any easier at the end of a cycle of erosion than at the beginning. Dense limestone, being nonporous, restricts the passage of subsurface water to its joints and partings; and being soluble, the passages are readily enlarged by solution, especially along the more soluble layers, so that water movement through dense limestone is greatly facilitated as an erosion cycle advances. Indeed, as subterranean passages are enlarged, water movement through them becomes so easy that surface streams frequently desert their subaerial courses and take to underground courses.

· · · · ·

Several writers have called attention to the importance of the concentration of subsurface water in limestone along selected passages as bearing on the production of caverns. . . . The concentration must involve a process of inorganic natural selection, whereby some embryo passages are much enlarged while others are little changed; and in consequence of such selection, it is only the favored embryo that grows to a great cavern.

Differences in the solubility of limestone layers are probably of large importance in guiding selection and thus determining the development of cavern galleries, even though the differences may be of moderate measure, not recognizable by the eye or detectable by the hammer, yet discovered with certainty by the long and intimate examination by the ground water. . . . It is of special importance to note in the present connection that, insofar as deep-lying galleries are opened by ground-water solution, the largest of them will tend, as interconnecting passages are developed, to draw to themselves some of the water supply that would, if all passages were equally opened, be evenly distributed. Furthermore, in virtue of the increased movement of water through an incipient deep-lying gallery, it should be more actively enlarged by solution; the enlarging process is therefore somewhat cumulative in its operation; and it is moreover increasingly efficient as water volume increases downstream from the divides. Thus solution of deep-lying galleries may continue to increase their enlargement until their growing size causes a disadvantageous decrease of velocity; but by that time the successful opening of many galleries has been assured, and they will be perpetuated thereafter even if at a decreasing rate of enlargement. But in contrast to galleries above the water table, ground water is not withdrawn from the smaller passages below the water table, and their network pattern therefore persists.

Moreover in a deep-lying gallery a slow circulation of ground water will be set up in consequence of its taking limestone into solution from the walls and roof. For the water in contact with the rock becomes a little denser than the rest; it therefore sinks and its place is taken by water containing less limestone. The convectional force thus provided is very weak, but in view of the extreme mobility of water and of the tomblike quietude of deep-lying galleries, the weak force may suffice to provoke a slow circulation. Thus even if the translatory movement of the ground water through the gallery is exceedingly slow, the solutional attack on the roof and walls will be continued until all the water volume is well charged with limestone. Even during the mature stage of the cycle, when ground water is chiefly supplied by imperfectly carbonated vadose water, some solution will still go on; for limestone is, it must be remembered, slightly soluble even in pure water.

### RESIDUAL CLAYS ON CAVERN FLOORS

The removal of calcite by solution in low-lying ground water should leave the insoluble, clayey residue of the limestone on the floor of the resulting cavity, where it would greatly retard if not wholly prevent further downward excavation; and in this respect caverns of ground-water solution must differ from caverns of vadose corrasion, in which downward excavation should be active until the corrading streams are graded. It therefore seems possible that clay beds on certain cavern floors, which are commonly attributed to deposition by inflowing streams, may be, in their lower part at least, of local origin while the cavern was water-filled. A minute study of cave clays might be profitable.

## Contrasts of Vadose-water and Ground-water Action

The action of deep-lying and slow-moving ground water may now be seen to differ from that of faster-moving vadose water in higher-lying shafts and galleries in several ways, which need to be carefully tested by critical observation. First, percolating vadose water should, it is believed, almost cease acting as a dissolving agent when the passage that it follows has reached such a size that it is usually occupied in good part by ground air: for reasons have been given above to show that vadose water is more or less self-regulating in the way of setting a limit to the size of a passage that it can dissolve without the aid of corrasion. There is, on the other hand, theoretically no limit to the enlargement of deep-lying passages by ground-water solution if it takes place at all, although as the passages enlarge their further enlargement may proceed at a slower and slower rate. Furthermore, the concentration of a vadose stream on a gallery floor withdraws all of its solvent action from the roof and walls; but all parts of a deep-lying, water-filled gallery are subject to solution.

Second, high-level galleries, initiated by vadose-water solution, are likely to remain of small size, still retaining an angular network pattern, because streams able to corrade them actively are soon withdrawn to lower levels; but low-level galleries little above the water table may be much enlarged by vadose-water action, aided by rock falls, whereby the gallery floors are graded with respect to some external control, usually a neighboring valley floor, and widened by lateral corrasion. As the widening takes place a gallery will most likely depart more and more from both the vertical joint and the extra dense or extra soluble stratum which first guided it, and the gallery floor may become sinuous, especially where its stream is deflected by rock heaps. Only the lowest blocks in such heaps can become stream-worn.

On the other hand, deep-lying galleries may be opened and enlarged to a considerable size along bedding planes at various levels by ground-water solution; for a deeper-lying gallery will not withdraw the water from one lying at a less depth. The gallery walls may be hollowed out in concave form, Fig. 32 A, so that the gallery width is greater above the floor, and not at the floor as it should be in corraded galleries, Fig. 32 E. As there is practically no selective corrasion performed by deep-lying ground water, its gallery floors will not be graded with respect to some external control; and the angles at the turns of slender galleries will be little rounded, as in Fig. 33. The galleries may be somewhat irregularly broadened laterally on soluble beds, as to the left in

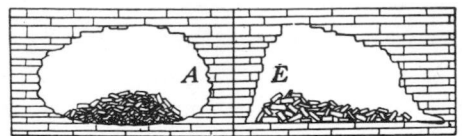

Fig. 32. Contrasts between solutional and corrasional galleries.

Fig. 33, and enlarged upward by rock falls from the roof, but such falls will be diminished by upward pressure from the water-filling. The blocks of early falls at the bottom of a rock heap should be rounded down to smaller size by solution, while those of later falls at the top of the heap should be larger and more angular, as in Fig. 32 A.

Third, the marks of water-wear by silt-bearing vadose streams may be preserved on the floor and walls and even on the roof of slender galleries; but as such galleries grow to greater size, largely by floor corrasion and rock falls from above, the early-made marks on walls and roof will disappear; only those on the floor will be preserved or renewed; but down-trickling water may modify the angular forms left on the walls by falling rocks; and where the trickle locally becomes a little stream the walls may be more or less smoothed or fluted.

On the other hand, the smooth forms produced by solutional excavation below the water table must be continually renewed on floor, walls and roof of a growing gallery; and even if they are removed from the roof by the fall of a rock slab, they will be produced again. Just what the nature of these forms may be it is not safe at present to assert; but it may be suspected that they are not unlike the irregularly rounded forms assumed by dense limestones under a leached-out soil cover; that is, they should have irregularly flowing curves which might be mistaken for curves produced by the wear of silt-bearing streams. No record of critical inquiry into this matter by cave explorers has come to hand; and in its absence one is tempted to wonder whether the walls of certain narrow passages which are described as smoothed

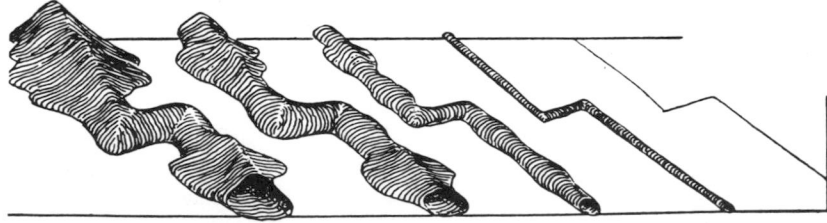

Fig. 33. Solutional enlargement of an angular joint-passage.

or polished by running water, and the walls of certain chambers which are said to be gracefully carved by water—with the implication of running water—may not be after all the work of solution by still-standing water. . . .

Fourth, the branchwork arrangement of low-level galleries with downstream gradients as produced by vadose corrasion has already been emphasized. Equal emphasis must now be given to the persistence of the arrangement of deep-lying galleries, without systematic gradients, as produced by ground-water solution. These galleries may develop and preserve outgoing branches and loops in abundance. An irregular interconnection of their parts should be one of their leading characteristics.

A fifth and highly significant contrast is to be found in the slopes of gallery profiles. It is not to be doubted that narrow galleries of immature vadose corrasion may have local steepenings of their downstream profile; but widefloored galleries of corrasion cannot have such steepenings because their widening cannot have begun until their floors had been reduced to fairly even gradients; nor can their profiles have reversals of slope. But galleries widened by ground-water solution may still have various irregularities of profile. When the great Carlsbad Cavern of New Mexico is described below this principle should be borne in mind.

There are, however, certain resemblances to be expected between the cavernous passages excavated by vadose water and by ground water. Both seem competent to produce high and narrow passages; running water will do so by progressive down-cutting, perhaps guided by a master joint, from a single minute passage well above local baselevel; dissolving water may do so by the gradual solutional opening of a joint at several levels until the different small openings blend into one

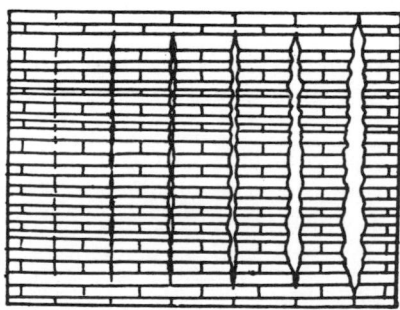

Fig. 34. Solutional development of a narrow passage.

large opening as in Fig. 34. Both should increase in size with increase in the volume of water engaged in their production; hence both should be small near the divides, and should increase in size downstream toward the cavern vents; but this increase in size should be more systematic in low-level galleries corraded above the water table than in deeplying galleries dissolved below the water table. Both are, at the outset, developed in network systems of interconnecting passages; but while the network is, as above noted, persistently maintained by the groundwater passages it must ordinarily be converted into a branchwork by vadose water. This final contrast will later be shown to be of large significance.

### LEISURELY CONTINUATION OF SOLVENT ACTION BY GROUND WATER

There is, furthermore, a combination of various factors which appears to act in favor of greatly increasing the measure of ground-water solution over what it might otherwise be in comparison with the measure of solution by vadose water. In the first place, little of the deeplying ground water is likely to run away so fast that it can not exert its solvent power to the utmost; thus it differs from the hurried behavior of concentrated vadose streams which, when they are of good size, may run so rapidly as not to allow all their water threads to exert their solvent power to best advantage and may thus prevent their all becoming saturated with calcite before they leave their cavernous courses. In the second place, ground water is continually pressed into complete and intimate contact with all the passages it follows. Vadose water has no such continuity or completeness or intimacy of contact; it sometimes drips or falls through the ground air. . . .

In the third place, although ground water acts slowly as a solvent agent, it has, as has already been pointed out, a much longer time for its action during the passage of a cycle of erosion than vadose water has. The excavation of cavernous galleries above the water table by vadose water largely ceases in the late-mature stages of a cycle, when many of the galleries are unroofed and transformed into valleys; but solution of galleries by ground water still goes on even through the longer-lasting stage of peneplanation, provided that no regional elevation occurs to interrupt it. In other words, the cavernous galleries that are hidden below a limestone peneplain have had a time-period for their slow excavation which must have included the preliminary solutional opening of joints and partings in the overlying limestone mass by percolating vadose water; the corrasional enlargement of some of the small, low-lying openings into great galleries; the unroofing of those galleries and their conversion into open or blind valleys, and the removal of the residual hills and swells between the valleys. Yet however long and leisurely may be the excavation of cavernous galleries by ground-water solution below the water table, they must always preserve their interconnecting network arrangement; and their floors must always, failing to develop the systematic downstream gradients that characterize corrasional galleries, persist in following rather closely along beds of most easy solution. Moreover, there need not be large galleries at deeper-lying levels below much smaller galleries at less deep levels, such as have been shown to be expectable in cavern systems developed by vadose water above the water table. Nevertheless, it must not be forgotten that the solvent action of ground water is extremely slow; and that it will be only under highly favoring conditions that it can excavate large, deep-lying galleries. Insofar as it does so, the water rising from them to issue as springs should be well charged if not saturated with calcite; and if saturated it would probably, on reaching the open air, form travertine deposits, such as have already been considered.

The importance of the time element in favoring the solutional excavation of deep-lying galleries by ground water must be further emphasized. This may perhaps be done best by recalling the value of this unescapable element in the aging of the soil on a peneplain; for such aging is believed to be largely accomplished by the solutional decomposition of minerals that are ordinarily regarded as insoluble. The occurrence of bauxite in the old soils of our Southern States is a case in point; for that mineral is, as Leith and Meade (1915), Adams (1927) and various others have shown, a hydrated aluminous residue that is left after the silica, with which it was originally combined, has been leached out. If this result can be reached by the intermittent action of small amounts of soil water through the long interval of time involved in peneplanation, important measures of limestone solution should be accomplished by the much more persistent action of deep-lying and relatively abundant ground water, year in, year out, during the same long interval of time. . . .

In any case, the excavation of even the largest cavern by ground-water solution requires only that its water-filling shall, after becoming saturated with calcite, be changed 30,000 times; and if an average of 33 years be allowed for a filling to become saturated (a month being given for the saturation of a very slender filling in a minute embryo passage, and half a century or more for the saturation of the filling in an enlarged, full-sized cavern), the time required for the total excavation would be hardly more than 1,000,000 years, even without the aid of carbon dioxide; and such a measure of time is surely available for cavern excavation below limestone peneplains. If a new water-filling is already somewhat charged with calcite when it enters the growing cavern, the time required for the total excavation will be prolonged; if the entering water-filling contains some unemployed carbon dioxide the time required will be shortened; if it is juvenile water, warm and carbonated, that enters the cavern from below the time of excavation will be shortened still more.

It therefore seems permissible, in view of these various considerations, to imagine that the development of cavernous shafts and galleries under the action, partly solutional but largely corrasional, of vadose water above the water table and their eventual destruction by subaerial degradation may be associated with the development of deeper-lying shafts and galleries under the action, almost wholly solutional, of ground water below the water table. In all events it must be true that whatever caverns are thus produced—and some have been so produced if the above-given interpretation of Marengo and Wyandotte caves in Indiana is correct—they must be developed in systematic order; they must grow from small beginnings to greater ends; that is, just as the work of vadose water proceeds from a fine-textured network at an early stage to a coarser-textured, low-level branchwork at a later stage, so the work of ground water must proceed from a fine-textured network at an early stage to a coarser-textured network at a later stage. But, while the branchwork galleries of a cavern produced by vadose water might be explored during their production, if one could be found in a dense-limestone upland in its first cycle of erosion, none of the network galleries produced by ground-water solution are accessible to exploration while they hold the attitude with respect to the water table in which they were produced.

As long as a region in which such deep-lying galleries of ground-water solution occur remains undisturbed, the deeper passages will be water-filled and will therefore be inaccessible. Only after elevation takes place and introduces the region into a second cycle of erosion, thus allowing the ground-water filling of the deeper-lying galleries to be drained away and replaced by ground air in which dripstones can be formed, may the passages that were dissolved during the previous cycle be entered and examined. Hence we must next inquire into the occurrence of caverns in limestone regions that are now, in consequence of regional elevation, moderately advanced in a second cycle of erosion after having progressed, before such elevation, far through an earlier cycle. . . .

It appears from this review, as well as from many diagrams not here reproduced, that limestone caverns are very generally attributed to the solutional and corrasional activities of subsurface water above the water table, and that no adequate cause is suggested for the change from their excavation to their more or less advanced replenishment with dripstone deposits; also that the excavation of caverns is usually held to have taken place since their region assumed its present attitude with respect to baselevel. This view as to the origin of caverns may be spoken of as the one-cycle theory of cavern excavation by vadose or by water-table streams; or more briefly as the one-cycle theory.

An alternative to this theory is that caverns may be produced largely by ground-water solution below the water table and then, after regional elevation, drained of their previous water-filling and on thus becoming filled with ground air made ready for dripstone deposition. This may be called the two-cycle theory of ground-water excavation and gound-air deposition; or briefly the two-cycle theory. It will now be set forth more fully. Grund appears to have been the first to state it clearly.

### Proposed Cause of Change from Excavation to Replenishment

It is proposed to consider in this essay the possibility, which has very likely occurred also to others, that large caverns are ordinarily excavated by ground-water solution during an epoch when the body of limestone in which they occur lies below the water table of its district; and that the change from this epoch of solutional excavation to the following epoch of depositional replenishment takes place when the water table sinks below the cavern level in consequence of regional elevation or other effective cause. After such change the ground water, which had completely filled the cavern during the progress of its excavation, is drained away and its place is taken by ground air, the presence of which provokes evaporation of percolating vadose water and escape of carbon dioxide from it, and thus compels it to deposit calcite and form dripstones on the cavern roof and floor.

The sinking of the water table in consequence of regional elevation or other effective cause as a means of dividing cavern history into two epochs is therefore an essential feature of the above proposal. It has at least the merit of providing an adequate reason for the change from an earlier epoch of excavation to a later epoch of deposition, even though the idea that cavern excavation may go on by solution with small aid from corrasion below the water table usually receives unfavorable consideration when it is considered at all. Such a process of excavation nevertheless seems worthy of examination. It is not intended, however, to deny the production of certain relatively slender, linear caverns by vadose-water solution and corrasion above the water table, for such caverns may often be produced in that way; but only to regard the action of vadose water in large caverns as usually subordinate and subsequent to the excavational work primarily accomplished by deeper-lying ground water. Similarly, the occasional formation of dripstones in small caverns without a change in the attitude of the water table is not to be excluded, but it is thought that great dripstone deposits in great caverns are best explained by a change in the attitude of the water table. . . .

# BECKE Friedrich Becke (1855–1931), Austrian mineralogist, received his doctorate from the University of Vienna in 1881. For several years he was associated with the University of Czernowitz and later with the University of Prague. From 1898 until his retirement he was Professor of Mineralogy and Petrology at Vienna. He was internationally famous for his perceptive studies of the structure and fabric of igneous rock bodies and his contributions to the understanding of the processes of metamorphism.

## STRUCTURE AND CLEAVAGE *

### 1. SCHISTOSITY AND FOLDING

. . . Parallel fabrics frequently develop in metamorphic rocks solely through the formation and orientation of crystalline constituents which are free of visible traces of mechanical influences such as cataclasis, mortar-structure, pressure-twinning lamellae, strain, undulatory extinction, and so on. . . . Such structures are believed to have been developed through the growth of the constituents under the influence of stress (i.e. according to the direction of differential pressure). This growth in rocks is possible, however, only if in various places simultaneous solution of the same constituents or different constituents (solution-transformation) takes place. Riecke's principle—a mechanically deformed crystal is dissolved while a nondeformed crystal will grow in the same solution—gives a physical explanation for the process.

. . . A simple parallel structure of this kind has been called crystallization schistosity, and the name has also been used to designate the process. Generally such structures have been called crystalloblastic. The term "crystalloblastic" is applied, therefore, not only to simple schistosity but also to lineation and folding in general of every structure which is brought about by the formation and orientation of mechani-

*From "Struktur und Klüftung," *Fortschritte der Mineralogie, Kristallographie und Petrographie 9* (1924), 185–220. Translated by Judith Frondel.

cally undamaged crystals—indeed, even to the isotropic hornfels structure.

According to more recent authors, parallel or otherwise directional crystalloblastic structures can be brought about in other ways than by directional pressure. I am in complete agreement that the term crystalloblastic should be used purely in a descriptive sense without any hypothetical implications concerning origins. . . .

One of the principal considerations in Sander's work is the search for componental movements in the fabric; these he identifies by their characteristics in thin-section. . . . For him, rocks of this kind are tectonites. He further attempts to distinguish the type of such movements, whether they have influenced the fabric by mobilization (which can be translated approximately as solution-exchange) or by mechanical deformation (rupture, cataclasis, or plastic deformation of the constituents).

Another characteristic of Sander is his clear-cut analysis of the time relations between the individual phases of metamorphism. The basic principle is the temporal separation of mechanical deformation and crystallization. Thus, he differentiates between:

   a) *precrystalline* deformed metamorphic rocks. The fabric shows traces of componental movements in schistosity, folding, and so forth; the constituents are, however, undamaged crystals. Crystallization has either followed or outlasted the componental movement.
   b) *paracrystalline* deformed rocks. Mechanical deformation and crystallization are simultaneous and affect each other.
   c) *postcrystalline* deformed rocks. Following crystallization, a phase of mechanical deformation, be it ruptural or constantly plastic, with the resultant optical phenomena. This group embraces all cases of cataclasis in the broadest sense, from the slightest bending of mica and the undulose extinction of sensitive quartz to the extensive internal fragmentation of rocks. Postcrystalline deformation can affect individual constituents; for example, quartz, whereas the carbonates may show no trace of deformation. . . .

According to Sander, paracrystalline deformation can be identified only if the rock constituents are partly mechanically deformed and partly in well-crystallized undamaged individuals. . . .

The author has . . . a somewhat different interpretation. If the deformation takes place under the most favorable conditions for crystallization, with suitable temperature and constant hydrostatic pressure and so slowly that the process of solution here and growth there may follow the mechanical stress, I do not know what will prevent the rock from showing in its fabric exactly what Sander describes as the result of precrystalline deformation.

Also, according to my interpretation, in many cases where Sander recognizes a temporal succession of deformation and crystallization, I must believe in one homogeneous process in which deformation and crystallization are genetically connected. . . .

Sander gives much importance to the greater permeability which a rock with already developed parallel structure has for penetrating solutions. This easier permeability in "S" accelerates the growth of the constituents in the same direction. The oblong form of garnet crystals and plagioclase grains can be explained in this way. . . .

Mügge . . . also speaks of the formation of parallel structure in crystalline schists. He begins with the observation that fractures in rocks frequently are filled with parallel fibrous aggregates of a mineral which commonly occurs as a constituent of the rock. His explanation assumes the presence of innumerable nuclei of the fibrous mineral on the walls of the fracture at the moment of its origin. As the cleft opens up, they grow in it at different rates in different directions. After a while . . . the largest crystals are those whose direction of most rapid growth happened to be perpendicular to the fracture wall. If the walls of the fracture separate more slowly than the least rapid rate of growth of the crystals, then they remain in constant contact with the retreating walls. Thus there develops a parallel fibrous aggregate of a mineral, the individual fibers of which have varying crystallographic orientation. If the movement of the fracture wall is greater than the smallest rate of crystallization but less than the greatest rate of growth of the fibrous mineral, then the slow-growing fibers will be suppressed and the developing hollow spaces will be filled with a lateral growth of the more quickly growing fibers; thus the fibrous aggregate will consist of parallel-oriented individuals for which the direction of most rapid growth was perpendicular to the cleft.

Mügge applies this concept to the microscopic and submicroscopic spaces which must develop through the influence of a unilateral stress by the separation of the rock constituents in the direction perpendicular to pressure. The neighboring rock-constituents grow and fill these platy spaces. In this manner they acquire a platy form perpendicular to stress and produce crystallographic orientation (i.e. positioning of a specific crystal plane parallel to the planes of schistosity) of such minerals that have a large difference in their rate of growth in different directions—the micas, for example.

Analogous processes produce lineation if the differential pressure is such that the separation of the rock constituents proceeds preferably in one direction within the planes of schistosity.

Mügge's concept is most enlightening, but I would like to suggest that if the growth of crystals within a rock is to take place in all directions along any plane, there must be an adequate supply of soluble material. Next to places of growth there must be places of solution, whether it be of the same mineral or of other minerals that can supply the material needed for the growing crystals. In short, if we accept Mügge's concept, we cannot avoid the necessity for the presence in a rock of neighboring places of solution and growth; this is the essence of our concept of crystallization schistosity or crystalloblasis.

Indeed, Mügge emphasizes correctly that such transformations and recrystallizations in a rock are effected by the action of solutions that cannot have a high concentration; that, moreover, the rate of transformation is very slow; and we are led to the postulate that long periods of time are an unavoidable necessity for metamorphism.

$$. \quad . \quad . \quad . \quad .$$

### 3. Porphyroblasts and Rolled Inclusions

The name porphyroblast was introduced to designate those crystals in crystalline schists that have grown to significant size in rocks which, though solid, yielded to the influence of metamorphism and in their growth have taken materials from the other rock constituents of the groundmass. . . . Porphyroblasts comprise constituents that were not present in the earlier state of the rock. Sander designates as holoblasts those constituents that have formed in the same manner as porphyroblasts but which do not stand out from the rest of the rock because of their size.

In German literature the name porphyroblast is often laxly used to designate any large crystal in a crystalline schist. This is not acceptable.

In American literature porphyroblasts are called idiomorphic or porphyritic crystals. C. K. Leith says that they develop through recrystallization after the fluid rock flowage has ceased. According to our concept, this is quite incorrect. Porphyroblasts develop and grow during crystalloblasis—in other words, while the mechanical deformation of the rock is taking place. . . .

In various rocks of the group, mica schists to phyllites, there are porphyroblasts of garnet or albite with inclusions that originated in the groundmass of the rock and are so oriented in the outermost parts of the porphyroblasts as to be aligned with the parallel pattern of the schistose rock. Within the porphyroblasts the rows of inclusions do not go straight through but are S-shaped. This phenomenon can be seen in the section perpendicular to the schistosity. If there are several porphyroblasts in the section, all the S-shapes have the same direction and manner. . . . Rolled inclusions can be explained most simply by a rotating movement of the growing porphyroblast in response to accompanying differential movements of the rock layers parallel to the planes of schistosity. . . .

W. Schmidt's description of the indications of movement in porphyroblasts . . . is of great significance; first, because of the proof that a differential movement such as a simple rotational strain is involved in the development of parallel structures; second, because of the proof that crystallization and growth of porphyroblasts take place during the differential movements within the rock, rather than before or after such movements, thus leading to the concept that the crystallization of metamorphic rocks is not catastrophic but proceeds slowly, gradually, and, at least in part, with continuous changes; third, because of the opportunity for clear determination of the nature of the differential movement. . . .

Helge Backlund refers to similar traces of movement in porphyroblasts. . . . Some very interesting phenomena are described in porphyroblasts of staurolite and garnet which are embedded in a groundmass composed predominantly of quartz and biotite. The indications of movement are very complicated and the differential movements obviously occurred, in part, during growth. The S-shaped orientation of inclusions in the garnet are reminiscent of Schmidt's description of the rotating motion of garnet crystals during growth. In the staurolite porphyroblasts one notices partially stretched columnar forms as well as partially crowded forms, without being able to distinguish . . . any relation to parallel structure. . . . In my opinion the inner portion of the inclusions seems to resemble an hourglass structure; the growth pyramids on the end faces are filled with inclusions but every prism face is free from them. Backlund believes that the inclusions in the staurolite and the orientation of the biotite in the surrounding groundmass indicate that the staurolite developed in the fold axes of compressed folds. . . . I would like to offer for consideration the idea that these structural features did not develop in this way, but rather that the growing staurolite crystals, because of their inflexibility, caused an unusual deviation of the directional stresses in the surrounding groundmass and thus produced the characteristic orientation of the biotite features. The fragments of decomposed crystals and the well-developed fine-grained quartz patterns in the intervening lineation aureoles indicate that the differential movements in the fabric continued after the growth of the porphyroblasts. Such lineation aureoles occur also with garnet crystals. . . .

## 4. FABRIC ORIENTATION

Fabric orientation is understood to be the phenomenon of orientation of individual minerals in a disturbed rock (i.e. a rock in which differential movements have taken place) in particular positions with reference to the plane of schistosity (or the direction of lineation) that are determined by the crystallographic regulations.

Such fabric orientation of micaceous minerals (mica, chlorite, talc) has long been known. The perfect cleavage plane (001) of most individuals is more or less parallel in the rock which because of this orderly arrangement has a good cleavage in one direction. Likewise, the orientation of hornblende prisms parallel to the planes of schistosity in amphibolites has often been described.

It is also known that near the valley floor and on the side walls of glacier tongues, where ice movement is considerable, the principal crystallographic axes of the ice grains lie almost normal to the base, and the translation surface (001) is nearly parallel to it.

# OLDHAM   Richard Dixon Oldham (1856–1936), British geologist and seismologist, was for many years the Superintendent of the Geological Survey of India and Director of the Geological Museum in Calcutta. His novel identification of the earth's central core was based upon seismographic data that today would be considered quite inadequate for such deductive reasoning, but it was an accomplishment of prime importance in the search for knowledge about the interior of the earth.

## THE CONSTITUTION OF THE INTERIOR OF THE EARTH AS REVEALED BY EARTHQUAKES *

### I. INTRODUCTORY

Of all regions of the earth none invites speculation more than that which lies beneath our feet, and in none is speculation more dangerous; yet, apart from speculation, it is little that we can say regarding the constitution of the interior of the earth. We know, with sufficient accuracy for most purposes, its size and shape: we know that its mean density is about $5\frac{1}{2}$ times that of water, that the density must increase towards the centre, and that the temperature must be high, but be-

*From *Geological Society of London Quarterly Journal 62* (1906), 456–475.

yond these facts little can be said to be known. Many theories of the earth have been propounded at different times: the central substance of the earth has been supposed to be fiery, fluid, solid, and gaseous in turn, till geologists have turned in despair from the subject, and become inclined to confine their attention to the outermost crust of the earth, leaving its centre as a playground for mathematicians.

The object of this paper is not to introduce another speculation, but to point out that the subject is, at least partly, removed from the realm of speculation into that of knowledge by the instrument of research which the modern seismograph has placed in our hands. Just as the spectroscope opened up a new astronomy by enabling the astronomer to determine some of the constituents of which distant stars are composed, so the seismograph, recording the unfelt motion of distant earthquakes, enables us to see into the earth and determine its nature with as great a certainty, up to a certain point, as if we could drive a tunnel through it and take samples of the matter passed through. The subject is yet in its infancy, and much may ultimately be expected of it; already some interesting and unexpected results have come out, which I propose to deal with in this paper.

So long ago as 1894 the late E. von Rebeur Paschwitz, recording the Japanese earthquake[1] of March 22nd, found that the record showed three separate disturbances or phases, but I believe that the true character of this threefold disturbance was not established until 1900, when I showed,[2] by a study of the available data, that the disturbance set up by a great earthquake was split up into three distinct forms of wave-motion, propagated at different rates and along different paths, giving rise to three distinct phases in its distant record. Of these, the third and latest was shown to be due to surface-waves, that is to say, wave-motion propagated along, or close to, the surface of the earth; but it was also shown that the other two phases, forming what are known as the preliminary tremors, represented the cropping-out of mass-waves which had travelled through the earth. It is these two phases alone with which I am at present concerned, for the third-phase waves can obviously give no information regarding the interior of the earth, as their wave-paths lie along its surface.

The researches of Dr. C. G. Knott[3] and Dr. P. Rudzki[4] have shown that no simple form of wave-motion can be transmitted through the heterogeneous rocks forming the outermost crust of the earth, and that

[1] *Petermann's Mitt. 41* (1895), 13–21, 39–40.
[2] *Phil. Trans. Roy. Soc. London* [A] *194* (1900), 135–174.
[3] *Trans. Seismol. Soc. Japan 12* (1888), 115–136.
[4] *Beitr. Geophysik 3* (1898), 519–540.

the records from instruments situated near the origin of an earthquake cannot show any sorting-out of different kinds of wave-motion. It is only in more homogeneous material that this sorting-out can take place, and it is only at a distance of 10 degrees of arc, or about 700 miles, from the origin that the three-phase character of the record begins to appear. The waves emerging at this distance have evidently traversed more homogeneous material for a part of their course; in this part there has been a sorting-out of the forms of wave-motion into which the disturbance has been converted, and the fact that the sorting-out can be detected at so comparatively small a distance from the origin shows that the outer crust must be, comparatively, very thin. I have not been able to collect sufficient data for an accurate estimate of its thickness, but this cannot be more than about a score of miles;[5] and below it comes material of a very different character, which not only allows a sorting-out of different forms of wave-motion, but, as has been shown by Prof. Milne,[6] transmits these at a velocity much greater than is met with in the outer crust. If the figures given in the following pages do not bear out in detail his further conclusions regarding the homogeneity of the whole of the core and the rectilinear propagation of the wave-motion, this must be ascribed to the accumulation of more data than were available when he wrote. As will be seen, they are confirmed in essentials, so far as the outer six-tenths of the radius are concerned, and in the central four-tenths the first-phase waves, which alone were dealt with by Prof. Milne, are so little affected that the change might easily have escaped recognition but for the clue given by those of the second phase. It is, therefore, desirable to devote a little space to the demonstration of the reality of a distinction in kind between these two sets of waves.

In my paper quoted above, I pointed out that the different rates of propagation of the first and second phases showed that they must be referred to different forms of wave-motion, which I interpreted as being, probably, the two known forms—compressional and distortional—which can be transmitted by a homogeneous solid. As regards the first phase, the conclusion was only one which had already been suggested, and is still generally held; but, as regards the second, my interpretation has been traversed in two separate ways.

The first is by the Rev. O. Fisher, who, believing my interpretation

[5] There is some seismological indication of a want of uniformity in this thickness, for earthquakes originating off the eastern coast of Japan exhibit a three-phase character at less distance from the origin than appears to be the case in Europe, indicating a lesser thickness of the outer crust in the former region.

[6] *Nature* (London) *67* (April 9, 1903), 538–539.

to be inconsistent with his theory of the earth, has propounded a most ingenious explanation of these second-phase waves.[7] It does not seem to me that there is any insuperable incompatibility between Mr. Fisher's theory of a fluid centre and the hypothesis that the second-phase waves are distortional. We know nothing of the behaviour of matter exposed to the pressures prevailing in the interior of the earth, and it is not wholly inconceivable that a fluid under pressure of millions of atmospheres might be enabled to transmit the distortional waves which it is unable to transmit under pressures with which we are familiar. I do not, however, insist on this point, as it is immaterial to my present purpose: all that is material is that the wave-motion, in the first and second phases, differs essentially; and this is accepted by Mr. Fisher.

It is also indicated, apart from the arguments which I have already urged,[8] by the records of Prof. Vicentini's type of seismograph, composed of two heavy masses, one free to move horizontally, the other free to move vertically. In the records of great earthquakes originating at a distance of 90° of arc or more, it is found that the former gives a very small displacement for the first phase, while the latter frequently registers the maximum displacement of the whole disturbance. In the second phase the conditions are reversed, and, while the mass free to move vertically seldom gives any indication of disturbance, that which is free to move horizontally gives a very large displacement. This difference in the character of the record in the two phases shows that the movement is different, and incidentally tends to support the interpretation that I have proposed: for, if the first phase represents the outcrop of a disturbance transmitted through the earth as a condensational wave, then vertical movement would preponderate over horizontal at distances of 90° or more; while, if the second phase is caused by distortional waves, horizontal movement should preponderate in it.

This difference in the character of the records of the two phases may also be used as an argument against the idea which has been adopted in Japan,[9] that the first and second phases represent wave-motion of similar character, transmitted at different rates through layers at different depths from the surface, but in both cases parallel to, and at no great depth below, it. As this contention is incompatible with the figures given below, it need not be dealt with in this place, and the facts may be left to speak for themselves.

[7] "On the transmission of earthquake-waves through the Earth," *Proc. Cambridge Phil. Soc. 15* (1903–1904), 354–361.

[8] *Phil. Trans. Roy. Soc. London* [A] *194* (1900), 162–166.

[9] A. Imamura, *Publications of the Earthquake-Investigation Committee in Foreign Languages,* No. 16, Tokyo, 1904, and later issues *passim.*

## II. THE DATA

In dealing with the data, it is necessary to make some selection from the large amount of material which has been collected, and to confine our attention to those records in which accuracy is *primafacie* probable; this limits us to those earthquakes the place and time of orgin of which can be determined with accuracy, and which were also of sufficient magnitude to give complete records on distant seismographs. This last reservation is necessary, for many earthquakes of great local severity are only imperfectly recorded at a distance of even a quarter of the circumference of the globe, and the portion lost is always that of the preliminary tremors.

These limitations leave only fourteen disturbances for consideration, some of which consisted of two or three distinct earthquakes, starting from the same origin at short intervals from each other. Of these, details have been published in a collected form in some cases only, in the others they are still in manuscript; but those that have been published will serve to show the manner in which scattered details are grouped and dealt with. . . .

. . . . .

Such are the materials available. As may be noticed, there are discrepancies, and the time-intervals do not increase regularly with the distance: the discrepancies being due, as has been explained, partly to inaccuracies in the distant records, and partly to errors in determining the time of origin. Another possible source of discrepancy is the possibility that the rate of propagation is not uniform in every direction, and that the time taken by wave-motion in travelling, say from Japan to Europe, is different from that taken by the same form of wave-motion in travelling from an equal distance in America. There are some indications that such is the case; but the difference is small, in comparison with the whole interval, and as the point is not material to the present investigation, it may be ignored, and the irregularities smoothed to a regular time-curve.

This is best done graphically, as is represented in Fig. 1, where the averages of groups, and the single observations not adapted to averaging, have been plotted, and average time-curves drawn for the first and second phases.

It will be seen that the time-curves of the first two phases are very similar in shape, up to 120° from the origin; but beyond this they differ radically in form. That of the first phase, after an irregularity between 130° and 140°, becomes very flat and proceeds almost horizon-

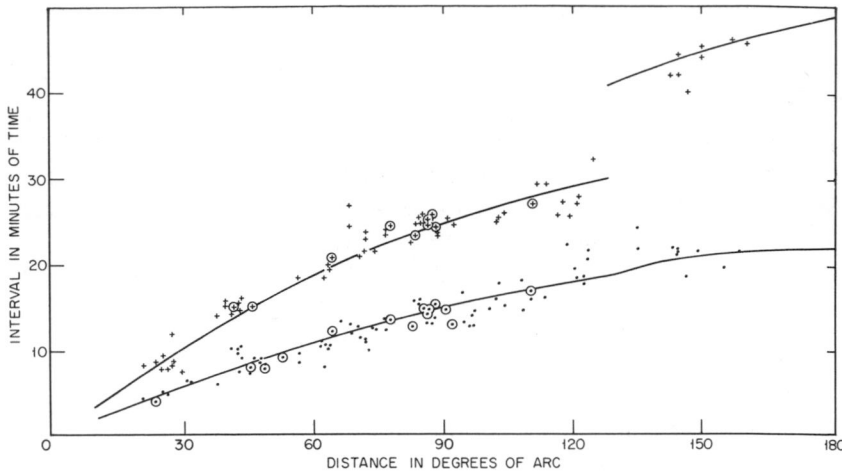

Fig. 1. Time curves of first and second phases of preliminary tremors. The marks surrounded by circles are averages.

tally from 150° to 180°; that of the second phase comes to an end at 130° from the origin, and is continued some 11 minutes farther up. It is the explanation of these irregularities with which this paper is mainly concerned. . . .

. . . . .

It should be noted that the intervals and resulting rates must not be taken too literally: the result of averaging observations is, indubitably, to increase the interval and lessen the apparent rates; but, besides this, an allowance ought to be made for the reduced rate of propagation of the disturbance through the outer crust of the earth. The amount of these corrections is not accurately determinable, but as they are in the same direction in every case, and as both together would, probably, not amount to a minute of time, they may be neglected so far as the conclusions drawn below are concerned.

### III. The Deductions

Wave-motion originating at any point in the earth will be propagated in all directions from it, and whatever the nature of these waves their wave-paths will be straight lines so long as the velocity of propagation remains constant; but, if this varies, the course of the wave-paths will be altered according to the laws of refraction, which are to be found in every text-book of physics. These laws hold good whatever be the nature of the wave-motion, although, in the case of elastic waves, the rate of propagation is dependent on two factors—the elasticity and density of the medium through which they are propagated. From this it will be seen that any information that we can get regarding the form of the wave-paths will indicate the changes, if any, in the rate of propagation, and thence in the physical condition, of different parts of the earth traversed by the wave-paths which emerge at different parts of its surface.

It will not be necessary to enter into details as to the manner in which the wave-paths can be determined from observations of the time of arrival of the disturbance; for the subject has been fully dealt with as a mathematical problem by Dr. Rudzki[10] of Cracow, and it will only be necessary to apply his conclusions.

In the first place, if waves are propagated along the surface of the earth, or at a short distance below but parallel to it, the mean apparent rate of propagation, as measured along the surface of the earth, will be constant for all distances. This is the case, or nearly the case, for the third-phase waves, which are, consequently, accepted as surface-waves, and can, therefore, give no information regarding the central portions of the earth. In the first and second phases this is obviously not the case: in the first phase there is a continuous increase in the apparent rate of propagation, and although there is irregularity in the rates calculated for the second phase, these are higher for distances beyond 90° than for lesser distances. These facts lead to the conclusion that the first and second-phase waves cannot be surface-waves, nor waves propagated a short distance below the surface, but must be mass-waves propagated through the body of the earth.

In considering the form of the paths along which these waves are propagated, it will be convenient to consider each quadrant separately, dealing first with the wave-paths which emerge at distances up to 90° from the origin, and then with those which emerge at distances beyond that.

If the rate of propagation through the earth were uniform in all directions and at all depths, the wave-paths would be straight lines, and the mean apparent rate of transmission, along the chord, would be the same for all distances. It is obvious that this is not so, for the apparent rate of propagation, as measured along the chord, increases continuously up to 90°, in the case of both first and second phase-waves. This means that the waves travel faster as they penetrate to greater depths, and consequently the wave-paths are not straight lines, but curves

---

[10] *Beitr. Geophysik 3* (1898), 495–518.

whose convexity is directed towards the centre. Besides this, the fact that the increase in apparent rate of propagation is proportionately greater in the case of the second phase, shows that the curvature of its wave-paths is greater than in the case of the first-phase waves.

It must, however, be noticed that, although the increase in apparent rate of propagation is greater in the one case than in the other, yet the rate of increase as between 30°, 60°, and 90° is practically the same in both cases. The actual figures are as follows:

| Increase of apparent velocity | | First Phase | Second Phase |
|---|---|---|---|
| along the chord | 30° to 60° | .055 | .118 |
| Ditto | 60° to 90° | .036 | .075 |
| Ratio of increments | — | .65 | .64 |

These figures show that the apparent rate of propagation increases with the distance about twice as rapidly in the case of the second as in that of the first-phase waves; that the rate of increase is not uniform, but diminishing with increasing distance; and that in both cases this alteration is in the same direction and at the same rate. This suggests that the increase in rate of propagation with increase in depth of the wave-paths is not due to their passage through material of a different character, but may be merely the effect of increased pressure and temperature, and consequently, that the substance of which the earth is composed—below the outer crust—undergoes no material change in composition or physical condition, at least to the depths reached by the wave-paths of earthquake-waves emerging at 90° from the origin.

This much is independent of any assumption regarding the nature of the wave-motion, but without making some assumption regarding this, no further information is attainable. I shall take it that the first-phase waves are condensational—this being generally acknowledged—and that the second-phase waves are distortional, an assumption which I regard as more than probable, and on these assumptions it is possible to estimate the proportion which the modulus of rigidity bears to the bulk-modulus, or resistance to compression. In making this estimate we may take the wave-paths for the two waves as being so nearly coincident that there is no material difference in the density of the medium. The calculation being simple, it is only necessary to state the results, which are that on wave-paths emerging at 30° from the origin the rigidity is .385 of the bulk-modulus, for paths emerging at 60° it is .446, and for those emerging at 90° it is .493; that is to say, the rigidity or power of resisting distortion increases at a greater rate than the solidity, or power of resisting compression.

If absolute values of these two moduli are required, it is necessary to make some assumption regarding the density of the medium through which the waves are transmitted, and if it be assumed that Laplace's law of densities is correct and that the mean density[11] of the medium traversed is about the same as that at the greatest depth reached by the chord, we get the following values for the mean rigidity and bulk-modulus, both being measured in C.G.S. units:

| | Assumed | Modulus of Resistance to | |
| Arc | density | Compression | Distortion |
|---|---|---|---|
| 30° | 3.00 | $151.6 \times 10^{10}$ | $74.7 \times 10^{10}$ |
| 60° | 4.25 | $219.4 \times 10^{10}$ | $132.3 \times 10^{10}$ |
| 90° | 6.20 | $322.4 \times 10^{10}$ | $223.2 \times 10^{10}$ |

These figures should be regarded as arithmetical curiosities rather than actual measures, for, apart from uncertainty regarding the density of the medium, the mean apparent rate of propagation, as measured along the chord, is certainly less than the true mean rate, as measured along the actual wave-path, and the maximum rate is greater than this again; yet, despite this, the figures indicate that the material traversed by the waves is endowed with a very high degree of rigidity and resistance to compression. In the case of the waves emerging at 90° from the origin, the material traversed has, on the average, nearly 12 times the resistance of granite to compression and 15 times its rigidity; if the density remains constant, these figures would be reduced by about three-tenths, but on the other hand the maximum values will be higher.

It must, however, be borne in mind that this high degree of rigidity, as against stresses of very short duration, is quite compatible with the yielding to stresses of long duration, which is required by known facts of structural geology, and need not necessarily be inconsistent with those movements, of the nature of convection-currents, which Mr. Fisher[12] believes to exist in the interior of the earth.

Turning now to the second quadrant, it will be convenient to take each phase separately, and to commence with the second phase.

. . . At 120° the increase in the mean apparent rate of propagation is more than maintained, but too much importance must not be attached to the exact figures, for the interval at 120° is somewhat uncertain. Most of the records from about this distance are late commencements, attributed to the second phase; and, if these be excluded, the interval will be a little longer, and the apparent rate of propagation a little less. . . .

[11] Strictly speaking, the square root of the mean of the squares of densities.
[12] *Physics of the Earth,* 2nd ed. (1889), Chaps. vi and xxiii.

At 150° from the origin we find a remarkable decrease in the mean apparent rate of propagation, which drops from an average of over 6 to about 4½ kilometres per second, and the most obvious explanation of the decrease is that these waves, penetrating to greater depths, have entered, and for part of their way traversed, a central core, composed of matter which transmits them at a much slower speed than that traversed by the waves emerging at lesser distances from the origin. The only other alternative is that the time-interval is wrong, and that we are not dealing with the second-phase waves at all.

As regards this hypothesis, I may point out that all the determinations used at distances of over 120° are derived from my own examination of the original records or copies from them. In every case the second phase, as adopted, presents the same characters as those which I had recognized at lesser distances; and if the times given do not refer to the second phase (in the sense used elsewhere by me), then this phase is not represented at all in the more distant records, and instead of a central core which transmits the waves more slowly, there must be one which is incapable of transmitting them at all, thus leading to the same conclusion, that the deeply penetrating wave-paths enter matter of very different constitution from that traversed by the shallower paths.

Rejecting the supposition that the second-phase waves are extinguished by the central core, and accepting the more probable one that the rate of transmission is reduced in it, there remain two important questions to be answered, namely, the size of the core and the rate of transmission of the waves in it.

As regards the size of the core, we have seen that it is not penetrated by the wave-paths which emerge at 120°; and the great decrease at 150° shows that the wave-paths emerging at this distance have penetrated deeply into it. Now, the chord of 120° reaches a maximum depth from the surface of half the radius, and we have seen that the wave-paths up to this distance are convex towards the centre of the earth, so it may be taken that the central core does not extend beyond about 0.4 of the radius from the centre.

As regards the rate of transmission of the waves, the data hardly deserve elaborate mathematical treatment until more have been collected, but it is easy to arrive at an approximate estimate of the rate of transmission and the nature of the wave-paths. The chord of 150° has a length of 12,297 kilometres, of which 8413 km lies in the outer 0.6 of the radius and, at a mean rate of 6 km/sec, requires 23.4 minutes, leaving 21.6 minutes for the remaining 3884 km, or a mean rate of 3 kilometres per second.

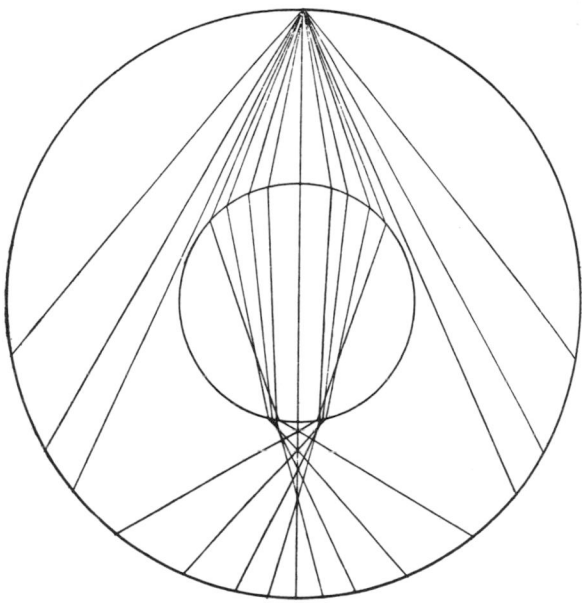

Fig. 2.

This reduction in speed has an important and unexpected result, for it means a refractive index of 2.0 and a great deviation of the wave-paths as they enter the central core. As a first approximation to the actual course of the wave-paths, I give, in Fig. 2, a representation of what they would be on the supposition of a central core, occupying 0.4 of the radius, in which the rate of propagation is one half of that in the outer shell; in this it will be seen that the wave-paths emerging at 150° reach their emergence after passing on the opposite side of the centre of the earth, and exhibit that concavity towards the centre which Dr. Rudzki's investigation requires where increase in depth of wave-path is accompanied by a decrease in the rate of propagation.[13] The actual wave-paths, however, are not, as has been shown, composed of straight lines, and the real wave-paths must be more like what is

[13]The wavepaths shown in Fig. 2 give, for an emergence at 150° and at a time interval of 45 minutes, a rate of transmission of 3.5 km/sec in the central core, and 7.0 km/sec in the outer shell. These values are higher than can be admitted; the explanation probably lies in the shortening of these long-distance wave-paths which results from their curvature, as shown in Fig. 3, and possibly also in a lesser ratio than that of 2:1 of the rates of transmission, or a lesser size of the central core. It may also be noticed that rates of 7.0 and 3.5 km/sec respectively give an interval for the diameter of about 42.5 minutes: and although this value cannot be accepted, it indicates a possibility that the emergence of the second-phase waves at the antipodes of the origin may actually be earlier than at a distance of 150°.

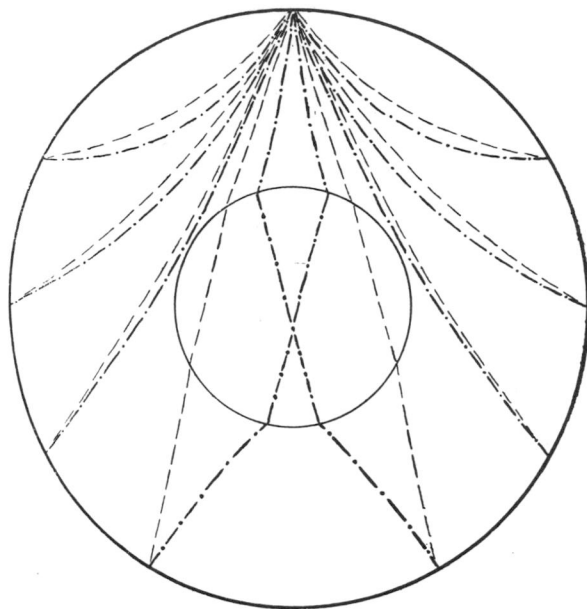

Fig. 3. The broken lines represent the first phase, the broken-and-dotted lines the second phase, and the continuous curve the third phase.

indicated in Fig. 3, which may be taken as correct in kind, though perhaps wrong in detail, as to the actual position of the wave-paths.

The high index of refraction prevents the formation of a complete shadow-band, for the most extreme of the rays which enter the central core suffer so great a deviation that their point of emergence at the surface overlaps that of the last rays which miss the central core; but an inspection of Figs. 2 and 3 will show that there should be a zone, at about 140° from the origin, where the second-phase waves would be so dispersed, and consequently feeble, that it would practically amount to a shadow, and the second phase should be absent in records from this distance, or much more feebly marked than in those from greater or lesser distances.

The effect will be modified by the fact that the transition from central core to outer shell is not abrupt but gradual, though comparatively rapid; yet it is worth noting that, so far as the limited amount of available material may be trusted, the second phase is certainly much less marked at about 140° from the origin than at distances of less than 130° or more than 150°. For instance, the Guatemala earthquake was recorded at Bombay, 144° from the origin, by three instruments. On one record no indication of a second phase can be found; on another it is so indistinctly marked that it can hardly be recognized as such; and even on the Milne pendulum, which shows what I take to be the second phase most distinctly, it is not at all characteristic. The Batavian record of this same earthquake, at a distance of 160° from the origin, shows it much more distinctly; and on the Cape-Town records of the Alaskan earthquakes at 150° from the origin it is easily recognizable.

These considerations lead to the conclusion that the time-curve of the second-phase waves is not a continuous line. Up to about 130° it is continuous, and represents the emergence of waves which have traveled directly from the origin; beyond that distance it represents waves which have been refracted, after passing on the opposite side of the centre of the earth, and it would be misleading to join the two into one continuous curve. For these reasons, the second-phase time-curve has been drawn as it is shown in Fig. 1.

We may now turn to the first-phase waves, and see how they are affected by the central core. At 120° the increase in mean apparent rate of transmission is maintained, but at 150° the rate has dropped to 9.76 km/sec, and the value is a good one. There can be no doubt that the drop is real, but it is much less than in the case of the second-phase waves, and merely represents a diminution of the rate of propagation by about one tenth.

From this it will be seen that the central core behaves differently from the outer shell with regard to the first, as with regard to the second, phase but the change is much less in amount, and would probably have remained undetected were it not for the very conspicuous alteration in the case of the second-phase waves.

## IV. CONCLUSIONS

From the considerations detailed in the foregoing pages, I conclude that the interior of the earth, after the outermost crust of heterogeneous rock is passed, consists of a uniform material, capable of transmitting wave-motion of two different types at different rates of propagation: that this material undergoes no material change in physical character to a depth of about six-tenths of the radius, such change as takes place being gradual and probably accounted for sufficiently by the increase of pressure; and that the central four-tenths of the radius are occupied by matter possessing radically different physical properties, inasmuch as the rate of propagation of the first phase is but slightly reduced, while the second-phase waves are either not transmitted at all, or, more probably, transmitted at about half the rate which prevails in the outer shell.

If these waves are to be explained as those of condensation and distortion, then the ratio between the modulus of rigidity and the bulk-modulus is only two-thirds of that obtaining in the outer shell; but whether this interpretation be adopted, or that of Mr. Fisher, or some other yet unproposed, we still have a central core the behaviour of which with regard to these waves differs materially from that of the outer shell. I do not propose to enter into speculative grounds, or to offer any opinion as to whether this central core is composed of iron, surrounded by a stony shell, or whether it is the central gaseous nucleus of others. On this occasion, it is enough to have shown that there is a difference which cannot be overlooked, and must be taken into account in any hypothesis that may be formed regarding the constitution of the interior of the earth.

# EVANS

John William Evans (1857–1930), British geologist, was engaged at various times in field work in Asia, Africa, and South America, was State Geologist in India from 1893 to 1898, first in Junagarh (Katheawar) and then in Mysore, and was Lecturer in Geology and Petrology at the Birkbeck College and the Imperial College of Science between 1906 and 1927. He was awarded the Lyell Fund in 1901 and the Murchison Medal in 1922 and was recognized as an authority on Devonian stratigraphy as well as a petrologist of distinction. He was apparently the originator of the term "ventifact."

## DREIKANTER AND VENTIFACTS *

With reference to the discussion . . . on the use of the word Dreikante, I should like to point out . . . that the term is more appropriately employed for the comparatively common form with three long, nearly parallel edges, than for the rarer type which is roughly tetrahedral and has typically six instead of three edges.

If a stone lies on a sandy tract, the wind may, by means of the sand that it carries with it, bevel the upper portion of the side turned toward it, and at the same time gradually remove the sand beneath till the stone falls, turning over towards the wind on its abraded surface. A new angle of abrasion will then be formed on the stone, making an angle of about 60° (a crystallographer would call it 120°) with the first, and, under favourable circumstances, by the repetition of the same movement a trigonal prismatic form with three parallel sides and edges will be more and more distinctly developed.

The tetrahedral or "tripyramidal" form and other more irregular

*From *Geological Magazine 48* (1911), 334–335.

shapes would appear to be due to the stone falling over obliquely instead of directly towards the wind, either on account of its shape or because the sand has been removed unevenly from below it.

If a general expression be required for any wind-shaped stone, we might speak of a "ventifact," on the analogy of artifact, sometimes spelt "artefact," which is already in use for an object, such as a palæolith, fashioned by men, and of "ventiduct," which has been employed in architecture.

# SCHUCHERT

Charles Schuchert (1858–1942), American paleontologist and stratigrapher, never enrolled in a formal course in geology or attended a college class. Yet, at age forty-six, he was appointed Professor of Historical Geology at Yale University and Curator of Geological Collections in Peabody Museum, posts which he occupied with great distinction until his retirement from museum duties in 1923 and from teaching in 1925. As a boy in his teens, he was an ardent collector of fossils from the richly fossiliferous outcrops in the vicinity of Cincinnati, Ohio, his birthplace and boyhood home. Despite heavy responsibilities in his family's furniture factory, he studied the available literature and organized his collections so expertly that in 1888 he was employed by James Hall as an assistant in the New York State Museum in Albany. After working for a time with N. H. Winchell in Minnesota and then with Charles E. Beecher as a preparator in the Peabody Museum, he joined the U. S. Geological Survey in 1893 as assistant curator of invertebrate fossils. A year later he was transferred to the National Museum, where he remained until 1904, when he accepted the appointment at Yale. He is best known for his taxonomic work with brachiopods, his emphasis upon the importance of geosynclines in stratigraphic studies, and his leadership in the development of paleogeography, but he is best remembered by his many former students in the Yale Graduate School as an inspiring teacher and beloved colleague.

## PRINCIPLES OF PALEOGEOGRAPHY *

### CLASSIFICATION OF METHODS

The methods or principles for determining the relation of ancient seas and lands are four in number: (1) The Paleontologic, (2) the Areal-Geologic, (3) the Petrologic, and (4) the Structural or Diastrophic.

*From "Paleogeography of North America," *Geological Society of America Bulletin 20* (1910), 427–606. The excerpts are from pp. 437–482.

## Paleontologic Method

The primary basis for a geologic chronology is furnished by the organic remains entombed in the stratified rocks. All methods for the exact determination of geologic time are at present dependent upon paleontology, yet it is not to be denied that locally other means than the paleontologic may become of prime importance.

.     .     .     .     .

. . . No paleontologist who has looked into the present dispersal of faunas understands how currents of similar temperature can keep shallow-water faunas from intermingling. It was the currents and the equable temperature of the ancient seas that facilitated the migration of the shallow-water life, and this is especially true of the larval and adult animals living near the surface of the sea. Land barriers and shallow-sea marshes, together with decided temperature and saline differences in the water, are the effective causes preventing the distribution of faunas. Temperature and saline barriers, however, are comparatively seldom effective in geologic time, but the land barriers are continually occasioning the localization of faunas, and by their breaking down permit the intermigration of the localized biota. The entire subject of sea-currents should not be used to explain faunal differences, but for the present should be laid aside. The first need is to establish paleogeography, a result which has as yet not been attained.

In making the maps herewith presented the greatest stress has been laid upon the distribution of faunas, both as to time and space, as known to paleontologists. When synchronous faunas were found to be different and a lapse of connecting strata occurred, these facts were interpreted as meaning that a land barrier more or less complete kept the faunas apart. It is fully realized that in the course of time it may be shown that these maps err on the side of too much restriction of the continental seas. It was thought, however, that by the present method of representation more certain progress would be attained than by assuming universal continental synthetic seas, which some paleontologists believe have not led to a proper understanding of the periodic encroachment of the oceans on the land.

An analysis of fossil faunas indicates that from the earliest Paleozoic times there have been three permanent oceanic realms that have furnished life to the continental seas of North America. In the order of their importance these are: (1) The Gulf of Mexico mediterranean, (2) the Pacific, (3) the Arctic and the Atlantic. The faunas of the North

Atlantic as a rule are restricted to Acadia and to the eastern portion of the Appalachian mountains, yet they frequently spread across these folds and mix with the life of the other regions. Those of the Pacific have a far wider range, and often occur as far east as Appalachia. The faunas from the Gulf or Mexican mediterranean are at times clearly tinged with an Atlantic facies, but oftener are more of the southern than of the northern European type, while at other times they are without doubt from the South American realm by way of the Pacific.

### AREAL-GEOLOGIC METHOD

Having ascertained the nature of a fauna and its stratigraphic position, the next point of greatest value is the geographic distribution of the formation. Here geologic maps are of the highest importance, especially those that give lists of the local faunas. In this connection the Folios of the United States Geological Survey were most helpful, but all maps issued by the more prominent national and state surveys were scanned for information. The recently published International Geologic Map was likewise found to be very useful, particularly so for outlying regions of the North American continent.

### PETROLOGIC METHOD

Marine conglomerates unmistakably indicate proximity to land, and are therefore of great value in paleogeography. Marine sandstones are also good indicators for shore conditions, shallow seas, and nearness to land, but are not so reliable as the conglomerates. In the interior region of the continental seas, however, sandstones are of rare occurrence. Mud deposits point rather to shallow seas, and black shales are thought to denote closed or stagnant arms of the sea, variably foul at the bottom, as in the Black sea of Russia. Such black shale deposits are the Utica, Genesee, Chattanooga, etcetera, the known faunas of which are of the nekton and plankton type. As a rule, limestones are indicative of seas of wider extent among low lands during times of moist and warmer temperature, while dolomites mark about the same conditions, but in shallower, evaporating seas. Oolites are formed in the littoral region of seas between tides where the lime salts accrete about a nucleus due to its repeated wetting and drying, and otherwise.

The interpretation thus given the various kinds of sediments has been applied in the construction of the present maps, but not with the same care as that given the faunas and the areal geology. Volcanoes and volcanic material have also been considered, but information regarding these has been plotted in only a few of the more striking times and areas of eruption. The positions of these are shown by asterisks.

## Diastrophic Method

Having ascertained the essential periods of emergence and transgression by the faunal method, the diastrophic principle was then used to fix the major time divisions. Taken by itself, the latter method is believed to be nearly as unreliable, where permanent results are concerned, as the petrologic method. In fact, the principle of diastrophism can rarely be used before taking the fossil evidence into account, for it is the latter that fixes and determines physical events. Diastrophism, however, is of much value in paleogeography, but it must follow, not precede, the evidence furnished by the fossils.

## Continental Seas, or Negative Continental Elements

All the Paleozoic seas now engaging the attention of American stratigraphers are of the "continental" type—that is, their deposits have been furnished by shallow seas within "great continental basins." . . .

These bodies of water and others to be named in the following pages are distinct faunal provinces whose successive biota are received from those great perpetual realms of marine life—the Pacific, Atlantic, and Arctic oceans. They are the "negative elements" of Willis,[1] yet as the oceanic areas are the true negative elements the writer has designated these seas as *negative continental elements*. They have been defined by Willis as follows: "By contrast with the positive elements of the continent which are recognized by absence of sediments and preponderance of unconformities, the negative elements are distinguished by the sediments which bury them."

According to the derivation of their faunas, these various elements or seas may be grouped as follows:

*Seas with Atlantic or Poseidon life*—Primarily (1) Saint Lawrence, (2) Potomac embayment; secondarily (1) Appalachian, (2) Mississippian, and (3) Hudson. By inference, Suwanee strait.

*Seas with Mexico-Caribbean life*—Primarily (1) Gulf of Mexico overlap, (2) Coloradoan, and (3) Mississippian; secondarily, Appalachian. By inference, Sea of Tehuantepec.

*Seas with Pacific life*—Primarily (1) Cordilleran, (2) Sonoran, (3) Logan, (4) Californian, and (5) Vancouverian; secondarily, Alaskan. At times primarily, but as a rule with slight Pacific incursions, Mississippian.

*Seas with Arctic life*—Primarily (1) Hudson, and (2) Alaskan; secondarily, (1) Cordilleran, (2) Coloradoan, and (3) Mississippian.

The foregoing arrangement of these seas will probably impress the

[1] Willis, *Bull. Geol. Soc. Am. 18* (1907), 398.

reader in two ways: First, the great number of North American seas, and, second, their rather free intercommunication. The multiplicity of seas, which in the main were of Paleozoic time, unmistakably indicates shallow bodies of water variously separated by more or less ineffective land barriers. A survey of the paleogeographic maps presented in this paper will make this fact abundantly evident, and it may be likewise observed that not only did the marine waters flow in on the land from the four sides of the North American continent, but that the seas were localized among lands that suggest an archipelago of large islands. Further study will show that the Paleozoic continental seas began in a small way, pulsated back and forth over the continent, and, if a few irregularities are disregarded, increased in area until they almost completely submerged North America in Middle Ordovicic time. This great inundation was dominated by the Pacific. The oscillatory nature of the seas continued, yet during the Siluric the Arctic waters were the dominating force. With each recurring climax of submergence, however, it is seen that the pulsations became smaller and smaller until the close of the Paleozoic, when North America was again as large as it had been at the beginning of this era. For a long period the entire continent then remained positive except along the border region of the Pacific, which ocean during the Triassic overlapped great areas and in the late Jurassic developed the Logan sea. During this period, however, contraction and subsidence of this immense ocean had gone on, and thrusting now took effect, giving birth to the Sierra Nevadas. About this time subsidence also took place over much of eastern Mexico, being probably caused by the thrusting of the Pacific ocean indicated in the appearance of the Sierra Nevadas. This thrusting was continued for a period equal in length to the Comanchic, and resulted in the greater extension of the Gulf of Mexico not only over the larger part of Mexico, but the syncline stretched into the United States as far north as Kansas. A marked but short withdrawal of this sea then took place, when the same syncline was further extended, giving rise to the Coloradoan sea connecting the Gulf of Mexico with the Arctic ocean. That this trough continued to subside is shown by the fact that in Montana it contains about 12,000 feet of marine deposits of Colorado and Montana age, and these series are said to be followed by a similar thickness of Laramie and Livingston beds. In the development of this trough must be assumed the gradual rise of the Rocky mountains in the West, a considerable portion of whose elevation has gone toward filling the syncline.

Along the northern Atlantic thrusting culminated with the early Permic revolution, since which time this ocean has gradually eaten its way westward, assisted by block faulting seaward either in late Jurassic or early Comanchic. This action continued until late in Cretacic times, when the ocean overlapped the continental shelf all along the coast from New Jersey southward, thus connecting with the Gulf of Mexico overlap.

·     ·     ·     ·     ·

A survey of the Paleozoic paleogeography here submitted shows that the seas are of a continental character, for the marine waters of the four quarters of the northern hemisphere flow in on the depressed inland basins of the North American continent; further, that this vast land-mass has in the main always been bordered by high lands. The sediments of these seas are derived from the elevated areas of the continental mass and there was no "contribution of rock material from outside or aid from the ocean's waves or currents, either those of the Atlantic or Pacific. For the most part, therefore, the growth of the continent . . . may be said to have been *endogenous.* It began to be *exogenous* on the Atlantic side in the Cretaceous era" (Dana).

These facts and others stated on later pages prove that the North American continent in its entirety has always been essentially positive, and was a greater land-mass just previous to the introduction of the Cambric and the Siluric seas than it is now. Moreover, during the Paleozoic its surface was variously buckled and elevated, but never very highly, owing to the inwardly moving Atlantic, Gulf, and Pacific margins, thus giving rise to shallow or continental island studded seas. During the early Mesozoic the North American continent was again larger than it is at present, but in late Mesozoic time, long after the Sierra Nevada deformation, another great syncline was developed giving rise to a continental sea that did vast endogenous work along the entire eastern side of the Rocky mountains extending from the Gulf to the Arctic ocean. Finally, since the disappearance of this, the Coloradoan sea, the North American continent has had throughout almost its present size and the work of its marine waters has been exogenous, due to overlaps of the oceans.

·     ·     ·     ·     ·

### PALEOZOIC EMERGENCES AND SUBMERGENCES

*General discussion*—From the preceding pages it may be learned that there are periodic recurrences of extensive emergences of the continents and that each one is later invaded or transgressed by continental seas of greater or less extent. The emergences mature far more rapidly than the transgressions. The former are thought to be due to the periodic subsidences of the oceanic bottoms, while the cause of the transgressions is not so clear. It is concluded, however, that the unloading of the combined continents into the seas is of primary importance in this connection. With each period of marked sinking of the oceanic areas the strand-line becomes negative and everywhere recedes to a lower level around the continental horsts. The lands then appear to stand higher. The continents therefore attain their elevation through two causes: (1) Low lands over vast areas, due to the negative eustatic character of the strand-line, and (2) a more or less high altitude resulting locally from the tangential lateral thrusts of the oceans or vertical movements due to isostatic readjustments. The smaller invasions made by the sea may therefore be caused by lands produced by tangential thrusts, such movements being apt to form synclines along the inner sides away from the oceans, or the water may vary in local distribution, owing to its being attracted by the land-masses. Further, as the detrital material from the land is unloaded irregularly and locally into the continental seas, the submergences may be locally accentuated. There are, therefore, various types of continental seas, and these may be named and defined as follows:

*Attracted continental seas*—During times of decided emergence due to the greater altitude and extent of the land-masses, the oceans may be drawn up the sides of these elevations several hundred feet, thus causing their margins or preëxisting depressions to be flooded. Such seas are met with after periods of actual elevation or eustatic negative movements. The resulting seas are small, and such are thought to be most frequently present in the Saint Lawrence sea.

*Synclinal continental seas*—During recurrent periods of unrest the oceans thrust the margins of the continents inward and away from their areas. In the early stages of such movements broad and low folds are produced, which together make synclinoria along the inner sides of the mass thus disturbed, the folds being most numerous, higher, and closer together toward the ocean. Therefore the deepest continental troughs appear immediately at the base of such lands; the sea flows into them and makes long but narrow waterways. In the developmental stages of such a synclinorium the sea is at first apt to be broader and shallower. As the folds are successively accentuated by the subsequent thrusting, the water areas not only become deeper, but also more complex; hence a series of troughs may finally appear that may or may not be in communication with one another. The Appalachian and Saint Lawrence seas, with their sinking Lenoir, Chazy, and Levis troughs, are good examples of such seas. The Appalachian and Great Basin synclines had each finally subsided in certain local areas to a maximum of at least 30,000 feet.

*Aggrading continental seas*—Being decidedly the areas of loading, continental seas are therefore aggrading seas; they are rarely degrading. Great quantities of detrital matter are transferred by the rivers to these seas, causing them either to spill over and inundate the other lands or causing their bottoms to subside. The strand-line is thus constantly affected either in a positive or a negative manner. In fact, this alternate loading and sinking explains the irregularity, at least, in the oscillatory nature of all continental seas. During a period of loading the waters are more and more displaced and submerge wider areas of land. If no subsidence of the sea-bottom takes place the basin will eventually become completely filled and all its water dispersed and added to other marine seas, thus causing the strand-lines to become positive. During a period of subsidence, however, the water is naturally contracted, and for a time parts of the former littoral region are exposed. In this way the strand-lines of aggrading seas are continually affected and made slightly positive or negative.

Again, if an area which is rapidly loading in vast quantities is constantly subsiding, there will result either some isostatic compensation in the way of land-making elsewhere, or where there is no compensation the entire adjacent areas will be dragged down. In the latter case, if such an area of a continental sea is close to the ocean the land barrier will be submerged, allowing communication between the two marine bodies of water. This is thought to have been the case during the deep subsidence of the New York basin, where every now and then the Atlantic has access to the Appalachian trough. In this region, either periodic isostatic compensation appears to have been operative or the tangential thrusting of the Atlantic ocean has repeatedly renewed the land barriers, which in the end were not only eroded, but again dragged down and submerged. Throughout the Paleozoic there was almost constant subsidence in the Mexico embayment, and the isostatic compensation must therefore have been farther removed than in the case of the New York basin. The Mississippian sea is an excellent example of an aggrading sea.

The "transgressive seas" are likewise aggrading seas, yet they owe their distinctive character not to minor local fillings, but to the combined deposits of all marine waters; also to the united effects of all the isostatic compensation having an upward movement, such as land-making and the elevation of the ocean-bottom as well.

*Transgressing continental seas*—These bodies of water, which are due to a general eustatic elevation of the strand-lines (eustatic positive strand-lines), are the great continental seas that more or less simultaneously affect all continents. They are slow in attaining their maximum expansion, but vanish fairly rapidly following the periodic shrinkage of the earth, which naturally exerts more influence on the oceanic areas than on the lands. The migratory reëxpansion of these seas is due to the combined unloading of the continents into the marine waters, with the added effect resulting from the settling back of the elevated continental borders. Probably there are also other causes, one of which may be the local raising of oceanic bottoms. Suess has well said: "Every grain of sand which sinks to the bottom of the sea expels, to however trifling a degree, the ocean from its bed." If the present continents above sea-level were unloaded into the ocean, the strand-line would become positive to the extent of 650 feet. Such a displacement of the sea would inundate North America in areal extent and distribution not unlike the submergence caused by the Siluric transgression, the third most extensive flood on this continent.

With these definitions as a foundation, the various emergences and submergences of the North American continent will now be described. A marked period of emergence combined with one of decided submergence completes a cycle of time, and according to the principle of diastrophism establishes a geologic system or period that may be recognized in all lands affected by inundations.

# JOHNSON Willard Drake Johnson (1859–1917), American topographic engineer and geomorphologist, was associated with the Topographic Branch of the U. S. Geological Survey throughout most of his active career.

## THE PROFILE OF MATURITY IN ALPINE GLACIAL EROSION*

My own acquaintance with the phenomena of glaciation of the alpine type had its beginning in the Sierra Nevada, in 1883, in the latitude of the Yosemite Valley—the so-called High Sierra. Prevailing opinion as to that region, it appeared, ranged between the two extreme views indicated; namely that, as regards quantitative effects in degradation more especially, glaciation had been widely destructive of the preglacial topography, on the one hand; on the other, that it had been relatively protective. But there was no recognition of distinctive forms —beyond "U-canyons" and moraines. I had little notion, therefore, as to what I should discover; only an open mind and a lively curiosity.

*From *Journal of Geology 12* (1904), 569–578.

I was a maker of topographic maps, of some experience, and had a topographer's familiarity with the erosion aspects of mountains; but only of unglaciated mountains. I had as well, however, something of the inquisitiveness of the physiographer as to the origin and development of topographic forms.

The first station occupied in this work of survey was Mount Lyell, one of the most widely commanding summits of the vast mountainous tract of the High Sierra.

From Lyell there was disclosed a scheme of degradation for which I had not been in the least prepared. No accepted theory of erosion, glacial or other, explained either its ground-plan outlines or its canyon-valley profiles; and, so far as I can see, none makes intelligible its distinctive features now. The canyons, at their heads, were abnormally deep; they were broadly flat-bottomed rather then U-formed, the ratio of bottom width to depth often being several to one; and their head walls, as a rule, stood as nearly upright, apparently, as scaling of the rock would permit. I characterized them, figuratively, as "down at the heel." In many instances the basin floor, of naked, sound rock in large part, and showing a glistening polish on wet surfaces, was virtually without grade, its drainage an assemblage of shallow pools in disorderly connection; and not infrequently the grade was backward, a half-moon lake lying visibly deep against the curving talus of the head wall, and visibly shallowing forward upon the bare rock-floor.

The amphitheater bottom terminated forward in either a cross-cliff or a cascade stairway, descending, between high walls, to yet another flat. In this manner, in steps from flat to flat, commonly enough to be characteristic, the canyon made descent. In height, however, the initial cross-cliff at the head dominated all. The tread of the steps in the long stairway, as far as the eye could follow, greatly lengthened in down-canyon order. In that order, also the phenomena of the faintly reversed grade and of the rock-basin lakes rapidly failed. Apparently, at the canyon head, the last touch of vanishing glaciation had been so recent that filling had not been initiated, while down-stream, incision of the step cliffs and aggradation of the flats had made at least a beginning in the immense task of grade adjustment; the tread of the step was graded forward, but so insensibly, as a rule, that its draining stream lingered in meanders on a strip of meadow, as though approaching base-level. These deep-sunk ribbon meadows, still thousands of feet above the sea and miles in length, reflecting in placid waters their bordering walls or abnormally steep slopes, presented an anomaly of the longitudinal profile in erosion no less impressive than that of the upright canyon heads.

In ground plan, the canyon heads crowded upon the summit upland, frequently intersecting. They scalloped its borders, producing remnantal-table effects. In plan as in profile, the inset arcs of the amphitheaters were vigorously suggestive of basal sapping and recession. The summit upland—the preglacial upland beyond a doubt—was recognizable only in patches, long and narrow and irregular in plan, detached and variously disposed as to orientation, but always in sharp tabular relief and always scalloped. I likened it then, and by way of illustration I can best do so now, to the irregular remnants of a sheet of dough, on the biscuit board, after the biscuit tin has done its work.

In large part, apparently, a preglacial summit topography had been channeled away. By sapping at low levels, by retrogressive undercutting on the part of individual ice-streams at their amphitheater heads in opposing disorderly ranks, the old surface had been consumed, leaving sinking ridges, meandering dulled divides, low cols or passes, and passageways of transection pointing to piracy and to wide shiftings of the glacial drainage. There was not wanting a scattering of the more evanescent sharp forms of transition which the hypothesis would require, as thin arêtes, small isolated table caps, needle-pointed Mätterhorn pyramids with incurving slopes, and subdued spires (in the massive granite tracts) with radiating spurs inclosing basin lakes. . . .

．　　．　　．　　．　　．

. . . The adjusted grade in river erosion is a smooth curve, lessening in declivity in the direction of flow. The glacier, however, by ablation, is diminished in volume as it lengthens; it is normally deepest close to its head, and possibly it is most effective in scour-erosion in pro portion as it is deep. It must, in that event, tend to produce a valley "down at the heel."

The reverse grade, on amphitheater floors especially, occurs with sufficient frequency to be regarded as a type form. Rock-basin lakes, beginning at the amphitheater head, sometimes have notable length, several times the canyon width. The upper surface of the glacier here, on the other hand, invariably declines forward. Thus, in specific instances, it is not merely inference, but fact, that the glacier is deepest at the rear, and excavates there to a forward-rising grade.

It is, furthermore, implied that forward inclination of bed is not essential to glacier movement. It is not necessary, merely to determine that question, to inquire intimately into the nature of glacial motion. Fundamental in that motion, apparently, is the weight of the ice; and if the glacier at bottom, under its own weight, is not strictly viscous, it is apparently at least viscoid, responding in effect to the law of liquid pressures.

A viscous substance, heaped upon a level surface, spreads in mounded disk form, deepest at the center. Its flow-curve, in any radial vertical plane, advances from the bottom. The tendency to flow movement is proportioned to depth—to load; it diminishes toward the outer margin. The outer portions, therefore, move too slowly, and are affected by horizontal, forward thrust. They are retarded at the same time by basal friction, and in consequence present a bulged and swelling front, implying, over a broad marginal tract, rising lines of flow. But the glacier is terminated forward, and is thinned toward its termination, by combined melting and evaporation—*i.e.*, by ablation; and, by ablation, it may be inferred, the constantly bulging front is planed away. The glacier may be regarded as made up of two layers—a superficial, relatively rigid layer, and a basal layer, mobile under the weight of the other; or of a zone of fracture and a zone of flow. In the thinning frontal region, the upper layer, or cover, is brought into contact with the bed. Rearward, it is lifted; though at the same time there it is planed away. Hence, rising lines of flow in effect extend to the surface; for the cover is to be regarded as a zone of rigidity merely, constant only as to position, and thickening, from the mobile ice below, as it is thinned by ablation above. Rates of glacial motion, measured along the surface, therefore will be deceptive. On these assumptions, the line of most rapid advance in the glacier mass is from near the bed, at the rear, to the surface, near the front. Along the bed, motion slows forward; and as pressure upon the bed diminishes in that direction, presumably abrasive erosion is most vigorous toward the rear. The accepted view as to the flow-curve of the river is that, normally, it advances most rapidly at the surface. Deep rivers, however, are found to advance from a point measurably below the surface. If rivers had the great depth of glacial streams, possibly it would appear that the curve of flow which they actually have is but the reverse curve due to bed friction, extended to the surface because the surface is near. It would seem to be a safe assertion that descending grade of bed is not essential to river motion, only decline of the river surface toward the level of discharge; and that, in a long canyon with level floor, terminating at the sea, a river, one or two thousand feet in depth and maintained at that depth at its head, would advance with essentially the same flow-curve as that here attributed to the glacier. The value of such speculation consists in the indication it affords that appeal to the observed flow-curve of the river, in rebuttal, may not be valid.

The long ribbon meadow of the lower canyon course, no less than the ponded amphitheater floor, I think, invites interpretation as the manifestation of a tendency on the part of the glacier to channel excessively up-stream. And in this overdeepening toward the canyon head, I suspect, the two agencies of horizontal sapping and of vertical corrosion powerfully co-operate.

The ultimate effect, upon a range of high-altitude glaciation, would be rude truncation. The crest would be channeled away, down to what might be termed the base-level of glacial generation. Where, among the determining causes of glaciation, high latitude rather than high altitude is operative, the base-level of degradation may lie below the sea, deepest centrally and shallowing outward. Given a land area initially, the glacier itself, as degradation approached its maximum, would replace the land, affording the necessary above-sea surface for snow accumulation. The degradation limit would be determined by the lifting power of the sea.

The hypothesis, at this stage, is of much less importance than recognition of the anomalies of fact, of which it offers a tentative, even venturesome, explanation. In the fiorded regions of the globe, notably in the Patagonian Andes, of which a well-controlled reconnaissance survey has recently been completed, we have examples not only of fiords deepening backward for many miles into rising grades, but of fiord lakes, in parallel series, penetrating from foothills on the one side to foothills on the other, transecting a range. In explanation of such deep channels, whether occupied by arms of the sea, by lakes, or by feebly moving streams on meander bottoms, the appeal to grades, it seems to me, will be most cogent.

# REID
Harry Fielding Reid (1859–1944), American glaciologist and seismologist, received his A. B. degree in 1880 and his Ph. D. degree in 1885 from Johns Hopkins University. After several years of teaching at Case School of Technology and the University of Chicago, he returned to Hopkins in 1894 as lecturer and then associate professor, becoming Professor of Geological Physics in 1901. Ten years later the title of his chair was changed to that of Dynamic Geology and Geography, in which he continued until his retirement in 1930. The earlier part of his career was devoted to the study of glaciers, especially their structure, composition, and movement; later he concentrated his research on seismology, with emphasis upon the mechanics of earthquakes and of recording devices. The report excerpted here is one of the great classics of twentieth-century geology, and the elastic rebound concept developed in it has stood the test of time.

## ELASTIC REBOUND: THE CAUSE
## OF TECTONIC EARTHQUAKES *

### The Movements Before and During Earthquakes

The following is the conception of the events leading up to a tectonic earthquake and of the earth-movements which take place at the time of the rupture, as developed by the observations and study of the California earthquake and by the comparison of these observations with what has been observed in other great earthquakes.

It is impossible for rock to rupture without first being subjected to elastic strains greater than it can endure; the only imaginable ways of rapidly setting up these strains are by an explosion or by the rapid withdrawal, or accumulation, of material below a portion of the crust. Both explosions and the rapid flow of molten rock are associated with volcanic eruptions and with a class of earthquakes not under present discussion; since earthquakes occur not associated with volcanic action, we conclude that the crust, in many parts of the earth, is being slowly displaced, and the difference between displacements in neighboring regions sets up elastic strains, which may become greater than the rock can endure; a rupture then takes place and the strained rock rebounds under its own elastic stresses, until the strain is largely or wholly relieved. In the majority of cases, such as when there is a general differential elevation or depression of adjoining areas, or where there are horizontal displacements, the elastic rebounds on opposite sides of the fault are in opposite directions. The directions of the slow relative displacements on the two sides of the rupture and of the elastic rebounds, all of which are practically parallel with each other, may be vertical, horizontal, or inclined.

The sudden displacements, which occur at the time of an earthquake, are confined to a zone within a few kilometers of the fault-plane, beyond which only the disturbances due to elastic vibrations are experienced. The distribution of the distortion of the rock at the time of the California earthquake shows that the elastic rebound, and consequently the elastic shear, was greatly concentrated near the fault-plane and was much reduced in intensity at even short distances from it; this concentration of the shear brought about a strain sufficient to cause rupture after a comparatively small relative displacement of the surrounding regions; if the shear had been more uniformly distributed over a wider region, a larger relative displacement would have been

---

*From The California Earthquake of April 18, 1906, *Carnegie Institution of Washington Publication 87,* vol. 2 (1910), "The Mechanics of the Earthquake," pp. 29-32.

necessary to cause a rupture and there would have been a greater slip at the fault-plane. Therefore, although it is quite conceivable that regions at a distance apart of, let us say, several times 20 km., might be relatively displaced and set up a state of elastic strain in the broad intervening area, it would be necessary that the relative displacements of the distant regions should be at least several times 6 meters, in order that the strain should become great enough to cause a rupture; and if the strain were less concentrated than it was in California, the relative displacements would have to be greater still. It is only in the case of very large earthquakes that a slip as great as 6 meters occurs; and we may therefore infer that it is only in the case of large earthquakes that the sudden elastic rebound is appreciable as far as 8 or 10 km. from the fault-plane.

The rupture does not occur simultaneously at all parts of the fault-plane; but, on account of the elastic qualities of the rock, it begins in a very limited area and spreads at a rate not exceeding the velocity of compressional waves in the rock.

We should expect that the slow accumulation of strain would, in general, reach a maximum value and bring about a rupture in a single, comparatively narrow fault-zone; and this is probably what occurs for the majority of tectonic earthquakes, but it is quite conceivable that the strains should become so great along two or more separated zones, that the vibrations, set up by the rupture of one, might be sufficient to begin the rupture of the second; or indeed, that the relief of strain at one might cause additional strain at the other and thus start the rupture there, though this seems improbable if they are as much as 20 or 30 km. apart. But it does not seem possible that large blocks of the earth's crust could be suddenly moved as a whole; if the material under the block slowly sank, the elasticity of the rock would allow the block to follow, still resting upon the substratum, and only a zone between the sinking area and the surrounding regions would be elastically strained and experience a sudden elastic rebound when the rupture occurred; and if the sinking area were large, the irregularity of the movement would probably bring about ruptures on different sides at widely different times. If a limited region should be elevated, exactly the opposite movements would take place. It must not be inferred, from what has been said, that small narrow blocks, from a few meters to a few kilometers in width, may not be raised or dropped as a whole, but they should be looked upon as small blocks, forming a part of a single fault-zone and playing a very minor part in the general disturbance of the earthquake.

The Mino-Owari earthquake of 1891, the Formosan earthquake of

1906, and the California earthquake of 1906 are good cases of earthquakes practically with a single fault-zone; whereas, the great earthquake in the central part of Japan in 1896 resulted from fractures along two roughly parallel fault-planes 15 to 18 km. apart, and the intervening region was elevated 1 to 3 meters; one of the fractures was considerably longer than the other; and there is no evidence of any connecting fractures, which would separate the elevated region into a block; the faults apparently die out, as faults usually do, and the elevation diminishes towards their ends and finally disappears completely. The two fractures occurred at about the same time, but no determinations were made exact enough to show that they occurred simultaneously. The sharply defined areas in Iceland over which the earthquakes of 1896 were severally felt suggest that they were due to the settling of successive blocks, and this idea is strengthened by the fact that the region is depressed and separated from the higher adjacent region by a fault. But the description given by Dr. Thoroddsen[1] does not indicate that the individual areas mentioned are bounded by faults, nor does he adduce any evidence that they sank at the time of the shocks, though he does describe some large fissures which ran across several of them. Iceland is actively volcanic, and the descriptions of it suggest a very mobile condition not far below the surface. If this condition really exists, it would be much easier for cracks to form at approximately the same time and break up the crust into blocks there than in regions where the crust rests on a firmer foundation.

The elevations and depressions about Yakutat Bay, Alaska, which Messrs. Tarr and Martin have described as due to the earthquake of 1899, strongly suggest the movement of blocks;[2] but they did not find evidences of faultings on more than three sides of a block, and that in only one instance; though it must be noted that they were unable to examine more than a very limited area and could not determine where the lines of fracture ended. It seems possible that the displacements they describe might be accounted for by an upward pressure, with or without a compression in a direction running north-northwest and south-southeast. Such a pressure and compression would bend the rocks into an arch, with the surface under tension, and the rupture would occur when this tension reached the limiting strength of the rock; the rupture would begin at the surface and extend downwards, and the ends of the broken rock would fly upwards, just as do the ends of a stick broken by bending, and an open fissure would be formed at the

[1] "Das Erdbeben in Island im Jahr, 1896," *Petermann's Mitt.* 47 (1901), 53–56.
[2] "Recent changes of level in the Yakutat Bay region, Alaska," *Bull. Geol. Soc. Am.* 17 (1906), 29–64.

principal fracture; but along the side cracks the relative elastic rebounds might be in opposite directions and the parts might remain in contact. The principal fracture would be that in Disenchantment Bay, but no soundings have been made there to discover the existence of a fissure. Fissures and displacements of this character, due probably merely to compression, but on a very small scale, have been described.[3]

We know very little about the interior of the earth or of the origin of the forces which produce such great changes at the surface. Great thrust faults exist which indicate tangential compressions; and normal faults, which indicate expansion. Great uplifts have occurred unaccompanied by compressions, due, apparently, to vertical forces; and the California earthquake has emphasized the existence of horizontal drags below the crust. Future study may reveal forces applied in other ways; but it is not going too far to say that whenever ruptures occur, they result from elastic strain, and the sudden movements produced are merely elastic rebounds; and, moreover, except in the case of earthquakes connected directly with volcanic action, the strains have not been set up suddenly, but are gradually developed by the slow displacements of adjacent areas. And severe earthquakes caused by shearing strains, vertical, horizontal, or oblique, where the elastic rebounds are in opposite directions on opposite sides of the fault, which remain in contact, will be more common than those due to the tensional strains of bending, where the elastic rebounds are in the same direction and a gaping fissure is opened.

### THE PREDICTION OF EARTHQUAKES

As strains always precede the rupture and as the strains are sufficiently great to be easily detected before the rupture occurs, in order to foresee tectonic earthquakes it is merely necessary to devise a method of determining the existence of the strains; and the rupture will in general occur in the neighborhood of the line where the strains are greatest, or along an older fault-line where the rock is weakest. To measure the growth of strains, we should build a line of piers, say a kilometer apart, at right angles to the direction which a geological examination of the region, or past experience, indicates the fault will take when the rupture occurs; a careful determination from time to time, of the directions of the lines joining successive piers, their differences of level, and the exact distance between them, would reveal any strains which might be developing along the region the line of piers crosses. In the case of vertical, horizontal, or oblique shears, if the surface becomes strained through an angle of about 1/2000, we should

[3]F. Cramer, *Am. J. Sci.* [3] *39* (1890), 220–225; *ibid. 40* (1891), 432–434. Mr. H. P. Cushing has shown me pictures of similar cracks with elevated lips in central New York.

expect a strong shock. It would be necessary to start with the rock in an unstrained condition; this could readily be done now in the neighborhood of the San Andreas fault. The monuments set up close to the fault-line (vol. I, pp. 152–159) were not placed with this object in view, but with the object of measuring actual slips on the old fault-line. Measures of the class described would be extremely useful, not only for the purpose of prediction, but also to reveal the nature of the earth-movements taking place, and thus lead to a better understanding of the causes of earthquakes. Less definite, but still valuable, information could be obtained by the simpler process of determining, from time to time, the absolute directions of Farallon Light-house and Mount Diablo from Mount Tamalpais; by this means northerly or southerly movements of 1 foot of either of the first two stations relative to the third could be detected; and we should know if strains were being set up in the intermediate region; but we could not tell where the strain was a maximum nor to what extent it may have been relieved by small displacements on intervening fault-planes.

It seems probable that a very long period will elapse before another important earthquake occurs along that part of the San Andreas rift which broke in 1906; for we have seen that the strains causing the slip were probably accumulating for 100 years. There have been no serious earthquakes reported along this part of the rift, except at its southern extremity, since the country has been occupied by white men, although strong earthquakes have occurred in neighboring regions. It seems probable that more consistent results might be obtained regarding the periodicity of earthquakes if only the earthquakes occurring at exactly the same place were considered in the series. The Messina earthquake of December 28, 1908, seems to have resulted from a movement on the great fault passing through the Straits of Messina. The last strong movement at the same place seems to have occurred in 1783; though the Calabrian earthquake of 1905 may have been caused by a movement on another part of the same fault.

It is quite possible, however, for strong earthquakes to occur on neighboring faults after short intervals. The ruptures of the Haywards fault in 1868 and of the San Andreas fault in 1906 are a fair example, though the interval is rather long. The Iceland earthquakes of 1896, already referred to, illustrate this much better. Five strong shocks occurred within fifteen days; but they were central, not in the same region, but in regions successively more and more to the west.

When a rupture occurs, the elastic rebound may carry the sides of the fault beyond their positions of no strain, and the friction may temporarily hold them there; or the friction may be so great that they do not entirely reach these positions. In either case further shocks may be expected before long; but they are apt to be slight, and are more likely to constitute *after-shocks* than independent earthquakes.

# LINDGREN

Waldemar Lindgren (1860–1939), Swedish-American geologist, was born in Kalmar, Sweden, and completed his formal education in 1883 at the Freiberg *Bergakademie,* in Germany, at that time the paramount school of mining and geology in all the world. He than emigrated to the United States and immediately joined the staff of the U. S. Geological Survey, with which organization he maintained official status until 1915. In 1912 he became head of the Department of Geology in the Massachusetts Institute of Technology, where he continued his illustrious career as an outstanding teacher of economic geology until his retirement in 1933. His contributions to the solution of the broad problem of ore genesis and his classification of ore bodies in terms of causative processes were among the most notable developments in the progress of geology during his lifetime. The paper, almost all of which is reprinted here, was his presidential address to the Geological Society of America in December, 1924.

## METASOMATISM *

### WHAT IS METASOMATISM?

I shall begin somewhat bluntly by asking the question, "What is metasomatism?"

Perhaps I am right in saying that there is a general impression abroad that metasomatism is a sort of replacement of one mineral by another, with addition of material and mainly of importance in ore deposits. I would like you to look at it from a far broader viewpoint— as a universal process based on the fact that the minerals of all rocks are soluble in the fluids of nature, particularly water, but also in the mixed emanations from magmas, and on the fact that these fluids change the minerals to others, of different composition, stable under the particular conditions of pressure and temperature prevailing. Remove metasomatism and there would be very little left of metamorphism.

I would define metasomatism as *an essentially simultaneous, molecular process of solution and deposition by which, in the presence of a fluid phase, one mineral is changed to another of differing chemical composition.*

*From *Geological Society of America Bulletin 36* (1925), 247–262.

*Replacement* is regarded as synonymous with metasomatism, but the latter term is preferred, as it may be adopted in all languages. *Alteration, dissemination,* and *decomposition* are synonymous with certain phases of metasomatism.

Metasomatism is, no doubt, governed by the laws of thermodynamics, but their application is greatly complicated by surface phenomena. The law of mass action helps to explain many reactions of mitasomatism in open space, but does not always afford a safe basis for the interpretation of changes going on in capillary spaces.

Metasomatism is at times governed by the phase rule, but in replacements in solid rocks and under stress the phase rule is not directly applicable; neither is it applicable in gel-replacements.

Metasomatism is at times governed by simple equations and definite stoichiometric relations; but replacements by crystalloids in solid rocks rarely follow these equations and in gel-replacements no formulas can be written. Nevertheless, the process is molecular in the sense that solution changes the equilibrium in the solvent, so that precipitation must occur; but the process does not always proceed "molecule for molecule."

In open space, in liquids and similar yielding media (gels), metasomatism is generally governed by the law of mass action and by the phase rule. I do not feel sure that it is so governed in rigid media.

Metasomatism draws no distinctions between partial and complete replacement. Pyrite replacing feldspar, galena replacing calcite, epidote replacing soda-lime feldspar, silica gel replacing limestone—all are phases of metasomatism.

Metasomatism may or may not proceed with changes of volume. In open space, in liquids, in soft rocks, and in gel-replacement there is usually a change of volume. In solid rocks the volume of the replacing mincral or minerals is substantially equal to that of the mineral or minerals replaced.

Specifically excepted from metasomatism are processes of paramorphism, in which by molecular rearrangement one mineral changes to another space lattice, as, for instance, when isometric chalcocite is transformed to the rhombic modification; also excluded are unmixing processes, as when a solid solution at a certain temperature ejects part of its dissolved material in crystalline form—for example, when in cooling galena silver sulphide is separated.

I have at the outset outlined my conception of metasomatism, for the current views on this matter are rather markedly divergent.

As stated above, some investigators divide metasomatism in these cases where no chemical reaction can be written, and in others where the process progresses according to certain supposed chemical equations. There appears to be no need of such a distinction. A precipitate may result from a double decomposition, but it may as well be caused by physico-chemical changes in the solution rendering insoluble a substance foreign to the attacked mineral.

Prof. V. M. Goldschmidt,[1] of Kristiania, in a paper of great merit, has recently proposed a definition of metasomatism. Grubenmann and Niggli,[2] in their splendid volume on metamorphism, also follow a similar trend of opinion. These authors wish to narrow metasomatism to rocks, speaking of metasomatic rocks when *essential* changes of composition have taken place. Goldschmidt defines the term as follows: "Metasomatism is a process of alteration which involves enrichment of the rock by new substances brought in from the outside. Such enrichment takes place by definite chemical reactions between the original minerals and the enriching substances." Water and carbon dioxide are excepted from "new substances."

I wish to enter a strong protest against such an unwarranted emasculation of a useful and fundamental conception. In the first place, metasomatism should be a term applied to individual minerals; if they are changed in composition by alteration, these new minerals are metasomatic. If the whole rock also changes in composition, then the rock also is metasomatic; and no exceptions are to be allowed for privileged substances. As to the last part of Goldschmidt's definition, referring to "definite chemical reactions," it is assuredly wrong. If calcite or limestone is replaced by quartz, or cryptocrystalline silica, then surely the new silica is a metasomatic mineral and the limestone is a metasomatic rock; but the process involves no definite chemical reactions, simply a precipitation of quartz or silica gel for which no equation can be written.

The absence of a definite word for the process here described is painfully felt in perusing the volume on metamorphism by Grubenmann and Niggli. They use such expressions as "Neubildung," "Umbildung," "Umsetzung," "Reaction." "Verdrängung," which is really the equivalent of replacement, is very seldom used.

### Crystalloid Metasomatism in Solid Rocks

For the present purposes I shall not deal in detail with these phases of metasomatism which take place in yielding media. The ordinary

[1]V. M. Goldschmidt, "Metasomatic process in silicate rocks," *Econ. Geol. 17* (1922), 105–123.

[2]U. Grubenmann and P. Niggli, *Die Gesteinsmetamorphose* 1. *Allgem. Theil.,* Berlin, 1924.

rules of chemistry generally hold here. The following remarks apply to metasomatism in rigid rocks, in part also to metasomatism in rocks subject to strong plastic deformation.

In the first place, I would like to point out that it is immaterial to the process of metasomatism, as outlined here, whether the metasome (the "guest") consists of elements foreign to the host—that is, galena in calcite or pyrite in orthoclase—or has one or more components in common—that is, fluorite in calcite, or chlorite in augite, or wollastonite in calcite. The process is essentially the same. Who shall say, for instance, when chalcopyrite replaces ankerite or pyrite replaces hornblende, just how much, if any, of the iron is derived from the host mineral and how much is introduced? Or how much, if any, lime is derived from the host when ankerite replaces oligoclase? Is it an entirely different process when ankerite replaces orthoclase?

Replacement may (1) preserve the form of the host by an individual metasome—for example, chlorite after biotite; (2) preserve the form of the host by aggregate structure—for example, chalcocite after pyrite; (3) proceed without preservation of form, as irregular aggregates—for example, calcite in feldspar—or by developing well-defined "metacrysts" in the host—for example, pyrite in hornblende; (4) replace one aggregate of several minerals—for example, cyanite in schist or pyrite in slate.

In the second place, I wish to reaffirm the thesis of which I have frequently spoken in the past, that in solid rocks the volume of the metasome, or metacryst, is substantially the same as that dissolved from the host. I say substantially, first, because of the pore space of subcapillary openings created when an aggregate like sericite replaces feldspar; and, second, because when the attacking solutions are sufficiently abundant active solution may run ahead of deposition and a drusy structure may result. In metamorphism[3] there are no drusy structures, because the changes proceed slowly. The rule of equality of volume has been found true by the work of many geologists who have paid any attention to the case. The textbooks, including the latest, generally preserve a discreet silence. Grubenmann and Niggli, in their latest edition of "The Metamorphism," 1924, admit that in some cases of "metasomatic ore deposits" constancy of volume may be true.

I would like to have the doubters carefully examine some crystals of epidote developing in soda lime feldspar or rhombs of calcite, dolomite, or ankerite replacing feldspars or tourmaline prisms developing

[3] The term "metamorphism" as here used excludes weathering.

in various rocks and see if there is any escape from this proposition.

To explain metasomatism (as here defined), Goldschmidt and Grubenmann and Niggli, as well as other authors of textbooks, depend entirely on the law of mass action and on the phase rule.

This is really a chemical problem, and I am not a chemist. Probably something will be said about rushing in where others fear to tread, to put it mildly. If in error, I shall be glad to be corrected.

It is certain, of course, that the phase rule does not apply to colloidal systems. Niggli admits that it does not hold where stress and unequal pressures in the system are present. It seems to be extremely doubtful whether it can be applied where capillary or subcapillary chemistry are concerned. Gibbs himself excludes the effects of capillarity; and if this is so, its use in metamorphism seems highly questionable. In a subcapillary system the surface tension and the adsorbed layer play important and not fully recognized parts. The phases become difficult to recognize and the pressures are probably not the same in all parts of the system. As well known, the phase rule can be applied only to systems of equilibrium.

At the meeting of the Geological Society of America in 1923 (volume 35, number 1), D. F. Hewett presented a paper on dolomitization in which it was pointed out that at the locality described there was no evidence of contraction in volume. In discussing this paper R. B. Sosman remarked "that the flow of liquids in capillary spaces is evidently accompanied by phenomena not yet clearly understood. It is very probable that some of the phenomena of replacement in nature are of this class and are not reactions which can be represented by the familiar balanced equations of chemistry." I have quoted this as the only example known to me where a chemist has shown an appreciation of the problems related to metasomatism. The fact seems to be that physical chemists are so used to consider systems in equilibrium and reactions in open space or in liquids that they give little attention to other conditions.

As for the law of mass action, it is a useful rule, but subject to many exceptions and irregularities. It seems doubtful to me whether it can be applied to the essentially capillary process of metasomatism in rigid rocks. The question simmers down to the query: Is the law of equal volume a fact in metasomatism of solid rocks or is it not? If solid zinc carbonate replaces limestone with complete preservation of structure, then the equation

$$ZnSO_4 + CaCO_3 = ZnCO_3 + CaSO_4$$

is obviously wrong, for a volume of calcite is replaced by an equal volume of smithsonite ($ZnCO_3$), which requires more Zn and more $CO_3$ than indicated by the double decomposition. If the equation is true, then contraction must take place. What has actually happened should be expressible by some kind of an equation, but I confess inability to formulate it. Perhaps gel replacement might solve the problem.

May I be permitted to suggest that many eminent geologists who have studied the crystalline schists do not fully realize the nature of metasomatism? It sometimes seems to me that they emphasize the phenomena caused by stress at the expense of the main underlying process, which is metasomatism. They speak, for instance, of the "quartz-tails" and of the peripheral rings of quartz, calcite, or chlorite, which so frequently surround metacrysts (porphyroblasts) in schists, and of the quartz along twinning planes and gliding planes as if they were fillings of open cavities. Grubenmann and Niggli speak of them as "Fefüllte Zerrungshohlräume," while it appears to me that they are nothing but replacements by quartz and other minerals. Entirely similar peripheral rings may be seen in the metasomatically altered rocks which have been subjected to hydrothermal action. The study of the crystalline schists should be preceded by that of ordinary "static," or hydrochemical metamorphism.

Is it not likely that most of the phenomena observed in schists are simple replacements modified in development by the influence of stress, so that solution without replacement predominates at points of maximum stress and deposition with replacement at points of minimum stress? Surely, it is common enough in schists to find inclusions in the metacryst of matrix and abutment of the mica foils of the matrix against the metacryst. This is in places modified by the stress which also tends to produce the rotations which have been so clearly demonstrated by F. Becke and others.

When we find aluminum concentrated in metacrysts of, say, cyanite embedded in a uniform schist matrix, does not this prove a considerable transportation of this element? It is not to be denied that metasomatism may result from the vapor phase between two adjacent grains, or by hydroxyl liberated, or by simple rock moisture; but movement and transportation on capillary openings appear to me as the governing factors. Even in hornfels such movement is in operation, for we find tourmaline and scapolite widely distributed in contact aureoles.

I will go so far as to say that all forms of metamorphism are accompanied by change in composition, though the changes sometimes may be small.

## Gel-metasomatism, or Replacement of Crystalloids by Gels

When the product deposited during metasomatism is a gel instead of a crystalloid, we may call this process gel-metasomatism. Little attention has been given to this in the past, but it looks now as if its importance had been greatly underestimated. Many chemists hold that any precipitate must pass through a gel-stage, even if it is only momentary. To any one familiar with the lightning-like development of crystals under the microscope, this seems an exaggeration; yet it may well be true. It is known, for instance, that many substances, like sodium chloride or barium sulphate, which ordinarily seem far away from the gel-state, can be obtained as jellies.

Gels are obtained in many ways, among which I shall only mention double decomposition, mutual precipitation of sols, or precipitation of sols by electrolytes. Even when obtained by double decomposition, they are rarely pure, but contain adsorbed material and, in the case of sulphides, more or less colloidal sulphur. When obtained by the two latter methods mentioned, no simple stoichiometrical relationships exist between the coagulated product and the precipitant, and adsorption is always an important factor.

In rocks the reactions are carried on as in crystalloid metasomatism on subcapillary fissures. Surface tension, surface energy, and the adsorbed layer play important parts. The phase rule as well as the mass law does not apply. Diffusion is of great importance, supplementing circulation, for electrolytes readily penetrate the gels. As a rule, no stoichiometrical formulas can be written. The precipitate takes the form of a gel, and it is probably of a high degree of concentration. The spaces provided by solution are practically at the same moment filled, and the law of equal volume undoubtedly holds. If larger pores and cavities are present in the rock, these will ordinarily be filled before metasomatism begins.

There is this difference, however; in gel replacement, the rock tends to become a mass of soft material, subject to contraction, fracture and crushing, so that ultimately sudden volume adjustments may take place.

The gel has a great tendency to colloform structure, replacing the host minerals in concentric rounded masses. This structure is not always developed, however.

Crystallization usually occurs sooner or later, and the gel becomes a metacolloid or a mixture of metacolloids, ordinarily a definite mineral or minerals and very frequently arranged in radial-fibrous forms. Sometimes crystallization may follow very closely on the heels of the separation of the gel. This is commonly accompanied by reduction of volume and expulsion of water. We, therefore, often find the metacolloids fractured or showing concentric contraction cracks, empty or filled with minerals of different kinds—calcite, for instance, or a new gel deposit.

Of course, the question may be raised whether gel-replacement is covered by the definition given in the beginning of this address. It may be said that a gel is not a mineral. A mineral is usually defined as an inorganic body of definite chemical composition found in the crust of the earth. A gel may not have a definite chemical composition and it may crystallize to two or more minerals. There are, however, many hardened colloids of varying composition—as, for example, the copper pitch ores and varieties of chrysocolla—and it is a question whether the "definite chemical composition" can be upheld.

It may also be pertinently asked, How do you know that these so-called "gel-replacements," now crystalline, have actually passed through the gel stage? What are the deciding criteria? In answer to this it may be said that at times the proof can be given along several lines and be wholly convincing, as I think I have done in case of the replacement of limestone by silica gel in Professional Paper 107, on the Tintic district. At times the proof can not be complete, especially when the colloform structure is absent. The safest criterion is undoubtedly that afforded by these concentric and concretionary structures.

The matter of spheroidal forms in minerals has been discussed by many authors since the days of Roth. Lately, A. F. Rogers and H. C. Boydell have contributed to the study of such criteria. Spheroidal forms result from weathering and abrasion, and they appear also in magmas, as shown by the occurrence of spherulitic and orbicular structures. Spheroidal forms may also result from diffusion of electrolytes in gels and in porous substances, as has been most efficiently pointed out by Liesegang.

In general, spheroidal development in a homogeneous substance strongly suggests the effects of surface tension in a viscous medium. Boydell says that "concretions of colloidal origin can result from inorganic as well as from organic processes. The mineral forms described as botryoidal, mammillary, reniform, spheroidal, stalactitic, are all manifestations of surface tension effects in viscous material, and therefore are indicative generally, though not by any means exclusively, of colloidal origin." It seems to me that when a homogeneous material develops such structures they are the best criterion of a previous gel state, especially when they are emphasized by the successive deposition of thin concentric layers of slightly different appearance or show distinct concentric contraction cracks. Such structures may develop by replacement as well as in open space.

In gel-replacement the concentric contraction cracks, when present, are directed with the convex side outwards in the general direction of the reaction. They do not follow the outlines of the space now occupied by the gel mineral, as would most likely be the case if the latter had filled a preexisting cavity.

## OCCURRENCES OF GEL-REPLACEMENT

### General Statement

It is perfectly natural that gel-replacement should be most prominent in the zone of oxidation and in semi-consolidated sediments. To some extent it may take place during sedimentation. It is also very common in the zone just below that of active oxidation. Its importance in ore deposits of the epithermal and mesothermal kind is just beginning to be appreciated. It is not common in ore deposits of hypothermal or direct magmatic origin. In metamorphism it is also generally absent, but it abounds in ordinary rock alteration under near-surface conditions.

### In the Zone of Oxidation

In the loose, or at least more or less softened, masses of decomposed rock many colloid precipitates are undoubtedly forming in open spaces and in pores, for precipitation favors open spaces; in this zone, particularly near its base, larger colloform masses are frequent—of limonite, of psilomelane, of barite, of wavellite, or smithsonite, or many other substances. I believe that in the majority of cases these represent replacements of the regolith by gels, which soon acquire crystalline structure. If occurring in the mass of rock, they either fill open spaces or they are replacements. Open spaces of this form and size are unlikely. The gel certainly did not push the rock apart. Therefore the probability rests with the replacements theory. The earlier work of T. L. Watson and E. C. Harder seemed to indicate this origin for psilomelane quite clearly; and recently D. F. Hewett has taken the definite stand that in most cases psilomelane develops by such a process, although he does not emphasize the original gel character of the mineral. It is evident that this manganese mineral replaces clayey soil as well as various inclusions of rock in the soil; and the same doubtless applies to limonite. The hydroxide gels are probably precipitates from carbonate or sulphate solutions.

### In Partly Consolidated Sediments (Diagenesis, Andree)

Solutions yielding colloidal precipitates are constantly at work in soft sediments. Glauconite and other iron silicates, phosphates, siderite, and many others are formed by adsorption, mutual precipitation of colloids, or electrolytic coagulation. In the oolites no doubt gel replacement is

73

going on to some degree (halmyrolysis, Hummel). I believe the majority of concretions like those of marcasite, siderite, and barite are gel-replacements in the first place which later have acquired crystallinity. That means that the soft material around the incipient concretion has been dissolved and that simultaneously a gel has been precipitated, at first assuming colloform outlines. Such concretions have been explained by Liesegang as caused by diffusion, and undoubtedly diffusion plays an important part; but they can not be caused by "cementation" (Verkittung, Liesegang), for they are essentially pure and must have *replaced* material once occupying their space.

## In Metamorphism

The tendency of many members of the chlorite group to assume colloform shapes is emphasized in many textbooks of mineralogy. Among these the iron-bearing chlorites predominate, such as thuringite, cronstedtite, diabantite, and delessite. No doubt the delessite lining amygdaloid cavities is a colloidal precipitate. Many petrographers have called attention to the frequent development of chlorite in "pseudo-amygdules." A chloritized greenstone may be filled with these rounded chlorite aggregates, which strongly suggest that from certain centers the rock substance has been dissolved with simultaneous precipitation—that is, replacement—of iron-magnesium-silicate gel. This subsequently acquired the cryptocrystalline structure of a metacolloid.

It has often occurred to me that serpentinization may also, in part, at least, be a gel-replacement, though of this I am not as yet able to furnish definite proof.

## In Ore Deposits

*General statement*—It is now evident that gel-replacement plays a considerable part in the development of some ore deposits, principally of the epithermal or mesothermal kind. We may differentiate between replacements of supergene and of hypogene origin.

*Replacements of probable supergene origin*—In the zone of oxidation gel-replacements are constantly going on. I shall only mention a few instances. Minerals like chrysocolla, copper-pitch ores, some malachites, some jarosites, and some zinc carbonates are clearly metacolloids and have passed through a distinct gel-stage. In a large number of cases it will be found that these are not deposited in open space, but owe their origin to gel-replacement.

Just below the zone of oxidation among the "secondary sulphides" we find many more examples. It is maintained by Tolman that many chalcocites are of gel-origin. This has been denied by Schneiderhöhn, but I believe it is true, particularly of these "sooty" forms which owe their origin to precipitation of cupric sulphate by hydrogen sulphide generated by the action of sulphuric acid on older sulphides. I think it is very likely that some at least of the replacements of pyrite, chalcopyrite, etcetera, by chalcocite are real gel-replacements.

The second instance is the development of marcasite just below the zone of oxidation. The first time I observed this was in an ore from the sulphide deposit of the Iron Queen Mine, near Mayer, Arizona. Here marcasite with colloform structure freely replaces the gangue minerals, mainly quartz, as well as sphalerite and perhaps pyrite (United States Geological Survey publication, in press). About the same time W. H. Newhouse, of the Massachusetts Institute of Technology, found entirely similar occurrences at Kokomo, Colorado, and in the ores of the Angangeo district, Michoacan, Mexico. Here, too, quartz and pyrite were replaced by marcasite showing colloform structure and, in places, contraction cracks (Economic Geology, paper in press). The process is later than the main mineralization, and it is believed that it took place just below the water level. . . .

*Replacements of hypogene origin*—Many geologists have explained the formation of certain kinds of chert in limestone and of silicified fossils with complete preservation of sculpture by means of a gel-replacement. Experimental demonstration of such replacement was furnished by A. H. Church many years ago.

The silicification of limestone and dolomite near ore deposits is often a normal crystalloid replacement. J. D. Irving was the first, I believe, to describe a different kind of silicification in the ore deposits of the Black Hills, South Dakota. More recently I have called attention to the entirely similar replacement phenomena in the Tintic district, Utah, and showed that we here undoubtedly had to deal with a gel-replacement at temperatures of, say, 200 degrees to 300 degrees centigrade. In contrast to the crystalloid replacement, which begins at numerous points in the rock by the development of individual quartz metacrysts, the gel-replacement proceeds like a wave, uniformly substituting a gel, which soon after crystallizes to a micro- or crypto-crystalline aggregate of silica, often with perfect preservation of structure.

A chemical explanation has been furnished later by Cox, Dean, and Gottschalk, who found that when a colloidal solution of silica containing $CO_2$ was allowed to act on calcium carbonate the silica is rapidly precipitated by the positively charged calcium ions of the dissociated carbonate. Without $CO_2$ no reaction takes place. It is evident that no equation can be written for this reaction, and that it is governed by no ordinary stoichiometrical rules.

Colloidal silica subsequently crystallized is often precipitated in the fissures of the epithermal deposits, and gold, for instance, is surely carried in the colloidal state in such solutions and so deposited. I hasten to add that I do not believe that the gel has been injected, but that it has gradually been deposited from aqueous solutions.

Seldom do we find evidence that the metallic minerals in ore deposits were precipitated as gels, either in open space or by replacement. There are some exceptions, however. Native arsenic or arsenic-antimony (allemontite) is characteristically deposited as colloform masses, and this occurs in many deposits. In part they may be formed in open space. Most of the cases I have seen indicate gel-replacement of calcite or quartz. The mineral occurs in the solid vein material as colloform, kidney-shaped masses crystallized soon after the replacement. Formerly I have held the mineral to be of supergene origin, not realizing the mechanics of gel-replacement. It is evident now that this view was erroneous. As far as I know, Prof. J. L. Gillson was the first to demonstrate the hypogene origin of native arsenic, this in a United States Geological Survey publication now in press. . . . It is well known that minerals containing vanadium and arsenic have a strong leaning towards colloidal behavior.

My attention has lately been attracted to the very strong tendency to colloform structure among the arsenides and sulpharsenides of cobalt and nickel. Perhaps this is most marked in niccolite. Over here we are disposed to regard the silver-bearing veins of Cobalt, Ontario, as something rather unique, with their gangue of calcite and their complex mineralization of niccolite, smaltite, chloanthite, arsenopyrite, löllingite, cobaltite, breithauptite, and many other similar minerals. However, if we glance through some such works as Hintze's "Mineralogie" or La Croix' "Mineralogie de la France," we soon find that this peculiar association of minerals and types of structure are exactly the same as those of a dozen long-known European deposits, though these latter may lack the phenomenal richness in silver peculiar to the veins of the Cobalt district. Concentric and concretionary structures are extremely common.

A careful study of the Cobalt deposits have led me to believe[4] that we have here one of the most instructive examples of gel-replacement at higher temperatures. As is well known, the narrow veins stand in

[4]This conclusion was reached simultaneously by Dr. H. C. Boydell, and the writer is referred to in Dr. Boydell's notable dissertation on "The role of colloidal solutions in the formation of mineral deposits," which has just been published in the bulletins of the Institution of Mining and Metallurgy (London). This writer, however, holds that the arsenides were deposited in a "carbonate gel."

genetic relationship to the thick, intrusive sheet of diabase. The veins have been described by many geologists, and at least six of them, William Campbell and C. W. Knight, W. G. Miller, E. S. Bastin, H. V. Ellsworth, and W. L. Whitehead, emphasize the concretionary and concentric structure of the ore, though they do not draw the inevitable inference as to the mode of origin. The veins are generally considered as mesothermal—that is, formed at intermediate temperatures, probably not exceeding 250 degrees centigrade.

At Cobalt the deposition may be divided in three stages:

1. The filling of the fissures by crystalline calcite and dolomite.

2. The replacement of the carbonates by gels of arsenides and sulpharsenides.

3. The introduction, mainly by replacement, of crystalloid native silver.

On polished faces the colloform arrangement of the arsenical minerals becomes particularly clear. Rounded, often concentric, aggregates appear in the carbonate and sometimes even extend into the wall rock. Niccolite cores are common and are usually surrounded by rounded, concretionary deposits of smaltite and other minerals. Under the microscope the solid aggregates are resolved into extremely intricate intergrowths, in which it is next to impossible to recognize any definite succession, but they are just what would be expected from the sudden crystallization of a complex gel. With considerable confidence I advance the view that the arsenical minerals are a gel-replacement of an older, crystalline carbonate filling.

It is obviously difficult to explain the chemistry of such a complex process, but here is a crude outline of what may have taken place.

The second stage consisted in the introduction of mobile solutions emanating from the cooling diabase. They may have been more or less mixed with water of magmatic or meteoric origin. They consisted of the chlorides of cobalt, nickel, and iron, and were mixed with arsenic sulphide (colloidal?) and hydrogen sulphide or alkaline sulphides. The immediate precipitation was inhibited for the time by the acid conditions resulting from hydrolysis of the ferric chloride. These solutions attacked the country rock—diabase or argillite—slowly or not at all, while an intense reaction was set up as soon as they encountered the carbonate filling. This resulted in the solutions becoming neutral and the sulphides, together with sulphur and arsenic, were precipitated as a complex gel, which took the place of the dissolved calcite after the fashion of gel-replacement. Needless to say, the liberated $CO_2$ must have played an important part in the system.

The complex gel was almost immediately transformed into crystalloids, resulting in the mixture of minerals which we now find. The crystallization was accompanied by contraction and fissuring, but the spaces were immediately filled by calcite or newly precipitated gel. The concentric gel-banding is often clearly visible. Because the crystallization followed so closely on the heels of the gel-precipitation, it is not surprising that we find places where crystals were formed directly in the country rock or in the vein filling, but they do not appear to be the principal mode of ore formation.

I believe the silver also came from the diabase magma, but in this reaction, as far as known, no colloidal processes were involved.

In the deposits formed at higher temperatures, definite evidence of gel-deposition and gel-replacement are lacking as a rule. We know of one instance, however. In 1916 Adolph Knopf described tin bearing veins in rhyolite from Nevada. The minerals consist of concentric wood tin, with opal, chalcedonic silica and specularite. Indeed, Mr. Knopf says that "locally the rhyolite has been replaced by wood tin, hematite and the various silica minerals." The author strongly maintains the colloidal nature of this occurrence.

### Conclusion

I fear having tried your patience by an address grown longer than anticipated. I have had two objects in view: First, to restore metasomatism in general to its proper place in the study of the alteration of rocks; and, second, to call attention to the neglected field of colloidal replacement. Substantially the process is of the same type, whether a chemical equation can be written for it or not, and whether the product is a crystalloid or a gel.

# HAMBERG
Axel Hamberg (1863–1933), Swedish geologist and geographer, concentrated his studies at Stockholm University on crystallography and mineralogy and subsequently taught those subjects there. In 1907 he became Professor of Geography at Upsala University, and from 1913 to 1927 he was President of the International Iceberg Commission. In the paper from which this excerpt was taken, he presented for the first time what seems to be an adequate explanation of the solifluction patterns attributable to frost action.

## MOVEMENT OF STONES BY FROST ACTION*

According to my experience, "mud islands" are occasionally found in the felsenmeer on the high mountains of Lapland. If they were so

*From *Geologiska Föreningens i Stockholm Förhandlingar 37* (1915), 604–610. Translated by Robert G. Wertheimer.

numerous as to touch each other, we would have to deal with a phenomenon called "polygongrounds" by Högbom[1] and "stone nets" by Meinardus,[2] formations which also occur in Lapland. Mud islands seem to be more frequent, however, on tundras almost bare of vegetation in fully arctic regions such as Spitzbergen, Siberia, and elsewhere. . . . Various authors have observed that stones and loam were at first intimately mixed, but that later a separation took place which rendered the loam parts almost free of stones. Thus far, no one has devised a reasonable theory for the separation of the stones from the loam. According to Meinardus,[2] no less than eighteen diverse hypotheses have been developed, or almost as many opinions as observers. The explanation most widely approved seems to have been that made by B. Högbom[1]: "Whenever the soil consists originally of a mixture of fine and coarser materials, a sufficient unevenness would exist so that in certain areas finer material would predominate. Owing to capillary action, these spots would absorb more water than the others. When ice forms, the material moves from these spots in a centrifugal direction. Afterwards, when thawing and shrinkage of volume set in, the finer material will be moved by adhesion whereas the stones will remain on the periphery. If this process is repeated often enough, a significant separation will result. This will strengthen the intensity of the procedure by increasingly localizing the origin of the changes in the mass and also at the same time by increasing the water-absorbing capacity of the central location."

This theory does not give a satisfactory explanation of the movement of coarser fragments within the finer because it does not explain why the coarser material, which is being shifted centrifugally by the freezing expansion, does not participate in the centripetal movement of the finer parts at the time of contraction due to melting and consequently return to its original position. . . .

The phenomenon of movement toward the surface of larger objects, such as stones and bones, from interior locations in earth and clay by the process of freezing is, according to Högbom, a known fact and one which I can only confirm. Ample observations of this phenomenon are found in inhabited regions of Sweden. However, as Sapper comments, we are presently unable to explain the mechanism of this phenomenon. We can only assume that freezing is the effective agent in this process.

In the paragraphs on ice-filaments I stressed the observation made by several scientists that the stemmed-ice forming on wet humus or clay at times carries dry layers of peat, foliage, and so on. The lifting up of stones above the surface of the clay could also be effected in

[1]Högbom, B., *Bull. Geol. Inst. Upsala 12*, (1914), 305–315.
[2]Meinardus, *Ges. Erdk. Berlin* (1912), 257–258.

this way, but after the melting of the ice prisms the stones would come to rest in about the same position they had had earlier. Movement of stones through the mud cannot be explained by this action.

An acceptable explanation can be found, however, if one compares the kinds of movement that will take place in freezing and melting masses of mud, on the one hand, and by enclosed firm objects, on the other.

It is not correct to assume in this analysis that a proportionate expansion of the mud masses in the freezing process and an equally proportionate shrinking while melting will take place, inasmuch as all changes in the warming-up process of the mud come from the outside and are transmitted to the interior. During freezing, a firm frozen crust forms first and then expands and thickens toward the inside. In thawing, while the interior is still frozen, a melted zone forms and enlarges toward the interior. Expansion and contraction therefore do not proceed at equal rates but are transmitted from exterior to interior. It is now obvious that enclosed stones which are sizable will move differently from the surrounding masses of mud, because in the freezing process the outer end gets frozen first in the crust, whereas in the melting process the inner end continues to be fixed in the frozen mass while the outer part is already surrounded by thawed material. The motion of the stones, therefore, does not coincide with that of the mud mass around the middle of the stone. In the process of freezing, the stone at its extreme end follows the movement of the mud, while in the melting process it follows the movement of the mud with its interior end. The centrifugal movement of the stone during freezing is thus greater than the centripetal movement during melting. At each completed cycle of movement, a permanent centrifugal shifting of the stone is thus accomplished.

The process is more clearly delineated in Figs. 7 to 12, which represent a vertical profile of fine material enclosing two round stones, one of which is tangential to the surface. Frozen parts are hatched. In Fig. 7 the mass is unfrozen. When the surface freezes, stone A becomes embedded in the crust, follows the movement of the crust, and will be

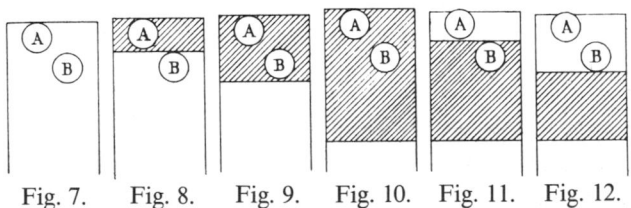

Fig. 7.     Fig. 8.     Fig. 9.     Fig. 10.     Fig. 11.     Fig. 12.

lifted upward by the expansion of the freezing mud (Fig. 8). The distance between A and B will at first be increased, until B also sits firmly in the freezing material. From that moment on, the distance remains constant and both will be uplifted equally during the freezing process (Figs. 9 and 10). When thawing sets in, the surface thaws first, while the stones are still encased in the frozen material. As long as they are fixed in it, they cannot participate in the contraction of the mud. As long as A is fixed, it remains at the same level as in Fig. 10, and if at the start it just touched the surface it now must be raised above it by the contraction of the mud from the same level (Fig. 11). Relative to the surface, A now keeps its position but otherwise follows the descending movement of the mud during the thaw. Stone B, at a lower level, is at first fixed, but when A descends, the distance between the two stones, earlier increased by the freezing process, will again shrink and gradually return to the original relationship (Fig. 12). In the final position after the thaw, the original distance between the stones is restored, but both stones have risen by an amount which depends on the effective height of the stones and the relative expansion and contraction of the mud during freezing and thawing.

The following calculation may serve to evaluate the effect of this process.

The "cubic" expansion of water on freezing is about 0.1 and the "linear" expansion is therefore about 0.03. The magnitude of expansion of wet mud is unknown, but it would probably be not much less than that of pure water, because of developing cracks, and so on. A mud layer 10 cm thick would thus expand by 3 mm. In a completed cycle of freezing and thawing, a stone of 10 cm "effective height"[3] would be permanently lifted upward by 3 mm. With the assumed expansion of mud, the upward movement of a stone would equal its effective height multiplied by 0.03. If a part of the stone sticks out from the mud, its effective height will be the part of the stone that is submerged in the mud. Large stones move faster than small ones. In general, the movement will be proportional to the linear dimensions; arriving at the surface of the mud, the amount of movement will decrease with successive freezing cycles and the stones will accumulate there.

In nature, this process is not so simple as here described. This is due especially to the fact that stones conduct heat better than the water-soaked mud subject to the freezing and thawing. . . . The conductivity and specific heat of objects enclosed in mud would presumably operate in such a fashion that the greater the former and the smaller the latter

[3] By effective height I mean the dimension of the mud-embedded stone projected in the transmitting direction of the freezing and thawing.

the more slowly will objects be thrust upward by frost action. One would expect that a piece of wood will be thrust out from the mud more rapidly than stones, and pieces of metal more slowly.

# BARRELL

Joseph Barrell (1869–1919), American geologist, made important contributions to the understanding of many phases of earth science, ranging from the genesis of metalliferous ore deposits to "the rise of air-breathing vertebrates and the origin of the Tertiary ape-man." Especially notable among his writings are those dealing with isostasy and the origin of continental and littoral sediments, excerpts from which are printed here. As a teacher of geology at Yale University from 1903 until he died of pneumonia and spinal meningitis at the height of his productive powers, he exerted a profound influence upon many grateful students who later achieved eminence in geological professions.

## CRITERIA FOR THE RECOGNITION OF ANCIENT DELTA DEPOSITS *

On the earth's surface, ranging from mountain crests to oceanic deeps, are wide gradations in geologic process and organic environment, but the line which most sharply draws division between two worlds of process and of life is the strand. In the study of the sediments, holding as they do the record of earth history and organic evolution, a fundamental question is therefore whether the strata were laid down in contact with the air or beneath the level of the sea. If fossils are present they commonly give an answer, but the absence of fossils from many formations leaves the problems of origin to be solved by other methods of attack. It is important that the criteria which are used for such purposes should be always subject to scrutiny in order that inherited errors may be detected and further progress made toward refinements of discrimination—refinements which though concerning small details may yet result in a disproportionately large increase of knowledge in the interpretation of the sediments. It is in delta deposits especially that the line of the ancient strand is difficult to draw, since it is not here coincident with the limits between erosion and sedimentation and the same formation is made in part above, in part below the level of permanent water. It is the purpose of this paper, therefore, to review the validity of the criteria which have been employed to discriminate between terrestrial and subaqueous sediments—critera whose use is preliminary to a knowledge of the physiography or climate of

*From *Geological Society of America Bulletin 23* (1912), 377–446.

those former periods where knowledge is drawn from the stratigraphic record; since building on an insecure foundation results in danger to the whole superstructure of knowledge.

But before a discussion of such criteria is given it is important that the view should be accepted that at certain geologic times deltas may have been of widely different character and have varied greatly in importance from the rather limited place which they now hold in the physiography of the lands. The field of progress in science is hedged in by the limits of the mental angle of vision, and the range of hypotheses should therefore be made broad before examining in detail the possibilities of a problem. The rise of geology as a science depended on the establishment of the principle of uniformitarianism—that the present is the key to the past. But applied too rigidly it narrows the visual angle, since the scale or rate at which various processes work may vary greatly in successive periods and their changing dominance is now believed to have resulted at times in great climatic and geographic contrasts. The highly variable importance of glaciation in geologic history may be used as an illustration of a similarly possible wide variation from period to period in delta-building. No *a priori* limit can therefore be set safely to the maximum area and thickness which under favoring conditions deltas may attain. In fact, as the successive geologic periods differ from one another in character, it should follow that the importance of delta-building will vary from age to age according to the physiographic stage-setting of the continents. A direct application of the growth of glacial theory during the past half century may be made to the problem of the relation of continental and marine deposits. The rise of geology in western Europe, where mountain glaciers and river deltas though interesting are relatively small and inconsequential factors at the present geologic time, and where marine erosion on the other hand is an impressive phenomenon, gave an initial trend to geology which underestimated the possibilities of continental glaciation and continental sedimentation. A truer perspective regarding glaciation has been attained by the study of the polar regions and of sedimentation by the study of other continents; but the records of delta deposits and their distinction from other forms of sedimentation are not so clear as are the marks of glaciation, with the result that the criteria for the recognition of delta deposits are still open to discussion and further elaboration. . . .

The strata of ancient deltas are now exposed for study as a consequence of uplift and partial erosion, and the broader concepts in regard to their original nature are derived from a synthesis of the observations on individual outcrops. Increase of knowledge rests on an accurate interpretation of the conditions of origin of the strata as seen in these outcrops. But, as noted in the introduction, it is the strand-line which separates the two widely contrasted zones of life, and the most fundamental use of criteria is therefore to distinguish deposits accumulated on the land surface, either by wind or water, from those originating under permanent bodies of water. As applied to deltas the initial problem is in consequence to determine the distinctive strati-graphic characters of the subaerial plain as contrasted to all the other parts of the delta, but especially to the rather closely related subaque-ous portion of the topset plain. In order to prevent undue reliance from being placed on indeterminate criteria it is necessary to discuss the degree to which they may occur in various situations and to find if possible in such cases minor distinctions which may be of determina-tive value. In general it may be remarked that considerable caution must be used in drawing distinctions between water-made structures of the land and sea. Evidences of exposure to the air, on the other hand, as shown by special structures or by fossils, are inherently of higher value.

Beyond the initial problem of the separation of the subaerial from the subaqueous portions, however, many subsidiary problems arise. The very complexity of chemical composition, of structure, and of fossil content make possible by their variations and combinations a highly significant geologic record. The stratigraphic characters of land de-posits especially bear the impress of climate and topography. The sub-aqueous deposits are related in their nature to life, depth of water, temperature, salinity, tide, and currents. According to the quality of this evidence will rest the conclusions as to the marine, estuarine, or lacustrine nature of the deposition.

It is evident that many criteria are subject to gradations in nature and in clearness of development, and in the following discussion of stratigraphic characters the method will be to pass from those of less to those of greater determinative value. . . .

Sediment carried by rivers is subjected to oxidation both while in transit and after deposition on the surface of the floodplain, until its burial by overlying layers carries a stratum below the level of ground water. Where the ground water level is coincident with or higher than the surface, organic matter accumulates and deoxidizing processes take place. A certain fraction of delta deposits, depending on the propor-tion of back swamps and coastal swamps, therefore show colors rang-ing from green to blue, according to the state of the iron oxide, and from white through gray to black, according to the amount of carbon.

But over the larger portion of the delta the iron of the soil is more or less completely oxidized during the seasons of dryness, and the corresponding colors—yellow, orange, red, or brown—are in evidence. The ratio of these oxidized and deoxidized sediments varies with the flatness of the delta and the character of the climate. Color is therefore in itself no criterion by which to distinguish between terrestrial and subaqueous deposition, but yellows, reds, and browns are the dominating colors of continental deposits save in certain geological periods. A red shale which grades laterally into a green, gray, or black shale gives therefore strong indications of terrestrial origin for the red portion. Such a relation is found in the Wamsutta Red Beds of the Rhode Island basin. The other portions may be swamp deposits of deltas or, so far as the color goes, of subaqueous origin. This evidence from red beds is especially strong when found in formations which are dominantly black, as in coal formations, but unless the transition can be traced is not a positive indication; as seen, for example, in the Lower Barren Coal Measures, where at Pittsburgh a marine fauna may be observed in a limestone band 2 to 3 feet thick, resting on red shale and succeeded by 1 foot of black shale, passing again into red shale. The evidence thus shows a time of red shale deposition, of possible marine origin, intervening in the Pennsylvanian when even the land muds gave normally a black shale formation. Taking the contrary case, lenses of gray or black shale in a formation which is dominantly red, such as the black shale bands in the Triassic rocks of Connecticut, is a suggestive though not positive indication as to the subaqueous accumulation of the dark bands, perhaps as swamp deposits if black; as lacustrine deposits if gray or olive in tone and associated with thin and regular bedding.

With respect to very early geological times, such as the Keewatin and Huronian, the absence of red is of doubtful significance, owing to the unknown composition of the air of those early periods and its possible ineffectiveness as an oxidizing agent.

Turning to the sea deposits, the dominant color of bottom muds at the present time, omitting the abyssal red clays, is seen to be blue or gray to black. There are, however, relatively small areas of red muds off the shores of certain tropical lands. In other localities, as the Red Sea, yellow muds occur. The dominance of blue muds corresponds with the known deoxidizing influences of the sea bottom, but at other times the oxidizing conditions which now give local areas of red muds may have been widely prevalent. Consequently in other geologic periods the dominant color effect may be reversed. In the Pennsylvanian, for example, the bulk of both terrestrial and subaqueous shales are dark with carbon. In the Clinton formation, on the contrary, the deposits of the shallow sea are brilliant with ferric oxide.

The influence of climate and the kinds of bacterial or inorganic reactions which it favors is therefore a factor of stronger control than conditions of continental or marine deposition. It is only in mean climatic states, such as the present, that the place of deposition exerts a dominating influence on color. . . .

*Lamination of mudstones*—Effects of subsidence from suspension— Lake or estuarine clays, if deposited below the depth affected by waves and currents, are characterized by a very regular lamination which is commonly closely spaced and may give rise to paper shales. The materials are wholly derived from suspension in water and are not marked by the intercalation of sand lenses. The same is true of marine mudstones, but the more powerful waves of the open seas are able to affect a greater depth of water and restrict to such depths the areas free from wave action. The preservation of perfect and fine-grained lamination in many ancient fossiliferous marine muds seems to show that the muddy ooze of deeper waters is not stirred by the bottom life to the same extent as is true within similar sediments on the land. The smothering nature of the deep, soft ooze is in fact unfavorable to most kinds of invertebrate bottom life and may be correlated with the sparingly fossiliferous character of thinly laminated non-calcareous marine shales.

Effects of waves—Where muddy sediment is supplied to shallow waters, as off the mouth of the Mississippi, the coast charts show intermixtures of sand and mud, some parts of the bottom soft and others hard. The waves of storms stir up such bottoms and shift its materials. The water becomes discolored with sediment and considerable thicknesses must settle on the subsidence of wave action. The stratigraphic result to be anticipated is a destruction of the fine and regular lamination of clays and their intermixture with sand and silt. Such a massive structure in clays is observed in certain fossiliferous marine formations —such, for example, as the Merchantville clay of the Upper Cretaceous of the Atlantic Coastal Plain, where bedding is characteristically absent except in the presence of laminæ of sand. Where two materials of unlike nature, such as clay and sand, are both present the results are quite different than in mud deposits alone.

Effects of subaerial actions—On floodplains extensive pelitic deposits are laid down in backwaters but little affected by currents, in shallow lakes, and on the frontal parts of the delta. Where such clays are exposed to the air various agencies tend to destroy the original lamination. The effects of earthworms and roots are well known, but over regions where the clays become mud-cracked a still more effective agency is in operation. The cracks break across the bedding and in thick clays may extend to depths of some feet. The next flood waters sweep more sediment into these cracks, the edges of the polygons slack and crumble and the cracks become obliterated. The following period of drying opens them again, but on more or less independent patterns. Thus the clay is subjected to a thorough vertical mixing through a period of time required for an accumulation equal to the depth of the mud cracks. Where the character of the sediment remains uniform, the filling is of the same material as the dried polygons and there results massive clay formations, in which both lamination and the evidence of mud cracking are absent. The latter are commonly revealed only when sand or sandy clay has been swept over the mud-cracked stratum, filling the cracks and protecting the stratum from further action. It is consequently the bottom of sandy strata resting on beds of shale which most commonly show the pattern of the mud cracks. This poorly laminated bedding is especially characteristic of the thick red shale members of the Catskill formation, which there is reason to believe is largely fluviatile and contrasts with the better lamination in the olive shales of the Chemung which represent the offshore deposition.

Thus, to sum up the previous discussion, it is seen that highly perfect lamination in pure pelites is characteristic of quiet subaqueous deposition, but an absence of such lamination is no proof of subaerial conditions, though most extensively developed in such situations. It is to be noted, however, that studies on the character of lamination in modern sedimentation is a subject which has received but little attention.

*Stratification of sandstones*—Effects of waves  The transporting agencies of marine sands are primarily waves, secondarily currents. In fluviatile work, on the contrary, currents are the controlling agency and the work of waves is limited. In neither region, however, is either one entirely absent and locally the minor activity may dominate the resulting structure.

Normal wave action tends to sweep sand in a direction opposite to that of the surface wave motion, but where the bottom shallows the wave becomes to some degree a wave of translation and carries the coarser bottom material which it can move with the water toward the shore and results in the building of bars. Waves over a broad bottom which is flat tend therefore to maintain an even depth of water and develop a regular bedding, the sand being swept under normal wave action from the slightly higher places to the quieter water of greater depth. The differing direction and force of storm winds tends also to shift the bottom materials. The action near the shore is different in character from that on the flat offshore bottom, since the material tends to be moved partly to deeper water, partly to shallower water, and the shoreward slopes are steepened, the outer slopes flattened. The shifting of bars results, further, in a continual cutting out and redeposition elsewhere of the sand beds. This is well illustrated off the New Jersey and Maryland coasts, irregularities of the bottom extending to depths of 10 fathoms at distances up to 15 or more miles from the coast. . . .

It is one of the important principles of sedimentation that the beds of sand which are laid down, and not later disturbed, are the results of the heaviest storms. These churn up the shallower bottom, loading the water with sediment and moving part of it to a greater depth of water whither minor storm waves can not transport the sand. Here the sand is laid down gently and without indication of the commotion which is reigning elsewhere. A sandstone bed may thus be deposited during a single storm and give the appearance of rapid sedimentation, when in reality years may elapse between the deposition of successive coarse beds. During such storms, although the sand is worked out to unusual depths, the silt of those depths has also been greatly stirred and is in part worked farther seaward, in part settles back in place. The resulting bed from a single storm, owing to this stirring, will show a sharply defined surface to the sand, frequently ripple-marked, witness to the culmination of the storm, on which another bed of mud or silt will come to rest and record the following period of lessened wave action. This is normal flagstone bedding.

The most striking effect of waves is in the production of ripple-mark as distinguished from current-mark. The size of the ripples is some function of the wave length, but the relation is not a simple one, and it is not possible at present to determine from the ripples the depth of water in which they were made. It is known, however, that ripple-marks may occur in depths of several hundred feet of water, and it may be produced by broad smooth currents of water affecting the bottom below wave base, and which by their evenness and breadth of movement may prevent the lack of symmetry which is especially characteristic of current-mark as contrasted to ripple-mark. The regularity of ripple-mark produced by wind action illustrates the possibility of currents simulating the effects of waves. River currents, however, tend to prevent regularity of bedding and symmetry of ripple-mark. It appears, therefore, that typical water-made ripple-mark associated with regularity of bedding in sandstones is especially associated with the subaqueous plain of deltas and the bottoms of shallow seas. It is developed, however, to a limited extent also over the subaerial portions of deltas, where shallow waters unaffected by strong currents have stood for a time before being drained away. Consequently it is not the presence of ripple-mark, but its dominance and association with other features which suggests offshore deposition.

* * * * * *

Effects of currents—Currents as carrying and depositing agents are especially characteristic of fluviatile action. In estuaries scoured by strong tides current action is also dominant, but they are in fact enlarged river channels alternately invaded by sea and river waters. In connection with irregularities in the coastline, waves also produce currents, as the result of concentrated undertow or obliqueness to the coastline. Such effects in seas and lakes are, however, local and exceptional as compared to the broad areas where wave action is dominant. The results of marine currents may be seen on the coast charts which show the entrances to Delaware and Chesapeake bays and also off Cape Hatteras. The conditions which give rise to wave-formed currents are connected especially with the inequalities of coastline resulting from a recent crustal movement and are rather closely restricted to shallow water and the vicinity of coasts. The waves and the currents which they generate are, however, in continual opposition, the one tending to fill up, the other to scour out. The leveling effects of strong wave action prevent in consequence such sharply defined and undercut channels as are developed by rivers. The slope of their sides probably does not average more than one in twenty-five, but the great volumes and consequent large cross-sections of water carried by shore currents permit of local excavation to depths of several fathoms. Where progressive subsidence permits such features to become preserved, there may result lenses of marine sandstones some tens of feet in thickness and marked by cross-bedding. The slopes are not so steep, however, nor the cross-bedding on so large a scale nor so dominant as in either river or dune structures. The marine bars and channels are also relatively fixed and do not migrate over the surface so freely as do river channels and desert dunes. . . .

River currents roll and jump material along the bottom in but one direction—a movement contrasted to the to and fro oscillating effects of waves. Typical ripple-mark is therefore exceptional, but in time of lessened velocity current-mark, an effect approaching it, is produced. The sand is caught between small back eddies on the bottom and the forward current, which is slightly higher. The result is the formation of crescents with gentle slopes facing upstream and steeper slopes facing downstream. The plan is more or less irregular and the individual ridges are limited in length. Current-mark is in fact analogous to dune structure, known as barchanes, rather than to the ripples made on the surface of the dune or the ripple-mark made by the oscillations of waves. As waves and currents may operate together, there are, however, all gradations between ripple-mark and current-mark. In the papers which treat of the theory of ripple-mark no distinction has commonly been made between the effects of waves and currents, both producing back eddies along the bottom. It seems, however, to the writer from repeated observations that where made clearly by a single cause the two structures can be separated, waves producing a symmetrical system of ridges; currents, on the other hand, resulting in ridges which are unsymmetrical in both plan and section.

The cross-bedded structures of fluviatile sands are the result of the cutting out and filling in of channels and the downstream migration of bars; the slopes of the cross-bedding are commonly steep, from 15 to 30 degrees. Although showing considerable variation, they tend to slope in one direction. The character of the cross-bedded strata of alluvial fans has been described by Hobbs, and several illustrations of cross-bedding ascribed to current action are given by A. Geikie. Such cross-bedded strata are especially discontinuous and indicate broken currents and shifting channels. The effects are presumably much more striking than the cross-bedding produced where waves are a powerful factor. On the other hand, the thickness of a single cross-bedded stratum of fluviatile origin is normally limited to a few feet, and in that respect is distinct from the cross-bedding which results from the migration of dunes. . . .

Effects of wind—Cross-bedding and ripple-mark of most noteworthy development occur as the result of wind action on river or beach sands. In semi-arid or arid climates during the dry season the shrunken streams lay bare large areas of loose sands which are swept to leeward for indefinite distances. The delta of the Indus furnishes an example of such a fluviatile deposit greatly modified by wind action. The dunes of such regions advance by the deposition of successive layers of sand on the leeward face. With each change of wind some shifting of the dune takes place. The marching of the dune involves the continuous destruction and construction of the bedding, but in regions of aggradation the basal parts of the dunes remain and become permanently buried. Huntington has called attention to the fact that cross-bedding of eolian origin attains a much larger scale than cross-bedding by water currents. He shows also that eolian cross-bedding is furthermore deposited on curved surfaces which approach tangency to a horizontal plane at the bottom. Aqueous cross-bedding, on the other hand, is commonly developed as plane slopes at a distinct angle to both the horizontal planes which limit the structure. These distinctions have been forcibly urged as evidence that the Triassic, and especially the white Jurassic sandstones of northwestern Arizona, are ancient desert sands. If gravels occur in connection with such wind-blown sands certain of the pebbles may be expected to show the smoothed facets and sharp edges which are developed by wind action, giving rise where carried to perfection to the form of pebbles known as dreikanter. Ripple-mark on marine sands is best developed on nearly horizontal surfaces, since the action of the waves is closely limited by depth. Winds, however, are not so restricted in action and develop ripple-mark on the long sloping sides of dunes. Furthermore, Cornish states that in wind-made ripples the coarser grains rest at the crest of the ripples—in water they remain in the troughs. These distinctions should be of aid in separating eolian and therefore terrestrial from water-laid sands. . . .

Wind wears fine sand much more rapidly than does water, moderate subjection to wind action giving a high degree of sphericity, which extends to grains which are less than a tenth of a millimeter in diameter, a size but little affected by water action. Subaerial exposure of loose sands is thus soon recorded in the form; but, as Sherzer notes, Sorby in 1880 called attention to the necessity of distinguishing between the age of the grains themselves and the age of the deposit in which they may be found. The same caution regarding age applies to the mode of origin of the deposit as distinct from the mode of origin of the grains. The sands which enter into both river and marine deposits may at some time in their history have been subjected to the wind, and this may happen in rather close relationship to the final deposition. The relative opportunities for wind action in these two classes of deposits must therefore be discussed and the problem raised of separating true desert deposits which imply aridity from those other deposits where the wind has been merely a cooperating factor and has but minor climatic significance. . . .

*Desert climates and dominant dune structures*—There is necessarily no sharp distinction between the combined wind and water structures of arid climates and semi-arid climates, especially as surrounding uplands may possess a semi-arid climate and furnish water to the true desert below, or great rivers like the Nile may flow from well watered zones through regions of arid climate. The following general distinctions may, however, be drawn: In the true deserts wind is the dominating activity. It not only shapes the sand but is the agent which abrades the rocks and which sorts and transports both dust and sand. Where thick sandstone formations show dominant dune structure and wind-

91

worn texture, as in the Jurassic white sandstones of Arizona, the inference is strong that ancient deserts probably prevailed.

*Semi-arid climates and dominant combined structures*—It would appear that the degree to which wind action may modify the fluviatile or marine sands in semi-arid or even in humid climates has not been appreciated by some who have written of past conditions, nor that sufficient distinction has been drawn between semi-arid and arid climates, widely different in their terrestrial development and their relations to life. Red color, feldspathic sands, and the presence of some wind-worn material have been taken as evidence of desert conditions in the Torridonian pre-Cambrian and the Old Red Devonian sandstones of Scotland, although saline deposits are not present and the bulk of the material is such as rivers and playa lakes could lay down. . . .

．　　．　　．　　．　　．

Gravels are transported by ice, by rivers, and by waves, giving rise to conglomerates of glacial, fluviatile, and marine origin. Glacial gravels may be eliminated from the discussion, leaving the distinctions between marine and terrestrial conglomerates to be considered. . . .

Where finer beds carry marine fossils the contiguous coarser beds are presumably in part if not wholly marine. Where, however, marine shales or sandstone are intercalated between conglomerate beds which are a hundred feet or more in thickness it is to be expected that at least the middle part of the conglomerates are terrestrial. Exceptional cases are known where these rules fail, chiefly on account of local accumulations of gravel through proximity to a bold shoreline, but it is thought that they have a high degree of generality. Thinner conglomerates may be either marine or terrestrial and their mode of origin must be determined on other grounds than that of thickness. The limit which has been rather arbitrarily drawn between sand and gravel by most writers is that of a diameter of two millimeters. For the application of these rules it should probably be raised to five millimeters.

Intraformational conglomerates made by wave action on shallow bottoms and not at the shore are readily discriminated, owing to the local origin and soft character of the pebbles and are not included in this discussion regarding the significance of thickness. . . .

．　　．　　．　　．　　．

From this review of the criteria which serve to separate the terrestrial portion of delta deposits from those of subaqueous origin several conclusions may be drawn. First, it is seen that it is more commonly the particular form of a feature, such as cross-bedding or the thickness of conglomerates or the mode of preservation of bones, which is of distinctive value, rather than the mere presence of cross-bedding or conglomerates or fossils; second, a single criterion is in many cases not absolutely decisive, and it is the convergence of evidence which makes strong the conclusion in regard to the origin of strata of a particular horizon; third, it is unsafe to extend the conclusion beyond the limits of the evidence to other portions of the same formation. Notwithstanding these limitations, it is thought that the criteria are sufficiently varied and numerous to determine the conditions of origin of the great majority of delta deposits. Finally, there should be emphasized the need of much broad study of a quantitative nature regarding modern conditions of sedimentation to determine minutely the characteristics which become a recognizable part of the buried formation as distinct from the passing surface features. The development of distinctive criteria must be studied, furthermore, in relation to the physiographic and climatic conditions of origin. This is a line of progress begun in the early days of geology, but then essentially of a qualitative nature, and by Lyell made the basis of the interpretation of earth history. Having grasped this idea the centers of scientific interest were transferred to the geologic record, and the interpretations made by the generation of Lyell were carried forward without material improvement till near the close of the nineteenth century. It is clear, however, that a more accurate and quantitative knowledge of that earth history which is now being recorded is needed in order to obtain in turn a more accurate knowledge of the past. Many of the criteria which in this paper are considered somewhat indefinite may become definite through a wide and more discriminative study of the sedimentation now in progress.

## THE STATUS OF THE THEORY OF ISOSTASY[*][1]

### OUTLINE OF THE THEORY OF ISOSTASY

Isostasy embraces the theory of relationships between the relative surface relief of segments of the earth's crust and the densities of those segments. It is a subject closely related to the geological history of con-

[*]From *American Journal of Science*, [4] *48* (1919), 291–338.

[1]This paper was written for the journal and was in the hands of the typist at the time of Professor Barrell's death, May 4, 1919. It is thought probable that it appears as he would have presented it. Here and there a few words have been added and minor changes in punctuation made. (Charles Schuchert)

tinents and ocean basins, and almost as closely to the nature of igneous rocks and the modes of deformation during periods of terrestrial revolution. Although one of the larger fields of geological theory, it is in a concrete form still relatively new and receives either no notice or but bare mention in the geologic texts published during the past ten to twenty years. The valuable literature on the subject is largely technical and removed from the field of the geologist. . . .

This article is written in enough detail to be clear to readers who have not closely followed the history of the subject. In the introductory sections the theory of isostasy is assumed to be true on the basis of work previously published by many investigators during the past half century. The later sections will discuss in detail certain recent adverse criticisms which may have seemed to some readers to undermine the solid basis on which isostasy was thought to rest. Those criticisms, in so far as they are against isostasy rather than against some subordinate or unessential hypothesis, are found here to be invalid. The conclusion therefore is reaffirmed that for regions sufficiently broad, and to variable degrees of perfection, the evidence is now convincing that the high or continental areas of the surface are underlain by lighter matter than are the low, or oceanic, areas. This relation is maintained closely enough over varied conditions to lead to the further conclusion that the relationship is one of cause and effect. Over broad high areas the mean elevations are high *because* the crustal densities are there low, and *vice versa*, the mean surface of low areas is low *because* the densities there are high. This is quite closely true for the relations of continents and ocean basins but to lesser and lesser degrees for the smaller and smaller subdivisions of these major segments of the crust. The subject remains problematic only in regard to closeness of adjustment and limits of area involved. The larger features of the earth's surface are, therefore, sustained in solid flotation, and at some depth the strains due to the unequal elevations largely disappear, the elevations being compensated by variations of density within the crust. In consequence the subcrustal shell is subjected to but little else than hydrostatic pressure. This conclusion regarding equilibrium of pressure in a subcrustal shell is embodied in the name *isostasy,* proposed by Dutton in 1889, meaning equal pressures. Above this shell, whose upper part though gradational is not more than 80 or 100 miles deep, every radial column of adequate area, say 100,000 square miles, contains very nearly the same mass as every other column of equal area, although the mean surfaces of ocean and continental columns may be several miles different in elevation.

Thus far we may speak of the *theory* of isostasy and regard its existence as demonstrated in the same way that astronomers have demonstrated the existence of small cyclic variations of latitude and the motion of the sun in space, namely, by the bringing into harmony, except for minor irregular discrepancies, of calculation and observation on large assemblages of precisely measured data. Beyond this broader demonstration of the existence of isostasy lies, however, the field of competing *hypotheses*. Such questions arise as: How closely related in horizontal area are the elevations and corresponding defects in density? How closely balanced are the elevations and densities? How near the surface are the corresponding variations and in what manner do they disappear with depth? What are the causes of variations of density and to what degree have they remained constant for each area through geologic time? To what degree are these questions determinate and to what degree indeterminate?

The quantitative data are mostly astronomic and geodetic, depending upon very precise measurements of the direction of the vertical and the intensity of gravity; the interpretation, however, is mostly geologic, having to harmonize the geodetic indications with other aspects of earth structure and history. Geodesists have been hampered in interpretation from the fact that they were not geologists; geologists have been hampered in weighing the force of the geodetic evidence because of lack of familiarity with the mathematics of the geodesist. . . .

In the analysis of the geodetic data bearing on isostasy, a simple mathematical picture is consequently introduced, but no one should imagine that nature is really so simple as the mathematical picture of hypothesis. The geodesist, while freely admitting this distinction, tends to minimize it; the geologist, familiar with the complexities of earth structure and seeing that topographic relief of the land is more dependent upon erosion than upon hidden density, tends to magnify the differences between nature and the mathematical picture.

The subject of isostasy has grown through the past half century, but has been brought into the field of exact analysis in the past decade by the comprehensive and very valuable geodetic researches of Hayford and Bowie. The writer, in common with some other geologists, was unable, however, to accept the geologic interpretation which Hayford gave to his work with the implication that whether geologists liked it or not they must accept it, and some years ago, in order to test the validity of the geodetic evidence and its geologic implications, made an extensive investigation of the geodetic data.[2] Since that time a number of articles of various values, some supporting the theory of isos-

[2] Joseph Barrell, "The strength of the earth's crust," *J. Geol. 22* (1914); *23* (1915).

tasy, some adverse to it, have appeared. As giving source material especially, should be mentioned Bowie's most important monograph,[3] which has greatly extended the data previously available and has treated them from some new standpoints. The time seems appropriate therefore for a further review and analysis of this subject.

As the following analysis must deal largely with the simple mathematical pictures, the impression might be given that a writer mistakes them for the realities of nature. It is desirable, therefore, before taking up the details of the subject, to state briefly the general conclusions entertained regarding the limits of isostasy. The writer believes the evidence demonstrates beyond controversy that the larger relief of the earth is in greater part balanced by corresponding variations of density within the outer fiftieth of the earth's radius, that the distortional stresses at a depth of a twentieth of the radius are only a small fraction of what they would be if the density of the outer crust were uniform. On the other hand, it is believed that the variations of density are irregular, imperfect, and mostly concentrated in the outer hundredth of the radius, with a tendency to progressively disappear with depth. The outer crust is very strong, capable of supporting individual mountains, limited mountain ranges, and erosion features of corresponding magnitude; but it is able to flex under broader loads, so that mountain systems and broad plateaus are in greater part related to regional deficiencies in subcrustal densities. The strength of the crust is believed to vary greatly in different regions and to shade off into the weaker zone below. The span and magnitude of the possible loads vary accordingly. The broader and gentler flexures of this thick, strong crust involve but little crustal stress and therefore but limited deformation within the crust itself, but imply a broad, deep, and slow creep in the subcrustal zone. This creep, provided the yielding zone is thick, involves but small distortion of a unit mass and is thought to be coexistent with the maintenance of a solid and rigid state. The probable mode of yielding is by recrystallization under strain, analogous to the mechanics of the flow of glacial ice.

This combination of a strong, thick crust resting on a weak but solid subcrustal shell is very different from the picture set up by the extreme isostasists, on the one hand, of a weak and failing earth, yielding isostatically in its outer part to each minor change of load; and is considerably different, on the other hand, from those hypotheses of the earth's internal nature and mode of deformation which have been

[3]William Bowie, *Investigations of Gravity and Isostasy,* Special Publication No. 40, U. S. Coast and Geodetic Survey, 1917.

elaborated without recognition of isostasy. These contrasts of interpretation point to the need for further discussion and investigation, with the object of bringing antagonistic points of view into harmony.

### DEFINITIONS INVOLVED IN ISOSTASY

In order to discuss in detail the problems of isostasy, the meaning of the phraseology must be held clearly in mind. For this reason Fig. 1 is given.

Let A be a section of the continental crust, and B a section of the crust beneath the oceans. They are both portions of the lithosphere or rock shell whose outer part is open to geologic study. The weight of the two sections of the crust is equal for equal areas. The mean density of A is therefore less than the density of a column whose mean surface is at sea level. The difference is known as the *defect of density*. The density of B is greater than the sea level column. The difference is a negative defect of density. The mass above sea level is balanced by a deficiency of mass below sea level. The deficiency of mass is known as the *isostatic compensation*. For the oceanic segments the isostatic compensation is an added mass. For convenience the sea level is used as the datum surface. Any other datum between the mountain summits and ocean depths could be used, since it is the difference of mass between A and B which is the quantity involved and this is independent of the datum. For convenience in computation, assumptions are introduced in regard to change of density at the datum surface which may require minor corrections according to the level of the surface.

At a certain depth, known as the *depth of compensation*, the differ-

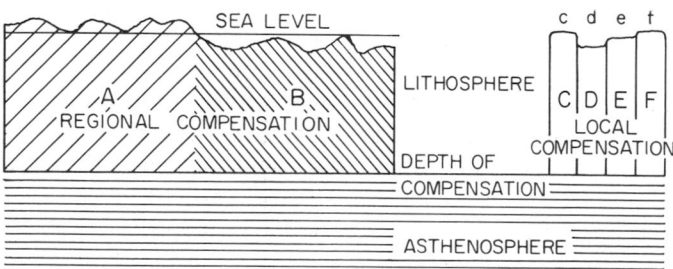

Fig. 1. Diagram to illustrate the principles of isostasy. In nature there are of course no sharp boundaries such as are drawn to make a diagram clear. The proportions are also different.

ence in density above will, for perfect isostasy, have completely neutralized the difference in surface elevations, and two sections A and B of Fig. 1, if of equal area, will contain the same mass.

The depth of compensation will depend upon the vertical *distribution of compensation*. . . .

If the depth of compensation is taken as 100 kilometers, the difference in densities between A and B for a differential relief of 5 kilometers would be 5 per cent. This is of the order of magnitude believed to exist.

The compensation may be conceived either: first, as existing in a certain part of the crust; second, as greatest near the surface and decreasing with depth; or, third, as uniformly distributed to the depth of compensation and there sharply terminating. Various other modes may be conceived as existing. A number of these modes of distribution satisfy the geodetic data and the most probable must be decided on geologic evidence. The depth of compensation will, however, vary according to the assumed mode of distribution.

The depth of the level of complete compensation under the *hypothesis of uniform distribution* Hayford determined at first as 114 kilometers, later as 122 kilometers, but the data do not form a sensitive index as to depth. The latest and fullest analysis by Bowie leads him to believe that future determinations will fall between 80 and 130 kilometers. Although the geodetic data do not yield a precise figure for the depth, they do show definitely that under any tenable mode of distribution practically all of the compensation lies within the outer fiftieth of the earth's radius.

In Fig. 1 *regional compensation* is indicated under areas A and B and *local compensation* under C, D, E, and F. The extreme of the hypothesis of local compensation is found in the assumption that each unit area, however small, is underlain by a corresponding density in its vertical column. The limit of regional compensation is to conceive a whole continent as underlain by crust of one density, an ocean basin by another density, without regarding plateaus and basins as related. The evidence indicates that neither of these extremes is near the truth. The truth, as is so commonly the case, lies between the two extremes. Regional compensation has indeterminate limits. It presumably varies in different regions, and certainly varies with the intensity and breadth of the loads to be supported. The assumption best adapted to mathematical calculation is, therefore, that of local compensation. Each unit area is given its appropriate density. Because gravity varies inversely with the square of the distance, near the geodetic station these unit areas are small. Far away they are large. They are chosen so that each unit area will have a unit gravitative effect. But no one conceives this extreme form of local compensation to be true, but calculations of the deflection of the vertical and intensity of gravity based on such local compensation agree essentially with those based on regional compensation over areas at least as large as a square degree. For mountain regions and those near continental borders the assumption of regional compensation restricted to radial distances of 60 kilometers or less appears to give slightly better results than the assumption of regional compensation over radial distances of 167 kilometers or greater, but the discrepancies involved in taking isostasy as regional with a radius of 167 kilometers are small in comparison with other disturbing factors. At the present time the best tests as to the horizontal relationships between relief and density appear to the writer to be geologic, based on the limits of the loads which can be imposed on the crust without yielding.

Since enormous strains exist in the crust above, which when too great produce folding or faulting, it seems clear that, in so far as isostasy is true, the absence of notable strains in the zone below, notwithstanding the existence of geological agencies which tend to bring stresses upon it, implies a lack of strength in that zone. Rock flowage, like glacial flowage, must occur nearly as fast as the strains accumulate. The writer has, therefore, proposed for that zone of ready yielding the name of the *asthenosphere,* the sphere of weakness, as contrasted to the *lithosphere* above, which by comparison is a sphere of strength, and the *centrosphere* below, which is probably also more resistant.

The geodetic evidence of isostasy is founded upon a comparison of the true and calculated directions of the plumb-line at numerous stations over the United States, and in later work also upon a comparison of the true and calculated values of gravity. By introducing the hypothesis of isostatic compensation of density corresponding to the relief, the discrepancies between calculated and observed values of the direction of the vertical and the intensity of gravity were reduced on the average, as previously noted, to a fraction of what they were if no such hypothesis of density variations was introduced.

Although the average disagreement between the observed and calculated values was reduced by the introduction of the hypothesis of isostasy, the disagreements for many stations remained larger. These outstanding quantities need careful study and must be frequently referred to. For the deflections of the vertical, the outstanding discrepancies are known as the *deflection residuals.* For the intensity of gravity, the variations which remain unaccounted for by the theory of isostasy are known as the *gravity anomalies.* . . .

DALY Reginald Aldworth Daly (1871–1957), American geologist, received his Ph.D. degree from Harvard University in 1896, studied at Heidelberg and Paris during the next two years, and was geologist on the Canadian International Boundary Commission from 1901 to 1907. For the next five years he was Professor of Physical Geology at Massachusetts Institute of Technology, and from 1912 until his retirement in 1942 he was Sturgis Hooper Professor of Geology at Harvard. Drawing upon his world-wide field experiences, his brilliantly imaginative mind ranged broadly over many diverse problems of geology and geophysics.

Two of his notably fruitful concepts are embodied in the following excerpts from his voluminous writings. In the first, his "glacial-control theory" concerning coral reefs, first presented in 1919, is reviewed ten years later in the light of subsequently available data and the criticisms it had received during those years; characteristically, some of his most pungent comments are in footnotes rather than in the main text. His "working hypothesis" that mud-controlled density currents could excavate submarine canyons, set forth in the second excerpt, is now generally hailed as the "turbidity current theory."

## SWINGING SEALEVEL OF THE ICE AGE*

. . . Personal study of shorelines of the Atlantic, Pacific, and Indian ocean basins, together with compilation of data published by others, has led me to suggest such a recent general sinking of sealevel to the extent of a few meters. To measure the exact amount of the sinking at any locality demands accurate knowledge of the relations of wave-cut bench or wave-built terrace to the sealevel at the epoch of its formation, and this datum is seldom to be obtained with certainty. However, the described lowering of sealevel appears to have averaged about five meters.

The recent negative movement of sealevel has been speculatively explained by a simultaneous increase of the existing ice-caps. During the late Neolithic age of Europe the average climate of the Northern Hemisphere at least was decidedly warmer than at present. About 3,000 years ago the earth's climate seems already to have attained its existing average character. Assuming the change from warm to cooler to have centered around the epoch of about 4,000 years ago, and that then the Antarctic ice-cap was thickened by 150 to 200 meters, we should be able to account for the world-wide five-meter drop of sealevel.[1]

*From *Geological Society of America Bulletin 40* (1929), 721–734.
[1]G. de Geer: *Ymer 45* (1925), 1 (abstract by E. Antevs, *Geog. Rev. 16* (1926), 170). R. Gradmann: *Hettner's Geograph. Zeit. 4* (1924), 249, 260. R. A. Daly: "Geology of Saint Helena Island," *Proc. Am. Acad. Arts and Sciences 62* (1927), 80, with references.

*Quaternary Oscillations of Sealevel*

Much greater eustatic shifts of sealevel must have accompanied each glaciation and deglaciation (melting of ice) during the pre-Recent, Quaternary time, the Ice Age as ordinarily understood. Both in Europe and North America the Quaternary ice-caps waxed at least four times and waned at least four times, though unequally, an earlier set of glacial stages being separated from a later set by an exceptionally long interglacial stage, when the earth was perhaps entirely ice-free (Toronto-Eemian deposits). Probably the changes were respectively simultaneous in the two continents. Thus the following correlations have been made: Jerseyan drift with the Günz of Europe; Kansan drift with the Mindel; Illinoian drift with the Riss; and Wisconsin with the Würm. Each glacial stage meant world-wide sinking of sealevel. Each of the interglacial stages, like the post-Glacial stage, was ushered in by a world-wide rise of sealevel.

The last, Wisconsin-Würm, oscillation of level can be discussed quantitatively. At least one of the earlier swings was of the same order of magnitude.

Only within the last few decades have required data been assembled and that only partially. In 1842, only two years after Louis Agassiz published his "Études sur les Glaciers," Maclaren guessed the lowering of sealevel in consequence of glaciation to have been 350 to 700 feet (107 to 213 meters). Many other estimates have since been made. The latest and probably the most reliable is that of Antevs, who gives 83 to 93 meters for the deepening of the ocean through the melting of the

---

In addition to the extensive data compiled and used in the preparation of the paper last mentioned, new discoveries of what appears to be the five-meter strand-mark have been reported from the Texas coast (Deussen); Jamaica (Matley); Gibraltar (Jessen); Mediterranean coast of France (Depéret and Denizot); the Red Sea coast and Zanzibar (Crossland); along 3,000 kilometers of the South African coast (A. V. Krige, who has carried out the most complete relevant field study ever undertaken in any one region); New South Wales (Harper); Fiji and Tonga Islands (Ladd and Hoffmeister); Marquesas Islands (Chubb); Nauru Island (Bohne); Oahu Island (Pollock); New Zealand (Ongley and Macpherson, Bartrum); Henderson Island (Aurosseau); Andaman, Chagos, Maldive archipelagoes, Persian Gulf, coast of India (Sewell).

Recent emergence of amounts that seem to correspond is described by W. M. Davis in his "The coral reef problem" (1928), at the following oceanic islands: Rocas Island, off Brazil; Aldabra, Silhouette, and Mahe Islands, Indian Ocean; Ovalau, Ono-i-Lau, Solo, and Vatu Vara Islands of the Fiji group; McKean, Enderby, Phoenix, and Birnie Islands of the Phoenix group; Niau, Rangiroa, and Matahiva Islands of the Paumotu group.

Concerning the date of the five-meter shift of sealevel and the Pleistocene shifts in general, see important papers by G. Dubois (*Annales soc. géol. du Nord 49* (1925), 120, and *Bull. soc. géol. France 25* (1925), 857, both with references). Compare C. E. P. Brooks, "The evolution of climate" (London, 1925), p. 164.

ice of the Wisconsin-Würm stage.[2] The larger value derives from the assumption that the Antarctic ice-cap attained its maximum volume simultaneously with the ice-caps of the Northern Hemisphere and has since diminished by a certain amount. A deepening of as much as 100 meters may not be out of the question.

For the remaining discussion let us assume the round figure of 80 meters (262 feet, or 47 fathoms) for the depth of the water which has been returned to the ocean since the epoch, some 30,000 years ago, when the ice of the Wisconsin-Würm stage began its slow melting.

### SOME CONSEQUENCES OF THE LAST GREAT MELTING

#### Distortion of the Solid Earth and of the Geoid

The transfer of water substance from the lands to the ocean through melting of the ice-caps of course raised the surface of the ocean everywhere and, in addition, had other complicated effects on levels. These latter effects were of two kinds: one immediate, the other delayed. The immediate effects were, in their turn, of two kinds, including the purely elastic distortion of the whole globe, and, secondly, the distortion of the geoid, or sealevel, surface itself.

The prompt, elastic reshaping of the earth was general, but it most affected levels in and near the glaciated tracts. The rocky surface at the center of each major glaciated tract, when relieved of the heavy ice-cap, rose several scores of meters, and at the edge of the tract nearly one-third as much. For several hundreds of kilometers outside the edge of the tract the rocky surface was elastically superelevated to a corresponding degree. It is possible that in this peripheral belt the earth's crust had been somewhat bulged upward because of earlier viscous outflow of the subcrust material under the weight of the ice-cap. If so, the peripheral bulge itself was elastically uplifted when the ice melted, and thus for two reasons a fairly broad belt of ground just outside the terminal moraine was elevated above the level of final equilibrium. Outside these peripheral belts of superelevation the rocky surface of the globe was elastically depressed somewhat below the level of final equilibrium.

The weight of water added to each ocean basin similarly caused an

[2] E. Antevs, "The last glaciation," *Am. Geograph. Soc. Research Series No. 17* (1928), p. 81. . . . The maximum lowering of sealevel by the glaciation of the lands, perhaps in Kansan time, may have well exceeded 80 meters. This maximum may be in mind when one is thinking of the depth to which rivers could sink their channels in the emerged banks and shelves of the glacial stages, but the maximum is not so important as a basis for estimating the extent to which the low-level waves and currents cut down into and smoothed the banks and shelves during the Wisconsin stage. In the latter problem the lower figure of 60–70 meters seems to be a better datum.

immediate elastic sinking of the floor of that ocean, in greatest amount near the center of the basin.

The other immediate effect on levels, that on the geoid, was smaller than the elastic effect and, with reference to the earth's center, was in the opposite sense. Thus the water substance removed from each glaciated tract no longer by its own mass attracted the ocean water toward the center of that tract; hence the sealevel sank at the center of the tract. For the same reason it sank about one-third as much at the edge of the tract. Beyond a moderately broad belt outside each of the glaciated tracts, the sealevel rose slightly because of the same disturbance of the gravitational field by removal of water substance from the continents. . . .

Outside of the glaciated tracts, the effects of distortion, whether of the solid earth or of the geoid, were, in relation to the vertical displacement of strandlines, decidedly subordinate to the effect of the mere addition of water to the ocean when the ice-caps melted. Similarly, when the Wisconsin-Würm ice-caps were of full size, the sealevel over most of the earth was not far from 80 meters lower than at present. We shall glance at some consequences of this fact. . . .

Just before the first glacial stage the deposition of inorganic and organic detritus had completed broad or narrow shelves or terraces along all sea shores. At present the water on a typical shelf, facing continent or old island, deepens rather rapidly from the beach outward; then more slowly. At the depth of 40 to 50 fathoms, or 75 to 95 meters, the surface of the shelf begins to drop rapidly to the deep, general level of the ocean floor. On account of erosion while the sealevel was lower than now, the profiles of the pre-Glacial shelves were somewhat altered, so that we can not be sure that any profile is now in equilibrium with waves and currents. However, we shall not make any essential error if we suppose that the break of slope of each well developed, pre-Glacial shelf was situated at the depth of 75 meters. The break of slope for most of the submarine landless banks would be at nearly the same depth.

With the onset of each of the four glacial stages, the sealevel began to sink, and for some thousands of years it continued to go down, until the volume of land ice reached its maximum. Each time, the level sank about 80 meters or a large fraction of 80 meters. At least twice the coastlines were moved out nearly or quite to the breaks of slope, the outer "edges" of the shelves and banks. During this slow process, then, the waves of the whole ocean were beating on little else than mud and sand, the dominant superficial materials of shelf and bank. The water was murky with mud to a degree which can not be matched under the normal conditions of a stable sealevel. Many shallow-water species of animals sensitive to the muddying of water were affected more or less seriously.

*Origination of the Existing Coral Reefs*

As the sea withdrew, a kind of elutriation, or sorting, of the sediment on shelf and bank took place. The fine muds were specially stirred up and in large amount carried out to deep water. The coarser sand was less readily removed and became concentrated in the form of a superficial layer on shelf or bank.

Because each of the four accumulations of ice on the continents was nearly at maximum for several tens of thousands of years, the waves beat long near the breaks of slope, about 75 meters below present sealevel. There especially was the removal of mud prolonged, with a corresponding concentration of coarser detritus, including the elutriated sand and also the shells and skeletons of the shore-dwelling organic species then existing.

The result was a considerable cleansing of mud from the old shelves and banks. Since the sealevel rose for the last time, the water on shelf and bank has been relatively clean, much less charged with suspended mud than it was in pre-Glacial time. During post-Glacial time, therefore, those shallow-water animals which are killed by abundant storm-raised mud have been enabled to live and multiply at an extraordinarily high rate. The reef-building corals illustrate the case. On account of their importance as rock-bodies, the problem of the living coral reefs appeals to any naturalist. Still more manifestly this problem continues to engage attention because of the prestige of Darwin's famous speculation on the subject, with its deduction of widespread instability of the earth's crust. Let us briefly consider the conditions for life for this one group of shallow-water animals, the corals, during the Pleistocene period.

Each existing atoll or barrier reef is characteristically wall-like. On the lagoon side the water is usually 50 to 75 meters deep and the reef rises more and more steeply from this depth. On the side toward the open ocean the face of the reef commonly drops off at a rapid rate into water which is thousands of meters deep. In such a case the structure rises from a belt which is nearly or quite identical with the break-of-slope belt characteristic of a detrital shelf or bank.

No atoll or barrier reef of pre-Glacial date of origin has yet been demonstrated. Because the water at the edge of the normal pre-Glacial shelf or bank was much too deep for the growth of these shallow-water species, and because of the lethal effects of storm-stirred mud, we may well doubt that either atoll or barrier reef of the kind just described could have been formed in pre-Glacial time. Doubtless fringing reefs existed, but their outward growth in the face of the destroying waves may have been decidedly limited by the muddiness of the shelf waters of the time.

Not only did each glaciation of the continents mean great accentuation of this mud-control; it meant also a prolonged, though temporary, general absence of hard bottom on which the corals could build stable structures. And, thirdly, it meant cooling of the oceans. Merely moderate cooling kills the reef-building corals, and this must be rated as another important reason why reef-growth was greatly inhibited during any one of the glacial stages. One can hardly be certain that a single reef was then thriving in the modern way, at the modern rate. Of course, the reef corals were not entirely extinguished. After each glacial stage the coral larvæ could issue from warm, sheltered inlets of the sea and with relative speed colonize the appropriate shallows. New reefs could thus be built wherever the warmer currents bore the larvæ in sufficient abundance.

The warming of the world climate long preceded the close of the last principal melting of land ice. The accompanying rise of sealevel was extremely slow, so slow as to permit extensive colonization and inception of new reefs at the outer edges of shelf and bank before the water got too deep for coral growth. The corals throve best at or near the edges; that is, in the case of the shelves, along the shores of the coastal plains, which were then dry because of the previous withdrawal of water from the ocean. Three reasons for this statement may be mentioned:

(1) Along those low-lying shores and sites of shallows the deleterious mud had been largely removed during the prolonged time when there was thick ice on the lands (tens of thousands of years). Thus, as we have already seen, a comparatively clean, sand-shell bottom was prepared for the colonizing larvæ.

(2) On the side toward the open ocean the water of the incoming waves and currents was almost entirely free from mud, and, like the waves and currents now bathing the outside of an existing atoll or barrier, were specially charged with the food and free oxygen which are necessary for the life of corals and their associates in reef-building.

(3) Finally, there is some reason for supposing that a hard bottom, such as is favorable to the most successful rooting of a coral reef, would be formed at the edges of the shelves and of any emerged banks; for the recently emerged sands of Florida and other tropical regions have been lithified to a large extent. Moreover, even between tide-marks,

siliceous and carbonate sands are now being converted into rather strong "beach rock" at intervals along our tropical beaches.

Hence, along the outer edges of continental and island shelves and detached banks, the conditions for the establishment of reefs are regarded as having been particularly favorable. It is usually in just such situations that the reefs are thriving best today, as barriers and atolls. We have already noted that the continued upward growth of the reefs was insured by the slow rate at which sealevel rose on shelf and bank.

Vigor of growth for fringing reefs also had been secured by the special conditions of the Glacial period. The removal of much mud from shelf and bank and the moderate lowering of the surfaces by wave erosion at the lower levels caused the water on the post-Glacial and interglacial shelves and banks to be abnormally clean. For this, among other reasons, isolated coral knolls have also grown up on non-barriered, detrital shelves, as well as within the greater atoll and barrier-reef lagoons.

That the pre-Glacial reefs grew with less vigor than the living reefs is further indicated by the strictly limited volumes of true reef structures among the uplifted limestones of the tropical belt. Coralliferous limestones are there in quantity, but few, if any, are shown to have been fast-growing, powerful reefs of the type represented in the living atoll, barrier, or fringe.

On the other hand, atoll, barrier, and fringing reefs of interglacial dates of formation are likely to have been formed according to the mechanism outlined for the post-Glacial living reefs. A few elevated atolls and barriers of the southwest Pacific may be examples.

To summarize: The Glacial-control theory, based upon the Pleistocene, eustatic oscillations of sealevel and the accompanying changes of world temperature, seems to account well for the wonderful structures which are still being built by corals, though these can not thrive in water deeper than 10 to 20 meters. In order to explain the heights of the living reefs, heights which commonly reach 75 or more meters, a rise of sealevel on the foundations of the reefs must be postulated. Melting of the Quaternary land ice appears to provide amply for the required change of level.[3]

[3] Most of the leading elements of the writer's Glacial-control theory are summarized in the *Am. J. Sci. 48* (1919), 136, where references to older statements may be found. The description of the theory by W. M. Davis in "The coral reef problem," *Am. Geograph. Soc., Spec. Pub. No. 9* (1928), is inaccurate in some of the essentials. Thus based on wrong premises, his argument has led Davis to the statement (p. 285) that the Glacial-control theory is of "small value." The main conclusion of this monograph is favorable to the Darwin-Dana theory of subsidence; and yet Davis, like all of his predecessors, has not been able to annul any of the more or less obvious and apparently fatal, objections to the Darwin-Dana theory.

A complete testing of the theory is a subject much too broad for present consideration, but a few tests may be mentioned.

First, the supreme test of prophecy. The theory foretold that material of the continental shelf should be found at the approximate depth of 75 meters under any coral knoll which has grown up in the central part of the broad lagoon back of the Great Barrier Reef of Australia. In 1926 a bore-hole was put down through such a knoll and disclosed sand and ooze typical of a continental shelf, beginning at the depth of 241 feet, or 73 meters, and continuing to the bottom of the hole, at 183 meters. Above the 73-meter level the material was coralliferous. Beneath that level not a single fragment of coral "in place" was reported.[4]

The theory foretold a submarine thickness of about 75 meters for the coralliferous limestone on the top of the Bermuda bank. A boring there made found the fragmental rock of a Tertiary volcano at the depth of 245 feet, or 74.6 meters, below sealevel.[5]

The celebrated bore-hole at Funafuti was wrongly placed and can therefore afford no clear test of the rival theories of coral reefs.

The two borings here more useful show that crustal subsidence is not a necessary accompaniment of the upgrowth of coral reefs. Sayles has brought weighty evidence that the Bermuda bank did not sink during the whole Glacial period, a time of the order of one million years, and that in spite of the enormous weight of the pre-Pliocene (pre-Miocene?) Bermuda volcano on the earth's crust.[6] The small depth of the volcanic surface, a surface of erosion, below sealevel proves similar failure of subsidence during several millions of years. So it is with the Australian case. The development of the broad shelf at normal depth, whether under the warm, reef-bearing sea or farther south, where the water is too cool for coral growth, spells crustal stability for some millions of years.

The prolonged stability of the earth's crust under many reefs and many reef-free islands is shown by the nearly uniform elevation of the strand-marks made before the last eustatic drop of sealevel, the 5-meter shift. Evidently the reefs and islands bearing these marks have not budged much, if at all, during the last 3,500 years or so. When mapping the Island of Saint Helena I was much struck with this evidence of its failure to sink, even though its volcanic cone represents a gigantic load on the earth's crust. The width and normal depth of the island shelf indicates practically perfect stability of the mass for much more than

[4] M. Nathan, *Geograph. J. 70* (1928), 541. Clearly the presence of shells of shallow-water foraminifera in the beds below the depth of 73 meters does not demonstrate subsidence.

[5] L. V. Pirsson, *Am. J. Sci. 38* (1914), 193.

[6] R. W. Sayles and T. H. Clark, *Bull. Geol. Soc. Am. 36* (1925), 141.

one million years. Saint Helena is merely an example of many hundreds of such cases among the islands of the tropical seas. . . .

To summarize: The swings of sealevel during the Ice Age seem best to account for the present abundance of the reef-building corals and for the forms and location of the living reefs. Hence it is not necessary to assume very recent widespread distortion of the earth, such as is implied by Darwin's subsidence theory. No sound physical reason for such distortion has been suggested. No sound theoretical reason can now be given for resting in the belief that this particular distortion of the globe ever took place. On the other hand, there is evident need of correlation between two utterly different processes in widely separated parts of our dramatic earth—between cold-engendered glaciation and the growth of the warmth-loving corals. No man liveth to himself. No part of our planet liveth to itself.

### CONCLUSIONS AND APPLICATIONS

Nor is any geological or geographical problem in a water-tight compartment. The study of eustatic shifts of sealevel during the Pleistocene leads to speculative explanations of (1) various strandlines, now high and dry; (2) drowned channels cut in the continental shelves; (3) the origin of many harbors; (4) the rarity of traces of shore-dwelling Paleolithic man; (5) the living coral reefs. But these questions are interrelated and they become more truly appreciated when they are seen to be vitally connected with major problems of earth science.

For example, the displacement of shorelines by the glaciation or deglaciation of the continents is not merely the direct effect of substraction of water from the ocean or addition of water to the ocean.[7] The loadings and unloadings with ice or water have meant a complex, rhythmical distortion of the whole globe—a kind of deep-toned tune played on our earth. As the facts become clearer, we shall know much more about the distribution of strength and viscosity in the earth,

[7]After this paper was prepared for publication, Dr. E. Antevs kindly sent to the writer the manuscript of an important memoir on "Quaternary marine terraces in non-glaciated regions and changes of level of sea and land," since printed in *Am. J. Sci. 17* (1929), 35. Dr. Antevs also discusses the position of sealevel on an ice-free earth. He does not specifically note the complicated effects of the earth's elasticity and plasticity on the positions of strandlines in non-glaciated regions. In connection with Dr. Antevs's correlation of Quaternary marine terraces, see the recently published "Étude géologique de la Tunisie septentrionale," Tunis, 1927, pp. 478, 481, 484, by M. Solignac.

P. A. Wagner (*Trans. Geol. Soc. South Africa 31* [1928], 12) reports that the marked 100-foot bench on the west coast of South Africa was formed when the sea water was warmer than it is now in the same belt. Does this bench mark the position of sealevel on an ice-free earth?

about the mode of isostatic adjustment, and about the time needed to adjust the earth isostatically for a widely extended load on the surface. Each waxing and waning of the ice-caps was a great experiment performed in Nature's laboratory. If we can grasp the full meaning of any one of these experiments, we shall have gained priceless information concerning the earth's interior, where the key to so many fundamental questions of geology and geography lies hidden.

## ORIGIN OF SUBMARINE "CANYONS"*

### THE PROBLEM

Recent discoveries of many valley-like trenches that interrupt the outer, steeper slopes ("continental slopes") of continental shelves are truly startling. Echo-sounding is responsible for the rapid increase of known examples. . . . The total number already charted approaches one hundred, with a distribution that may be fairly called world-wide. The distribution is planetary, not merely regional.

The recorded facts permit some generalizations bearing on the origin of the huge "canyons," a question as baffling as it is weighty for earth science.

(1) Most of the grander trenches lie along seaward prolongations of the axial lines of great rivers. Some of these rivers, including the Mississippi, Fraser, Indus, Ganges, and Niger, are now building deltas of the first rank. On the other hand, no important delta accompanies the submerged "canyon" off New York City.

(2) Many trenches have no direct topographical relation to existing rivers. This is obviously the case at the isolated Georges Bank, which, moreover, could not supply any large river if the bank were to emerge from the ocean. Lack of genetic connection with old rivers of size is again shown by the close spacing of the trenches along Georges Bank, a feature appearing also in other regions.

(3) Some continental shelves, inside the 100-meter isobath, are interrupted by valley-like furrows, graded oceanward and reaching maximum depths not greater than 100 meters. These comparatively shallow furrows seem clearly due to erosion by rivers when extended out over the shelves during the Glacial stages (hereafter called "epochs") of the Pleistocene period. Then glaciation of the lands lowered sealevel everywhere, at maximum probably 75 to 100 meters, so that river mouths were a long time far out toward the continental slopes or fall-offs.

*From *American Journal of Science* [5] *31* (1936), 401–420.

(4) With floors 500 to 1200 or more meters, in individual maxima, below the adjacent surfaces of the continental slopes, many trenches have been traced to depths ranging from 1000 meters to nearly 3000 meters below sealevel. These deeper parts are hardly to be explained in the same way as the shallower incisions traversing the broad flats of the shelves inside the 100-meter isobath.

(5) Each trench is comparatively straight, with axis directed in the sense of the general continental slope, as if it had been cut by a stream "consequent" on that slope. Some trenches branch at their upper ends, suggesting analogy in a poorly developed dendritic pattern of river drainage. According to the mapped isobaths some trenches widen, flare, at their outer ends, toward the deep ocean.

(6) As a rule the longitudinal gradients of the deeper parts of the trenches range between 1:100 and 1:10, and are continuously ocean-ward. In a few cases the bottom is somewhat irregular, hummocky, as if recently laden with the debris of slides from the trench walls.

(7) Toward their tops the walls may be remarkably steep, with slopes between 20° and 45°.

(8) At Georges Bank, Stetson's dredge tore from the trench walls lithified blocks of Upper Cretaceous sediment, and also late-Tertiary clays, tenacious enough to form blocks and yet decidedly plastic and weak. He has evidence that most of the material of the walls is not hardened into rock in the ordinary sense of that term. Shepard reports late-Tertiary "rock," dredged from the walls of trenches off California. As Stetson has pointed out in personal discussion, the steepness of the walls at Georges Bank need imply rigidity of the material in general no greater than that illustrated in the visible clay of the Island of Martha's Vineyard, where the clay, like typical loess, is tenacious enough to stand in nearly vertical cliffs and yet offers little resistance to attack by running water.

(9) So far as examined, the floors of the trenches are covered with mud of specially fine grain, indicating deposition there, rather than active erosion, for some time past. If so, the trenches must have been formed during a geologically recent period when the oceanic régime differed from that at present.

(10) The general resemblance of the trenches all over the world is most simply understood if their development was nearly or quite simultaneous. . . .

·    ·    ·    ·    ·

*A New Conception of Origin*

However, the more moderate eustatic oscillations of sealevel due to the fourfold Pleistocene glaciation and deglaciation of the lands represent a set of facts on which may be based a rational hypothesis concerning the development of the submarine trenches. Each of the four sets of ice-caps grew slowly and melted slowly, each process taking at least 25,000 years. Hence for more than 200,000 years, out of the million years or so that have elapsed since the Ice Age dawned, wind waves and tidal waves were beating on the mud and sand of the continental shelves—a condition utterly unlike that now ruling. These more or less mobile sediments had been built into embankments with widths measuring scores of kilometers and with depths averaging at least tens of meters. The volume of fine sediments was therefore enormous and sufficient to keep the tidal currents and storm waves of the lowered ocean well charged with solid particles for a large fraction of the 200,000 years. The waves were especially muddy because the depth of water on the outer, still submerged parts of the shelves was small. Then, too, the average storminess of the world was doubtless more pronounced during the Glacial epochs than at present. Storms no more intense than those now affecting the shelves must have made the water overlying the continental slope (the fall-off of each shelf) much richer in suspended sediment than the water of similar location in pre-Glacial, Interglacial, or post-Glacial times. The tidal currents and gales of the twentieth century disturb the bottom of the North Sea so powerfully that sand is thrown up from depths of 40 to 50 meters to the decks of laboring ships. So long as sediment was "suspended" in the water on the Pleistocene shelves, that water was effectively denser than the clean water farther out to sea or the water below the zone of rapid stirring. There must have been a tendency for the weighted water to dive under the cleaner water, to slide along the gently inclined bottom of the shelf, and to flow still faster down the steeper continental slope. Since the solid particles kept settling out, the horizontal distance through which any such density current operated was limited. It is therefore important to remember throughout the discussion of the general hypothesis, that the belt of strong agitation by waves was, at the times of lowered sealevel, much nearer to the continental slope than now. In principle the imagined bottom current would be similar to the flow of ink or muddy water placed at the appropriate point in a tilted, partly filled glass of clear water. Each of those denser fluids slides down along the inclined "floor" of containing glass.

We thus picture a special kind of density current or convectional movement. Were these bottom currents strong enough to have excavated the submarine trenches now under discussion? The question is much too hard to answer offhand, but some facts suggest that an affirmative answer may not prove to be entirely wild.

If a thick, uniform sheet of mercury were kept continuously pouring out from the whole shore of a continent, it is easy to see what would happen in a general way. The mercury would quickly seek and flow down any slight, initial, transverse depression in the continental shelf and erode the depression deeper. With this progressive deepening, more and more mercury would be drawn into the new trough from both sides, thus increasing the thickness, velocity, and eroding power of the stream of mercury that occupies the trough. To him "that hath shall be given."[1] Reaching the much steeper continental slope, the mercury flood, so concentrated, would slide down yet faster and dig a deeper trough in the soft sediments beneath the slope. Continued long enough, a submarine "canyon" would there be produced. This fanciful analogy may help to clarify the hypothesis now to be elaborated.

Discussion would be easier if we knew what amount of sediment can become suspended in strongly agitated water adjacent to the continental slope; and, again, what proportion of the maximum amount remains in suspension for say ten hours after the loaded water has sunk below the level where wind waves and tidal currents cease to keep sediment and water mixed together. Some idea of the maximum amount may be gained from measurements of the sediment in torrential rivers. According to A. Geikie's *Textbook of Geology* the lower Rhone River, even when only two-thirds of the way up to highest water, carries sediment to the extent of 2.2 per cent by weight. Corresponding figures for the Vistula and Durance rivers at high water are about five per cent and three per cent (at rare intervals as much as ten per cent) respectively. If the maximum for the agitated Pleistocene seawater was normally only one or two per cent, the added density could hardly fail to produce a powerful current at the bottom, down the continental slope. . . .

Many geologists hold, without specific qualification, that sedimentary material settles in sea water many times faster than in fresh water. As Sidell showed long ago, this is true when the solid particles are clayey and exceedingly small. The law does not hold for particles as large as those prevailing in river silts or of larger diameters. Thus Vernon-Harcourt found the silts of the Hugli (Ganges), Rhone, Dnieper, and Missis-

---

[1] It is worth noting also that, with each Glacial lowering of sealevel and emergence of the continental shelves, old rivers were extended over the new lands, where, in addition, many consequent streams were born. Each stream must have quickly trenched the soft materials of the shelves to some depth less than 100 meters. Until such new valleys became filled with wave-swept and tidally swept detritus during the next eustatic rise of sealevel, those furrows could hardly fail to guide and concentrate the flow of loaded water. Since each eustatic rise of sealevel probably lasted through at least 25,000 years, this control over the direction of the bottom currents of loaded water and over the rate of trenching would have long existed.

sippi rivers to settle in sea water only about ten per cent faster than in Thames River water and about twice as fast as in distilled water. The observed average rate of settling in sea water was small, namely 72 centimeters per hour. The experimental results of Wheeler were similar in principle. For solid particles of similar size Rubey showed that the relevant Stokes law is obeyed with considerable exactness, the observed velocities of settling in fresh water being nearly the same as those recorded by Vernon-Harcourt in the case of sea water. Hence, while ionic coagulation of minute clay particles hastens the clearing of merely "turbid" sea water, it does little to speed the fall of the larger particles that make up most of the sediment in strongly agitated seas.

Since the rate of settling was low in absolute measure, it seems credible that a thick layer of bottom water on the continental slopes in Glacial times may have had its effective density temporarily increased 0.005, if not 0.01 by suspended sediment.

Similarly the silt carried out over the continental slope by the larger extended rivers of the Glacial epochs would slowly settle into and through the underlying sea water, and, for the many hours occupied by the settling, increase any relative excess of density of the deeper water. It can hardly be doubted that this denser layer of bottom water would slide down the continental slope. . . .

. . . It appears that the problem of horse-power for the imagined density currents during the major storms and tidal flowings of the Glacial epochs is decidedly complicated. The potential energy is conceived to have originated in: (1) the contrast of density between clean sea water and sea water loaded with sediment (whether incorporated by marine turbulence or by settling from overlying, silty river water); (2) the difference of level between continental shelf and deep ocean bottom; (3) banking of coastal waters by violent onshore winds. It is suggested that an initial density current of the Pleistocene may have triggered off the potential energies listed under headings (2) and (3), and so considerably increased the velocity of that initial current, in spite of the braking action of new turbulence and new frictional resistance that must have been developed by such increase of velocity.

Each of these speculative mechanisms involves the principle of self-acceleration, a principle already seen to apply for quite a different reason, namely, the deepening of the current by inflow of loaded water from the two sides of a trench.

In any case we should expect trenching to have progressed at variable rates. Most of it may well have taken place during exceptional storms of the Glacial epochs, averaging perhaps one such paroxysmal event in a decade of years. On the other hand, wherever the topography of the continental shelves, then covered by shallow water, caused strong tidal currents, the density currents due primarily to the agitation by these turbulent flowings may have been eroding more or less constantly. . . .

An origin by erosion under the peculiar conditions of the Glacial epochs has been pictured in the light of certain facts and their logical consequences. Some of these need not be restated. Others, perhaps more liable to be lost to sight in an attempt to value the hypothesis, are: (1) The relatively small depth of water on the continental shelves during the four Glacial epochs;[2] (2) The absolute slowness with which muds sink in sea water; (3) The close proximity of the belt of shore breakers to each continental slope when the ice-caps were voluminous;[3] (4) The paroxysmal effects of major storms and of spring tides at the time, including extraordinary increase of suspended sediment and corresponding increase of potential energy in the mixture of water and sediment; (5) The probability that the "fore-set" sediments under the continental slope were close to the angle of rest, and hence in danger of sliding where dragged by a localized bottom current; (6) The increase of density of sea water by receipt of the silt that settles out of overlying river water as this, by its own momentum, forces its way out over the open ocean; (7) The self-acceleration of the density currents by lateral addition of loaded water on each shelf and within each deepening trench, and by increase of the density where turbulent erosion of the bottom added to the sediment in suspension; (8) The smallness of the excess of density (probably no more than 0.004) required in a bottom layer of water 60 to 100 meters thick, in order to cause that layer

[2] Although the conditions of the Glacial epochs are emphasized in this paper, the possibility of some trenching of the continental slopes in pre-Glacial time is not thereby excluded from a full discussion of the general problem. According to both theory and observation, the continental shelves were truncated by wave erosion during each Glacial epoch. Hence, just before the first major glaciation began, the average depth of water on stable shelves may have been something like 25 meters smaller than at present. In other words, at that earlier time the shelves may have been more closely adjusted to wave-base, as defined for ordinary storms, than the shelves are now. If so, the sediments of the shelves may have been stirred up by exceptional, quasi-hurricane storms operating in pre-Glacial time. The question arises as to whether density (muddy-water) currents of prolonged, pre-Glacial time actually began the development of the trenches. The answer must be difficult and not to be satisfactorily made until the depths of wave-base for both ordinary and extraordinary storms and the relation of those depths to shelf profiles have been more accurately defined than has yet been done. The narrower the detrital shelf of pre-Glacial time, the greater would have been the likelihood of such earlier trenching.

[3] F. P. Shepard explains the absence of trenches along the northern edge of Georges Bank (see Fig. 1 of his paper, *Bull. Geol. Soc. Am. 45* [1934], 281) by assuming glacial erosion there, sufficiently intense to have removed "all signs of stream erosion." However, is it not possible that the thick ice, responsible for the morainal material found on the northern part of the bank, prevented the trenching by bottom currents while the trenches along the ice-free, southern edge of the bank were developed?

to flow down a continental slope at the rate of two to three kilometers per hour—an eroding rate; (9) The expectation that the erosional effects of the assumed bottom currents would rather closely resemble those due to rivers on the land, even to the point of making systems of branching trenches that recall the dentric ground-plans of visible rivers. . . .

In view of the many uncertainties the idea of mud-control must now be rated as merely a working hypothesis. Yet its troubles seem incomparably less serious than those of the older explanations of submarine "canyons." On the other hand, it would be manifestly wrong to suppose all furrows crossing the continental shelves to have been excavated by marine density-currents. Here and there canyons and other types of valleys, cut by ordinary rivers in pre-Glacial time, have been drowned by strong, local subsidence of continental borders. Such old, rock-hewn valleys, if they had not been quite filled with fine-grained detritus, would naturally have attracted the water loaded with sediment during the Glacial epochs. The resulting, localized currents would have been likely to remove some of the filling of each of the old trenches, and thus have revived the open-valley form more or less completely. Illustrations of this speculative process might be looked for particularly along the coasts of California, Japan, and other uneasy parts of the continental borders.

# RUTHERFORD Ernest Rutherford (1871–1937), British

physicist, studied at the University of New Zealand in his native land, and after further studies at Cambridge University became in 1898 the Macdonald Professor of Physics at McGill University, Montreal. In 1907 he was appointed Longworthy Professor of Physics at Manchester University and in 1919 Cavendish Professor at Cambridge, accepting in addition, in 1920, the professorship of physics at the Royal Institution in London. He was awarded the Nobel Prize for chemistry in 1908, was knighted in 1914, and was created a baron in 1931. His brilliant pioneer work in nuclear physics provided the indispensable foundation for the burgeoning of that science in the middle third of the twentieth century. In his Silliman Lectures, delivered at Yale University in March 1905, from which the following brief excerpt is taken, he directed attention to the possible use of radioactive timekeepers in geochronology.

## RADIOACTIVE TIMEKEEPERS *

The helium observed in the radioactive minerals is almost certainly due to its production from the radium and other radioactive substances

* From *Radioactive Transformations* (New York: Charles Scribner's Sons, 1906).

contained therein. If the rate of production of helium from known weights of the different radioelements were experimentally known, it should thus be possible to determine the interval required for the production of the amount of helium observed in radioactive minerals, or, in other words, to determine the age of the mineral. This deduction is based on the assumption that some of the denser and more compact of the radioactive minerals are able to retain indefinitely a large proportion of the helium imprisoned in their mass. In many cases the minerals are not compact but porous, and under such conditions most of the helium will escape from its mass. Even supposing that some of the helium has been lost from the denser minerals, we should be able to fix with some certainty a minimum limit for the age of the mineral.

In the absence of definite experimental data on the rates of production of helium by the different radioelements, the deductions are of necessity somewhat uncertain, but will nevertheless serve to fix the probable order of the ages of the radioactive minerals.

It has already been pointed out that all the $\alpha$ particles expelled from radium have the same mass. In addition it has been experimentally found that the $\alpha$ particle from thorium B has the same mass as the $\alpha$ particle from radium. This would suggest that the $\alpha$ particles projected from all radioactive substances have the same mass, and thus consist of the same kind of matter. If the $\alpha$ particle is a helium atom, the amount of helium produced per year by a known quantity of radioactive matter can readily be deduced on these assumptions.

The number of products which expel $\alpha$ particles are now well known for radium, thorium, and actinium. Including radium F, radium has five $\alpha$ ray products, thorium five, and actinium four. With regard to uranium itself, there is not the same certainty, for only one product, UrX, which emits only $\beta$ rays, has so far been chemically isolated from uranium. The $\alpha$ particles apparently are emitted by the element uranium itself; at the same time, there is some indirect evidence in support of the view that uranium contains three $\alpha$ ray products. For the purpose of calculation, we shall, however, assume that in uranium and radium in equilibrium, one $\alpha$ particle is expelled from the uranium for five from the radium.

Let us now consider an old uranium mineral which contains one gram of uranium, and which has not allowed any of the products of its decomposition to escape. The uranium and radium are in radioactive equilibrium and $3.8 \times 10^{-7}$ grams of radium are present. For one $\alpha$ particle emitted by the uranium, five are emitted by the radium and its products, including radium F. Now we have shown that radium with its four $\alpha$ ray products probably produces .11 c.c. of helium per gram per year. The rate of production of helium by the uranium and radium in the mineral will consequently be $\frac{5}{4} \times .11 \times 3.8 \times 10^{-7} = 5.2 \times 10^{-8}$ c.c. per year per gram of uranium.

Now, as an example of the method of calculation, let us consider the mineral fergusonite which was found by Ramsay and Travers to evolve 1.81 c.c. of helium per gram. The fergusonite contains about 7 per cent of uranium. The amount of helium contained in the mineral per gram of uranium is consequently 26 c.c.

Since the rate of production of helium per gram of uranium and its radium products is $5.2 \times 10^{-8}$ c.c. per year, the age of the mineral must be at least $26 \div 5.2 \times 10^{-8}$ years, or 500 million years. This, as we have pointed out, is a minimum estimate, for some of the helium has probably escaped.

We have assumed in this calculation that the amount of uranium and radium present in the mineral remains sensibly constant over this interval. This is approximately the case, for the parent element uranium probably requires about 1000 million years to be half transformed.

As another example, let us take a uranium mineral obtained from Glastonbury, Connecticut, which was analyzed by Hillebrande. This mineral was very compact and of high density, 9.62. It contained 76 per cent of uranium and 2.41 per cent of nitrogen. This nitrogen was almost certainly helium, and dividing by seven to reduce to helium this gives the percentage of helium as 0.344. This corresponds to 19 c.c. of helium per gram of the mineral, or 25 c.c. per gram of uranium in the mineral. Using the same data as before, the age of the mineral must be certainly not less than 500 million years. Some of the uranium and thorium minerals do not contain much helium. Some are porous, and must allow the helium to escape readily. A considerable quantity of helium is, however, nearly always found in the compact primary radio-active minerals, which from geologic data are undoubtedly of great antiquity.

Hillebrande made a very extensive analysis of a number of samples of minerals from Norway, North Carolina, and Connecticut, which were mostly compact primary minerals, and noted that a striking relation existed between the proportion of uranium and of nitrogen (helium) that they contained. This relation is referred to in the following words:—

"Throughout the whole list of analyses in which nitrogen (helium) has been estimated, the most striking feature is the apparent relation between it and the $UO_2$. This is especially marked in the table of Norwegian uraninites, recalculated from which the rule might almost be formulated that, given either nitrogen or $UO_2$, the other can be found by simple calculation. The same ratio is not found in the Connecticut varieties, but if the determination of nitrogen in the Branchville mineral is to be depended on, the rule still holds that the higher the $UO_2$ the higher likewise is the nitrogen. The Colorado and North Carolina minerals are exceptions, but it should be borne in mind that the former is amorphous, like the Bohemian, and possesses the further similarity of containing no thoria, although zirconia may take its place, and the North Carolina mineral is so much altered that its original condition is unknown."

Very little helium, however, is found in the secondary radioactive minerals, *i.e.,* minerals which have been formed as a result of the decomposition of the primary minerals. These minerals, as Boltwood has pointed out, are undoubtedly in many cases of far more recent formation than the primary minerals, and consequently it is not to be expected that they should contain as much helium. One of the most interesting deposits of a secondary uraninite is found at Joachimsthal in Bohemia, from which most of our present supply of radium has been obtained. This is rich in uranium, but contains very little helium.

When the data required for these calculations are known with more definiteness, the presence of helium in radioactive minerals will in special cases prove a most valuable method of computing their probable age, and indirectly the probable age of the geological deposits in which the minerals are found. Indeed, it appears probable that it will prove one of the most reliable methods of determining the age of the various geological formations.

### SIGNIFICANCE OF THE PRESENCE OF LEAD IN RADIOACTIVE MINERALS

If the $\alpha$ particle is a helium atom, the atomic weights of the successive $\alpha$ ray products of radium must differ by equal steps of four units. Now we have seen that uranium itself probably contains three $\alpha$ ray products. Since the atomic weight of uranium is 238.5, the atomic weight of the residue of the uranium after the expulsion of three $\alpha$ particles would be $238.5 - 12, = 226.5$. This is very close to the atomic weight of radium 225, which we have seen is produced from uranium. Now radium emits five $\alpha$ ray products altogether, and the atomic weight of the end product of radium should be $238.5 - 32, = 206.5$. This is very close to the atomic weight of lead, 206.9. This calculation suggests that lead may prove to be the final product of the decomposition of radium, and this suggestion is strongly supported by the observed fact that lead is always found associated with the radioactive minerals, and especially in those primary minerals which are rich in uranium.

The possible significance of the presence of lead in radioactive min-

| Locality | Percentage of uranium | Percentage of lead | Percentage of nitrogen |
|---|---|---|---|
| Glastonbury, Connecticut | 70–72 | 3.07–3.26 | 2.41 |
| Branchville, Connecticut | 74–75 | 4.35 | 2.63 |
| North Carolina | 77 | 4.20–4.53 | |
| Norway | 56–66 | 7.62–13.87 | 1.03–1.28 |
| Canada | 65 | 10.49 | 0.86 |

erals was first noted by Boltwood,[1] who has collected a large amount of data bearing on this question.

The accompanying table shows the collected results of an analysis of different primary minerals made by Hillebrande. Five samples were taken of the minerals from Glastonbury, three from Branchville, two from North Carolina, seven from Norway, and one from Canada. In minerals obtained from the same locality, there is a comparatively close agreement between the amounts of lead contained in them. If helium and lead are both products of the decomposition of the uranium radium minerals, there should exist a constant ratio between the percentage of lead and helium in the minerals. The percentage of helium is obtained from the above table by dividing the nitrogen percentage by seven. Since probably eight $\alpha$ particles are emitted from the decomposition of uranium and radium for the production of one atom of lead, the weight of helium formed should be $(8 \times 4)/206.9 = .155$ of the weight of lead. This is based on the assumption that all the helium formed is imprisoned in the minerals. The ratio actually found is about 0.11 for the Glastonbury minerals, 0.09 for the Branchville minerals, and about 0.016 for the Norway minerals. It will be noted that in all cases the ratio of helium to lead is less than the theoretical ratio, indicating that in some cases a large proportion of the helium formed in the mineral has escaped. In the case of the Glastonbury minerals, the observed ratio is in good agreement with theory.

If the production of lead from radium is well established, the percentage of lead in radioactive minerals should be a far more accurate method of deducing the age of the mineral than the calculation based on the volume of helium, for the lead formed in a compact mineral has no possibility of escape.

# KAY George Frederick Kay (1873–1943). American geologist, received his baccalaureate degree in 1900 from the University of Toronto in Canada,

[1] Boltwood, *Phil. Mag.*, April 1905; *Am. J. Sci.*, October 1905.

his native land, and after further studies there, as well as field work for the Ontario Bureaus of Mines, he was granted a fellowship at the University of Chicago, where he was awarded the Ph. D. degree in 1914. From 1904 to 1907 he was an assistant professor at Kansas University, and in the latter year he accepted a professorship at the State University of Iowa, where he remained until his retirement, serving at various times, and often simultaneously, as Head of the Department of Geology, Dean of the College of Liberal Arts, Director of the Iowa Geological Survey, and State Geologist. His research concerning Pleistocene deposits in the Mississippi Valley led him to the early recognition of four major glacial "epochs" in that "period"; although this interpretation of the data has been fully supported in subsequent years, the names he proposed for the four "epochs" have not come into general use.

## CLASSIFICATION AND DURATION OF THE PLEISTOCENE PERIOD*

### Time Involved in Gumbotil Development

It has been emphasized in this paper that in the upland Iowan till and upland Iowan gravels the depth of leaching is approximately the same, namely, about 5 feet 6 inches, and that there has been insufficient time since weathering began on the Iowan till for gumbotil to be developed. On the other hand, Illinoian upland gravels have been leached to a depth of about 12 feet, and about 5 feet of gumbotil has been developed on the Illinoian till. When these and other facts are analyzed carefully the judgment is reached that the gumbotil phase of weathering begins to appear on till soon after leaching of calcium carbonate has extended downward from the surface to a depth of somewhat more than 5 feet. If the upland Illinoian till and similarly situated Illinoian gravels were leached somewhat more than 5 feet when gumbotil began to be formed on the Illinoian leached till, then the 5 feet of Illinoian gumbotil was developed on the till from the surface downward during the time that an additional 7 feet of leaching in Illinoian gravels took place below the 5 feet which had been previously leached (see Fig. 9). Again, the thickness of Kansan gumbotil on Kansan till is about 12 feet and the depth of leaching of Kansan upland gravels about 30 feet, 5 feet of which are interpreted to have been leached before gumbotil development began. In this case, 12 feet of gumbotil was formed during the time of leaching of 25 feet of Kansan gravels. Furthermore, the thickness of Nebraskan gumbotil on the Nebraskan till is about 8 feet, and the depth of leaching of Nebraskan gravels is about 20 feet, 5 feet of which were presumably leached before the gumbotil

*From *Geological Society of America Bulletin 42* (1931), 425–466.

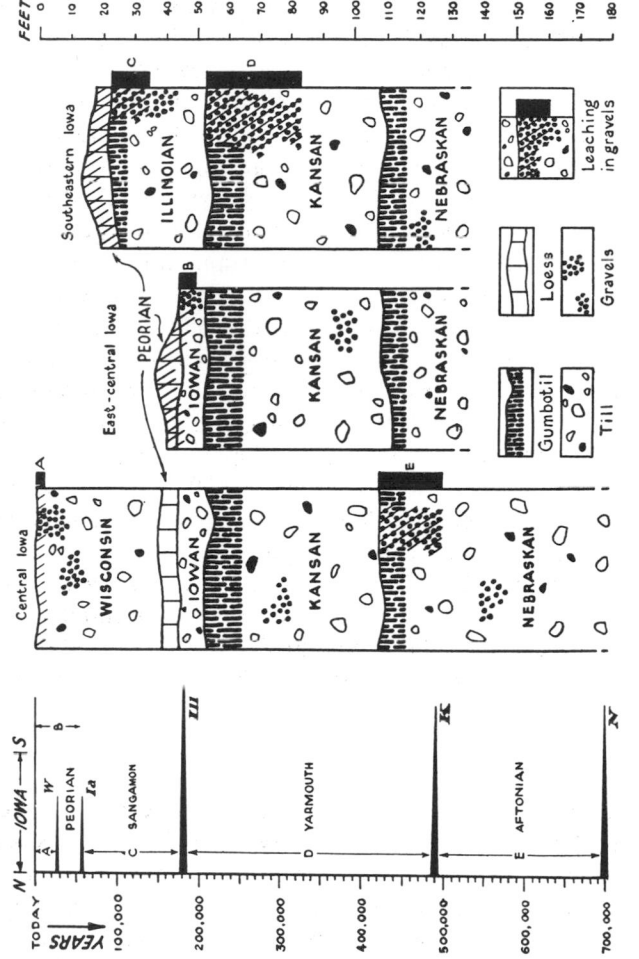

Fig. 9. Minimum duration of Pleistocene period in Iowa, based on relative depths of leaching in upland gravels. The diagram indicates relative depths of leaching of upland gravels in Iowa and the estimates of minimum duration of glacial and interglacial ages and of the Pleistocene period as a whole.

began to be formed. Hence, during the formation of 8 feet of Nebraskan gumbotil about 15 feet of additional leaching of Nebraskan gravels took place.

These facts indicate that as gumbotil thickens the length of time involved in the development of each additional foot is relatively longer than the time involved in the leaching of each additional foot of gravels. In other words, with increasing thickness gumbotil is formed progressively more slowly than gravel is leached. Thus, while 5 feet of gumbotil was formed, 7 feet of gravel was leached beneath 5 feet of gravel already leached; while 8 feet of gumbotil was formed, 15 feet of gravel was leached beneath 5 feet of gravel previously leached; and while 12 feet of gumbotil was being developed, the leaching of gravels was extended downward 25 feet beneath 5 feet of overlying leached gravels.

The minimum time involved in the development of the gumbotil on each of the three tills—the Nebraskan, the Kansan, and the Illinoian—can be estimated from the known data. The gumbotils developed in each of the interglacial ages, the Aftonian, the Yarmouth, and the Sangamon, only after more than 5 feet of upland gravel had been leached. The leaching of the gravels to this depth at the rate of post-Wisconsin leaching, namely, $2\frac{1}{2}$ feet in 25,000 years, involved in each case about 50,000 years. The time involved in the development of the 8 feet of gumbotil on the Nebraskan till was therefore 50,000 years less than the 200,000 years which has been estimated for Aftonian interglacial time, that is, 150,000 years, for the 12 feet of gumbotil on the Kansan till 50,000 years less than the 250,000 years involved in Yarmouth interglacial time, that is, 200,000 years, and for the 5 feet of gumbotil on the Illinoian till 50,000 years less than the 120,000 years involved in Sangamon interglacial time, that is, 70,000 years. These too are minimum estimates.

### CONCLUDING STATEMENTS

Deposits of the Pleistocene or Glacial Period have been subjected to detailed study in America for more than fifty years. In the Mississippi Valley in particular the records of this most fascinating chapter in the earth's history have been remarkably well preserved and thoroughly investigated. In fact, this area has been made a classic one as the result of the researches of T. C. Chamberlin, McGee, N. H. Winchell, Leverett, Calvin, and many other geologists. Here evidence has been found which is conceded to be the most reliable in interpreting the history of the Pleistocene, in classifying the deposits of this geological system, and in estimating the duration of the Period.

In this paper the classification and the duration of the Pleistocene

Period have been discussed. It was pointed out that when the most significant facts of Pleistocene history are analyzed critically in relation to what might be considered as a logical classification it is evident that from the time of the advance of the first ice-sheet, the Nebraskan, to the retreat of the last ice-sheet, the Wisconsin, there were recurrences of similar geological events with accompanying similar geological results. In other words, there were within the limits of the Pleistocene Period a succession of cycles, the most significant evidences of which are recorded in the deposits which were made during each cycle and in the changes which the deposits underwent before the coming of the succeeding cycle. Reasons were given for the interpretation that Pleistocene history involved four cycles. The judgment was expressed that it would seem to be desirable at the present time to bring together for distinct recognition in Pleistocene classification the sedimentary units which are the chief products of the cycles, and that the cycles be designated epochs and the sedimentary units, each of which consists of the intimately associated glacial and interglacial materials formed during an epoch, be given the rank of series.

A revised classification of the Pleistocene has been presented. It recognizes four epochs (series), each of which is divided into ages (stages) which continue to have the well-established names of the present classification. New names have been chosen for the four epochs (series): Grandian, Ottumwan, Centralian, and Eldoran. These names were chosen from localities where the materials of the different stages have been studied in all their relationships and where they have areal distribution.

Estimates of the minimum duration of the Pleistocene in Iowa have been given. The evidence used in reaching judgments as to the durations of the interglacial ages was gained chiefly from extensive field studies in Iowa of relative depths of leaching of calcium carbonate in similar materials which throughout their times of leaching were similarly situated topographically and climatically. Leached gravels of known ages were compared. The differences in depths of leaching are the results of the differences in lengths of time to which the gravels were subjected to weathering agents. The depth of leaching of upland gravels in the Late Wisconsin drift was determined to be about 2 feet 6 inches. This leaching is the result of exposure to weathering since the retreat from Iowa of the Late Wisconsin ice-sheet, that is, through a period estimated to be about 25,000 years. With this rate of leaching of gravels as a unit, estimates were made of the lengths of time involved in the leaching of other gravels of known ages. The results for Iowa as given in this paper are as follows: Post-Late Wisconsin time,

25,000 years; post-Iowan time, 55,000 years; Sangamon interglacial time, 120,000 years; Yarmouth interglacial time, 300,000 years; and Aftonian interglacial time, 200,000 years. The combined durations of Aftonian, Yarmouth, and Sangamon interglacial ages, and of post-Iowan, total about 675,000 years.

The durations of the glacial ages in Iowa were estimated from present-day consensus of opinion as to the rates of advance and retreat of ice-sheets. For the retreat of the Late Wisconsin from Iowa the rate of one mile in ten years was adopted. The same rate was assumed for the advance of this ice-sheet into Iowa and also for the advances and retreats of earlier ice-sheets. The minimum duration of glacial time in Iowa was calculated to be about 30,000 years.

In accordance with the methods of evaluation adopted in this paper, minimum interglacial time in Iowa was determined to be approximately 675,000 years, and minimum glacial time in Iowa about 30,000 years, the combined estimates giving for the whole Pleistocene in Iowa a minimum duration of about 700,000 years. How far this estimate of the minimum duration of the Pleistocene falls short of the actual duration can not be determined from reliable quantitative evidence. However, it would seem safe to state that the Pleistocene involved probably a million years, possibly twice this length of time.

Evidence was presented also for the judgment that the 5 feet of gumbotil on the Illinoian till involved in its development about 70,000 years, the 12 feet of gumbotil on the Kansan till 250,000 years, and the 8 feet of gumbotil on the Nebraskan till 150,000 years. Gumbotil development was preceded in all cases by leaching of calcium carbonate.

As investigations of Pleistocene deposits continue into the future, better and better standards of measurements will be established, and hence more and more accurate determinations of Pleistocene time will be made. The classification of the Period will no doubt have to be revised from time to time as further refinements of study of glacial and interglacial deposits enable more definite interpretations of their origin and history.

# ANDERSSON

Johan Gunner Andersson (1874–    ), Swedish geologist and geographer, received his doctorate from Upsala University in 1902, was a professor there from 1906 until he joined the faculty of Stockholm University, where he became Professor of Geology in 1925. He was Secretary-General of the XIth International Geological Congress, meeting in Stockholm in 1910. He was the originator of the term, solifluction, connoting a type of geologic action that has since proved to have great significance.

## SOLIFLUCTION, A COMPONENT
## OF SUBAERIAL DENUDATION *

During the last few years I have had the opportunity of studying, under high northern and southern latitudes, regions where the removal of the waste is now going on under peculiar conditions, and in another case was working during a bygone climatic depression in a most effective manner almost all over the area of the islands under consideration.

I have thought it possibly useful to publish a short preliminary review of my observations, as they may add to the understanding of an important component of subaerial denudation. The phenomenon I am going to describe is by no means new to science; on the contrary, it has been noticed and clearly described by many skilled observers from different parts of the world, where the conditions are favorable for its development. But it seems to me that there has been a tendency to depreciate its importance as a link in the series of denudative agents, and to look at it as only a curiosity of mere local nature. No one, as far as I know, has collected the scattered material, as I will try to do in the following pages, and probably few have had an opportunity like mine to study the phenomenon in its fullest development.

### SOLIFLUCTION IN BEAR ISLAND

This islet situated in $74\frac{1}{2}°$ N. L., in the Atlantic part of the Arctic Ocean, is a small remainder of a once larger stretch of land. Sea cliffs, in some places rising to the height of 400 meters and fringing the island almost all around, tell us of the destructive action of the abrasion. The northern and larger part of the island forms a lowland plateau rising very slowly from the recent coastal outline to the interior and cut out through slightly dislocated Devonian and Carboniferous beds. Several reasons, among others the occurrence of old, somewhat obliterated coastal cliffs at the inner margin of this plateau, incline me to consider it as worked out by marine abrasion.

The southern part of the island is mountainous, with tops rising to 460–539 meters. In this region the ground is composed of a great variety of sedimentary rocks from Silurian to Triassic age, and the older strata are cut up by vertical dislocations into a few parallel blocks. In some cases the denudation has laid bare parts of the precipitous surfaces of the faults, but as a rule the land-sculpturing agents show a marked tendency to smooth the tilted blocks to rounded hills and broad river valleys with gentle slopes. Thus the land forms of the interior of the island are in a striking contrast to the perpendicular cliffs on the sea side.

*From *Journal of Geology 14* (1906), 91–112.

On the hill-slopes and valley sides of Bear Island there are almost everywhere clear indications of a moving of the waste from higher to lower ground. Many of the small hills show a very marked streakiness of surface, which is due to the peculiar arrangement of the detritus; sometimes the flowing soil forms real streams which have much likeness to a glacier in miniature, and often in the depressions between the hills there are numerous small circular or semicircular walls composed of rock fragments and including a patch of muddy material, often hardened through desiccation. Evidently all these phenomena only represent different facies of the displacement of the waste.

It is not very difficult to find out the mode of formation of the "mud-glaciers" mentioned above. When in summer time the melting of the snow has reached an advanced stage, often the bottom of the valleys are free from snow, while big masses still rest in sheltered places on the valley sides. Every warm and sunny day new quantities of water trickle from these melting drifts into the rock-waste at their lower edge. As the masses of detritus are composed not only of coarser rock fragments such as blocks, slabs, and gravel, but also of finer particles filling the interspaces between the coarser material, they are able to absorb considerable quantities of water. When once saturated, they form a semifluid substance that starts moving slowly downhill. This process, the slow flowing from higher to lower ground of masses of waste saturated with water (this may come from snow-melting or rain), I propose to name *solifluction* (derived from *solum*, "soil," and *fluere,* "to flow").

As the snowdrifts of Bear Island diminish in the course of the summer, new ground is exposed, its waste is thawed, and then, saturated with water, it follows the slow downward movement. The flowing detritus does not generally move as a "sheet-flood" with a broad front, but more often flows in some slight depression of the slope, taking the form of a narrow tongue, offering a most striking parallel to a glacier. The névé region is represented by the area of water-saturated detritus at the lower edge of the melting snowdrift, and the flowing tongue of mud is the glacier proper that moves down the valley. The terminal moraine even is often to be seen in the shape of slabs and pieces of rock that the mud-stream has pushed together in front of its lower end.

These mud-streams do not consist of finer particles only, but also of coarse material, gravel and blocks, frequently intermixed with, and also carried on the top of the muddy substance.

$$\bullet \quad \bullet \quad \bullet \quad \bullet \quad \bullet$$

### The Stone-rivers of the Falkland Islands

This island group, situated in 52° S. L. in the South Atlantic, consists of two large and a great number of small islands. The East Falklands, and to some extent also the western large island, present an undulating land surface built up by slightly folded Devonian beds and evidently subjected for a long time to subaerial denudation. With the exception of some resistant quartzite ridges, they, and especially the eastern island, are far advanced toward the peneplain. The land is woodless over large areas, and occupied by peat-bogs, the drier places forming grass steppes and the very driest heaths covered by *Eupetrum rubrum*.

This landscape, as bewildering through the monotony of its outlines as deterring through its ugliness, boasts a natural phenomenon that may be unparalleled in the world. The "stone-rivers," which form a beloved object of the fancy of the population, were lucidly described by Charles Darwin, though he could not find a satisfactory explanation; but a later visitor, Sir Wyville Thomson, got very near to a proper understanding of the thing. . . . [His] explanation . . . referring the formation of the stone-rivers to the slow removal of the waste down the slopes, must be willingly accepted by everyone who has studied the "stone-runs" in nature. The only objection, and that a very essential one, is against the idea of the phenomenon as a product of present conditions and of the process as still working with full effectiveness underneath the vegetation that now partly covers the stone-rivers. . . .

Solifluction, in its quite typical form, is still at work in the Falkland Islands, but only on a small scale in favorable localities where the hillsides are steep, the vegetation scarce, and the trickling water saturates the soil.

· · · · · · ·

The large old stone-runs of the Falkland Islands evidently were formed in a period of the past with a climate more severe than the present, with heavy snowfalls in winter, but also with summers characterized by active snow-melting, causing an intensive solifluction which was ever victorious in the fight with the then poor and scattered vegetation. I fancy that in these days the state of the Falkland Islands was very much like that which I have actually studied on the Bear Island of today.

It is very inviting to connect this birthtime of the Falkland stone-rivers with the great climatic depression of a bygone time that has been demonstrated in the adjacent southern lands. . . .

To the west, east, and south the Falkland Islands are surrounded by lands deeply furrowed by an old ice age. In our islands, on the contrary, there are no traces of an old ice-sheet, no grooving of the rock-surface, no moraines, and some very characteristic relief forms are directly incompatible with the hypothesis of an earlier ice-action upon the islands.

But, on the other hand, it seems impossible that the great wave of cold, which has set its mark so severely upon the surrounding lands, should have left no traces on the Falkland Islands. Nothing is then more natural than the presumption that the birth of the stone-rivers is a facies of the ice age of the southern lands. In the Falkland Islands the climatic depression was not severe enough to cause a glaciation, but only an intensive frost-weathering and flowing slopes, quite as to-day in Bear Island we have no glaciers, but only a marked solifluction.

.　.　.　.　.

## Conclusions

From the evidence given in the preceding pages it is easy to recognize the climatic features which form the optimum of the solifluction. In the polar and subpolar regions, where the ground is not covered with ice, we find this process working with more or less intensity almost everywhere, and in the same manner, the alpine tracts of lower latitudes are favorable for the development of this phenomenon. In these regions, characterized by a "subglacial" climate with heavy deposits of winter snow melting in summer, solifluction is a chief agent of destruction. The unceasing succession, summer after summer, of mudstreams and moving slopes indicates that here the removal of the waste runs on at a rate that may be unsurpassed in other parts of the earth's surface—except in the deserts.

But this effective removal of the waste must be balanced on the one hand by a rapid production of new waste, and on the other, by an effective clearing out of valley bottoms by running water. The "subglacial" climate is most favorable for both these processes. In the extra-glacial regions the frost-weathering works with an intensity well known to every student of polar lands and alpine mountains, and the violent summer floods caused by the melting of the winter's snow give to the rivers of these regions an erosive power that is quite surprising.

When all these conditions are taken into consideration, the "subglacial" climate must be looked on as an optimum of destructive action. In fact, the high mountains, the large folded ranges, where all the agents mentioned work in high intensity, are found to be short-lived features in the earth's surface. In fact, one might be tempted to raise the question whether complete peneplanation is possible in regions where the action of running water is not supported by an effective removal of the waste, such as is produced by solifluction. With this premise, every peneplain found a climatic token of the same kind as the stone-rivers of the Falkland Islands and the limestone breccias of Gibraltar. Still I think that such a presumption hides a dangerous exaggeration. It is very possible that in many cases, under other climatic conditions of less erosive power, the process has had time to reach, though at a very slow rate, the end of the cycle of erosion.

But, on the other hand, it seems certain that solifluction has often been an important agent toward peneplanation. The importance of the process, because of its humbleness, has been much undervalued. But I feel sure that it is not until we get a knowledge of all the contributive agents that we can reach a full understanding of all the varied and complicated forms of land-sculpture.

# WRIGHT AND LARSEN Frederic Eugene Wright

(1877–1953), American mineralogist and petrologist, received the Ph. D. degree from Heidelberg University in 1900, taught in the Michigan College of Mines at Houghton for three years, and was then engaged in geologic mapping in Alaska for the U. S. Geological Survey until in 1906 he joined the staff of the Geophysical Laboratory of the Carnegie Institution of Washington, where he continued his research until his retirement in 1944. His authoritative treatise, *The Methods of Petrographic Microscope Research,* published in 1911, did much to stimulate the use of the petrographic microscope in America, and his comprehensive book, *The Manufacture of Optical Glass and of Optical Systems,* published in 1921 by the Ordnance Department of the U. S. Army, has been for many years the standard treatise on that subject.

Esper Signius Larsen, Jr. (1879–1961), American mineralogist and petrologist, graduated from the University of California in 1906, was associated with Wright in the Geophysical Laboratory for two years, and in 1909 joined the U. S. Geological Survey, where he was in charge of the petrology section from 1918 to 1923. In the meantime he returned to the University of California as acting professor for the academic year, 1915–16, and was awarded the Ph. D. degree in 1918. He was appointed Professor of Petrography at Harvard University in 1923 and continued his career there until his retirement in 1949. Returning to Washington, he pushed forward his research at the Geophysical Laboratory as long as his failing health permitted.

The jointly authored paper, excerpted here, was the first systematic attempt to establish criteria for determining temperatures within the earth and still stands as one of the great contributions to mineralogy.

## QUARTZ AS A GEOLOGIC THERMOMETER *

Geologic phenomena take place at different temperatures, but at present very little exact information on the entire subject is available,

*From *American Journal of Science* [4] 27 (1909), 421–447.

and in many instances the temperatures are merely guessed at. Direct temperature measurements are seldom possible, and even then only rough approximations can be obtained because of the disturbing factors entering into the problem. Experiment and laboratory tests must, therefore, be largely relied upon for exact data bearing on such problems. . . . Accurate data, relating to equilibrium conditions and stability ranges of different minerals and aggregates of minerals over different temperatures and pressures, are of prime importance.

To illustrate: crystallized calcium metasilicate (wollastonite or pseudo-wollastonite) fuses at 1512°, but at 1190° passes from wollastonite to pseudo-wollastonite, which on cooling does not revert in the solid state to wollastonite. The temperature of inversion, 1190°, can, therefore, be used as a point on the geologic thermometer scale, for the appearance of wollastonite in a rock signifies at once that at the time of formation of the wollastonite the temperature of the magma or solution was below 1190°, otherwise pseudo-wollastonite, the form stable above 1190°, would have been precipitated. Since the specific volumes of wollastonite and pseudo-wollastonite are practically identical, it is probable that the effect of pressure on this inversion point is very slight, and can therefore be neglected.

Melting points of minerals and of definite aggregates of minerals (eutectics), melting regions of rocks, inversion temperatures of minerals and stability ranges for different forms of the same chemical compound, furnish the geologist with fixed points on his geologic thermometer scale, just as the freezing and boiling points of water are the two standard fixed points on the ordinary thermometer scale.

In like manner, experimental data may furnish points of reference for a geologic pressure gage, which is of equal import to the geologist.

Equipped with a satisfactory geologic thermometer scale and geologic pressure gage expressed in terms of stability ranges of different minerals and aggregates of minerals under different conditions, the geologist would be in a position to attack many problems which, at the present time, defy all solution. Exact data of this sort in turn tend to act as a governor on geologic theory establishing limits of temperature and pressure beyond or below which it is not safe to assume certain conditions; and at the same time they strengthen materially the foundation of fact on which geologic reasoning is based.

For such geologic thermometric purposes, quartz has been found by experience to be well adapted. It is plentiful in nature and occurs in many different kinds of rocks. $SiO_2$ in the form of tridymite melts at about 1625°, while between that temperature and about 800° tridymite is the stable phase; below about 800° quartz is the stable phase. From evidence thus far gathered, it is probable that pressure has but slight effect on raising or lowering such an inversion point, and that, therefore, wherever quartz appears in nature, it was formed at a temperature below about 800°.

Quartz itself undergoes a reversible change at about 575°. This was first observed by Le Chatelier[1] in 1890, who noted a sudden change in the expansion coefficients and circular polarization of quartz heated to and above 575°. At the same time Mallard and Le Chatelier[2] found noticeable changes in the birefringence at about 575°, and recently O. Mügge[3] has considered the problem in detail, and by means of etch figures combined with crystallographic reasoning has been able to show that while the low temperature form of quartz stable below 575°, and called by him $\alpha$-quartz, crystallizes in the trapezohedral-tetartohedral division of the hexagonal system, the high temperature $\beta$-form, stable above 575°, is also hexagonal but in all probability trapezohedral-hemihedral in its symmetry, the axial ratios of the two forms being, however, very nearly identical. Practically the only crystallographic change which takes place on the inversion is a molecular rearrangement, such that the common divalent axes of the high temperature $\beta$-form become polar in $\alpha$-form, and this fact involves certain consequences which can be used to distinguish quartz which has been formed above 575° from quartz which has never reached that temperature. At ordinary temperatures all quartz is $\alpha$-quartz, but if at any time in its history a particular piece of quartz has passed the inversion point and been heated above 575°, it bears ever afterward marks potentially present which on proper treatment can be made to appear just as an exposed photographic plate can be distinguished at once from an unexposed plate on immersion in a proper developer, although before development both plates may be identical in appearance.

To corroborate the data of Mallard and Le Chatelier, and at the same time to locate the inversion point more accurately, if possible, the birefringence and circular polarization of quartz were remeasured by means of a specially constructed thermal (electric resistance) microscope. For the measurement of the birefringence, polished plates of different thickness cut parallel with the principal axis were used and readings with the Babinet compensator taken, both in white light and in sodium and lithium lights.

. . . . . .

The above measurements and data prove definitely that quartz undergoes a small energy change at about 575° and that the change is

[1] *Compt. Rend. 108* (1889), 1046, and *109* (1890), 339; *Bull. Soc. Mineral. 13* (1890), 112, 119.
[2] *Compt. Rend. 110* (1890), 339; *Bull. Soc. Mineral. 13* (1890), 123.
[3] *Neues Jahrb. Festband* (1907), 181–196.

reversible or enantiotropic. The amount of energy involved is, however, so small that thermal methods of study are relatively unproductive compared with optical methods.

It is of interest to note that in a substance like quartz, which in some respects is exceedingly inert and sluggish, certain changes of equilibrium are extremely sensitve to temperature differences, a difference of one tenth of one degree being sufficient to cause the shift from the one form to the other. It is indeed difficult to form an adequate and satisfactory picture of a mechanical system which shall satisfy the conditions of such nice equilibrium and adjustment. In the case of quartz, however, it is fortunate for the observer that certain physical properties which can be determined with great accuracy at different temperatures are extremely sensitive to the inversion, since the actual change in energy content, or amount of heat involved in the transformation, is extremely slight, and too small, in fact, to be detected by ordinary methods for measuring temperatures. Notwithstanding the comparatively insignificant amount of energy required in the transformation, it is still sufficient to cause a readjustment of the crystallographic forces, such that the low temperature $\alpha$-quartz and the high temperature $\beta$-quartz crystallize in all probability in different subdivisions of the hexagonal system, and at the same time, intricate twinning phenomena may be set up, the effects of which are in general sufficient to enable the observer to distinguish $\alpha$-quartz from $\beta$-quartz. . . .

. . . In passing from the tetartohedral $\alpha$-form to the hemihedral $\beta$-form, the bivalent common axes lose their polarity and the tendency in the latter form to form twins, therefore, is much less strong than in the $\alpha$-form. On reverting later to the $\alpha$-form, the common axes of the $\beta$-form become again polar and the tendency during the molecular rearrangement is again to form twins, and, in this instance, twins with irregular boundary lines, since the change takes place rapidly and in the solid state.—The form and character of twinning on basal sections of quartz can therefore be used as one of the criteria in determining whether or not quartz has been formed above or below 575° C. . . .

Still a second fact of observation can be used to advantage in ascertaining the original temperature of formation of quartz.[3] Quartz is circularly polarizing and may rotate the incident plane polarized light waves either to the right or to the left. Experiments on the crystallization of circularly polarizing bodies have indicated that a slight change in the mother solution is often sufficient to change the character of the rotation of the crystal being precipitated. In quartzes formed at low temperatures, vein quartzes and the like, one might expect intergrowths of right- and left-handed crystals more frequently than in magma quartzes where rapid changes in the composition of the solutions are less likely to occur.—In the low temperature quartzes crystallizing out of quietly circulating solutions, moreover, the conditions are less violent than in a magma above 575° and the processes of precipitation might well be considered to proceed with more regularity and uniformity at the lower temperatures than above the inversion point. The tendency of intergrowths of right- and left-handed crystals of the low temperature phase should accordingly be toward regularity of outline of the intergrowths and toward hexagonal symmetry.—The fact of intergrowths of left- and right-handed quartz and the character of such intergrowths is a second factor to be considered in the investigation of any particular quartz.

A third feature which is of service in this connection is the shattering and cracking of quartz crystals on passing the inversion temperature as a result of the abrupt change in the coefficient of expansion. This occurs both on heating and on cooling. It is safe to assume, therefore, that large clear quartz plates free from fractures have in all probability never reached the inversion temperature. The fracture cracks in many small grains are present only potentially, and appear so distinctly on etching that an apparently clear plate of quartz which has been heated above 575° may crumble down in the etching acid and break up into a number of small grains, while the purely α-quartz remains intact and is etched with much greater uniformity.—The fact that thin plates of quartz may warp and bend temporarily at the inversion temperature, thus finding relief from the strains set up on the change, while thicker plates bend less easily and tend to fracture more readily, is a factor which should be considered in any particular case. Small grains, being thus less liable to fracture, may not show the phenomena of shattering as clearly as might be expected.

Crystallographically, the difference in crystal class between the α- and β-forms finds expression in the crystal habit. In the β-form, the pyramid faces are equally developed; trigonal trapezohedrons are absent, the habit of the crystals being usually that of the simple dihexahedrons observed in quartz porphyries and allied rocks. Crystals of the low temperature α-form, on the other hand, are usually prismatic in habit and often show marked differences in the size and character of the rhombohedral faces. Trigonal trapezohedrons may occur and stamp the crystal on which they do appear at once as a low temperature form.

·　　·　　·　　·　　·

Summarizing these data . . ., it may be stated that the quartzes from veins and geodes and certain vein pegmatites are in general clear and free from intricate fracture-cracks and show frequent regular intergrowths of right- and left-handed quartzes; they are also frequently twinned after the unit prism and the outline of the twinned areas is usually regular and hexagonal in aspect. The quartzes from graphic and granite pegmatites, granites and porphyries, on the other hand, are smaller in size, frequently fractured and cracked in an intricate manner; they show rarely intergrowths of right- and left-handed individuals and the outlines of such intergrowths may or may not be regular. They are as a rule intricately twinned and the twinned areas are usually small and irregular and bear no apparent relation in outline to the hexagonal symmetry.—The observed characteristics of the first group of quartzes are those deduced theoretically for low temperature $\alpha$-quartzes, while the features recorded for the second group are essentially those deduced theoretically for $\beta$-quartzes formed above 575°. This places the temperature of final solidification of an intrusive granite mass above 575°. With the quartzes examined in the course of this investigation, a number of other minerals, garnet, magnetite, albite, lepidolite, etc., were associated, and in certain instances where, from the degree of idiomorphism and similar criteria, the relative periods of precipitation of the associated mineral can be ascertained, temperature limits of formation of the latter can thus be established. By thus determining stability ranges of certain minerals, points on the geologic thermometer scale are gained which in turn serve to fix limits for the temperatures of formation of other associated minerals.

# JONES
Owen Thomas Jones (1878–    ), British geologist, received his geological training at Aberystwith University in Wales and Trinity College in Cambridge, England. From 1903 to 1910 he was a member of His Majesty's Geological Survey, from 1910 to 1919 he was Professor of Geology at Aberystwith, and from 1919 to 1930 he held a similar post at Manchester University. In 1930 he became Professor of Geology at Cambridge University, retiring in 1943 as Professor Emeritus. He is well known for his research concerning the geology of Wales and his geophysical studies of continental shelves. The paper excerpted here was based upon the address he delivered as he retired from the presidency of the Geological Society of London in 1938, an office to which he was re-elected in 1950.

## SEDIMENTATION IN GEOSYNCLINES *

Our knowledge of the history of any geosyncline is based primarily on the study of the sediments and other materials that accumulated

*From "On the Evolution of a Geosyncline," *Geological Society of London Quarterly Journal 94* (1938), pt. 2, Proceedings, pp. lx–cx.

during its development. Sedimentary rocks may be divided broadly into (1) carbonate rocks composed of limestones and dolomites, and (2) argillo-arenaceous, or clastic, rocks which were originally gravels, sands, silts and muds. Many of the Lower Palæozoic carbonate rocks possess, however, some of the depositional structures which are characteristic of clastic sediments and may have been deposited in the same manner.

The clastic sediments accumulated during a given period of time vary from place to place in thickness, grain-size, degree of sorting, and the distribution and kind of organic contents. These characters together constitute a facies, and were controlled by the conditions of sedimentation and the life, if any, in the area of deposition. The interpretation of past conditions is largely a matter of inference, based in part on a study of modern sediments and in part on the assumption that physical and climatic causes operated in former times as they do at the present day.

·     ·     ·     ·     ·

It is convenient at this stage to anticipate some of the major results that accrue from the study of the Lower Palæozoic clastic sediments. It has long been known that among the Ordovician and Silurian rocks two main facies can be recognized, which have been termed the shelly and the graptolitic facies, and the general distribution of these is well known. The distributions of these faunal facies are related to some extent to those of the sedimentary facies, which are in turn related to the trend of certain parts of the geosyncline and its bordering regions.

The rocks laid down in different regions of the Lower Palæozoic seas are distinguished notably by their constitution, thickness, grain-size, degree of sorting or washing, bedding, and other characteristics which will be noted in dealing with individual formations. During the Ordovician and Silurian periods, shelly deposits were mainly laid down in shallow seas which fringed the land areas. The characteristics of these deposits are as follows: they vary greatly from point to point in a horizontal sense and often from bed to bed in a vertical sequence, and bedding planes are usually sharply defined. The deposits are well sorted, so that the argillaceous constituents have been cleanly separated from the arenaceous materials; the latter frequently exhibit strong and variable current-bedding. Breaks in the faunal or lithological sequence are not uncommon, and are often accompanied by obvious signs of erosion. Calcareous matter is usually abundant in the form either of banks of shells or shell debris, and often there is evidence of transport and sorting of these according to size and shape by strong currents; occasionally true coral reefs may occur. The surfaces of calcareous beds are often current-swept, as if the rocks had consolidated rapidly, thus holding organisms firmly while any unconsolidated materials were removed. Oolitic structures may occasionally be found in the limestones, while phosphatic beds concentrated in definite bands and glauconite grains all indicate shallow-water conditions. Ripple-marks, sometimes of considerable size, may be found. Deposits having some of these characteristics in association are usually of limited thickness, and they have, in general, suffered relatively little from subsequent earth-movements. In the Lower Palæozoic, such deposits were laid down in the region bordering the geosyncline; this region was sometimes of considerable extent. They constitute Haug's neritic facies.

Marr's "belt of variables," a term applied to the deposits that form at the present day around the coasts, possess many characteristics which have been noted in ancient sedimentary formations. The chief rock-types exhibiting these characteristics are conglomerates, sandstones, muds of every grade of fineness, and limestones, both bedded and in reef masses. The grains of the sandstones often show a conspicuous degree of rounding, though this may be due in some cases to derivation from an adjoining land area where wind erosion prevailed. Sandstones associated with muds or sandy muds are often laminated, with sharply defined upper and lower surfaces. They are frequently of the types known as streaky sandstones. Some of these lithological types have many of the characters associated with deltaic deposits, but in general the latter are of greater thickness. The seas in which they were laid down have been termed "platform-" or "shelf-seas."

In their typical development, the sediments of the geosyncline stand in sharp contrast to those of the shallow shelf-seas. The arenaceous and argillaceous constituents are intimately mingled, so that sandstones are either muddy sandstones or have a considerable proportion of finely divided chlorite and muscovite disseminated through them, giving rise to grey or green rocks. Many of the muddy sediments are of a type for which no more satisfactory name exists than sandy mudstones; abundant grains of quartz are associated with fine muds or silts, and some are of considerable size. Deposition appears to have been continuous, apart from occasional indications of bottom disturbance or "bottom stir" in some types of mudstones or siltstones. The bedding is uniform and usually well marked, sometimes with an appearance of rhythmic deposition. The graded, bedded sandstones which Bailey (*Geol. Mag.* 1930, p. 84) has suggested should be named "greywacke" are essentially deposits of the geosyncline and are characteristically found near one or other of its margins. Such sandstones are so frequently associated with grey or greenish mudstones of similar constitution that they might be referred together to a greywacke suite. The coarser particles in these sediments are not rounded and are frequently very angular, though beds of conglomerate with rounded pebbles of quartz and other rocks may occur under special conditions. Organic remains are in general distributed sparsely through a great thickness of deposits. These may include shelly and graptolitic remains. Carbonate rocks are usually absent, but may occur as nodules. Deposits of this type were termed "bathyal" by Haug. This name is, however, open to objection, inasmuch as it suggests that some of these deposits were laid down in a great depth of water, which is not necessarily, if at all, the case.

Several thousands of feet of sediments having the general characteristics noted above were laid down during several periods of the Lower Palæozoic era, and since they bear clear evidence throughout that they were deposited in no great depth of water, it is obvious that the area in which they occur was sinking *pari passu* with the accumulation of the sediments. In many areas, the graded, bedded sandstones show a peculiar internal structure which has been described under various names, such as "curly bedding," "hassock bedding," "slip bedding," and "internal crumpling." It affects individual sandstone beds and sometimes the underlying mudstones for an inch or two, but the overlying bed is unaffected. This structure is due to movement or creep of the materials while the sand was full of water. Bailey has suggested that it may have been caused by earthquake shocks.

In some districts, the muddy sediments have slumped on a large scale, producing very remarkable structures. The consistent occurrence in all sections of a graded bed resting on the upper surface of the slumped masses proves conclusively that the slumped masses formed the sea floor at the conclusion of the slumping. In certain parts of the geosyncline, fine-grained, dark or almost black shales occur; they are usually free from admixture with sand, though material of silt grade normally occurs. Carbonate matter, if present, occurs in nodules, and pyrite is often abundant. This is the type commonly associated with an abundant graptolite fauna. It may, however, be associated with grey, green, dark-blue or sometimes maroon-coloured, fine-grained mudstones for which the conditions of sedimentation appear to have been similar to those of the graptolite shales but the life conditions different. The fine-grained sediments seem to have been laid down in parts of the geosyncline where relatively little material arrived from the land area.

At any one period the limits between the sedimentary types distinguished above are not in general sharply defined, and one facies passes gradually into the adjoining facies. Further, the boundaries are liable for various reasons to fluctuate in different periods, so that sediments of a given facies in one period may overlie those of another facies, and be covered in turn by those of a third facies.

The thickness of sediments deposited at any one place during a given period was controlled largely by two factors: (1) the sum-total of the vertical movements which occurred during that period, and (2) the amount of sediment which arrived at the place from the land area. If an area initially under shallow-water conditions did not subside, little, if any, sediment could accumulate, since any material that settled on the floor of the sea was disturbed repeatedly by currents and transported elsewhere; its final resting-place could only be in some other area where the depth was too great to allow bottom currents effectively to transport it. If, in turn, that area ceased to subside, after a time accumulation so reduced the depth as to bring the sediments under the influence of bottom currents, and the deposit that formed thereafter would be limited in thickness. The materials that were prevented from accumulating there would, as before, be transported elsewhere. The only region in which sediments could accumulate without interruption was one that was undergoing continuous subsidence.

At the same time there was a degree of sorting of the clastic sediments that found their way into the subsiding area, with the result that the finest grades occurred farthest away from the shore, and in a region situated at a considerable distance from a land area the thickness of the sediments depended to a greater extent upon the amount of sediments that reached it than upon the subsidence of the floor of the sea. The grain-size of the materials depended also upon the relief of the adjoining land whence the sediments were derived: their mineral composition reflected the character of the rocks of which that land was formed, while the climatic conditions prevailing during the period may have had some influence upon the characteristics of the sediments that were formed in the seas.

There are some more or less obvious principles which allow conclusions to be drawn regarding the direction from which certain types of sediments were derived. Thus, if the deposits laid down during a given period in a shallow sea near the land area were fine muds or limestones which required a clear sea for their formation, it is unlikely that coarse sands could have been transported during that period across the area in which such sediments were accumulating. Consequently, if coarse sands were laid down in an adjoining area they must have been derived from some other direction. If, however, there is evidence of substantial breaks or gaps in the sedimentary record of the shallow-water facies, accompanied by obvious signs of disconformities or unconformities, then it was possible during the time intervals represented by such breaks for coarse sediments to have been transported across the shelf-sea region.

Again, if the deposits of the shelf-sea were current-washed coarse sandstones or conglomerates, it is probable that the silts or muds which must have been at one time associated with the coarse-grained constituents were transported into an adjoining area, and if conditions there were favourable for continued accumulation, then a considerable thickness of mudstones and siltstones would occur.

In general, where there is evidence of continuous sedimentation, as in a geosyncline, the region where the deposit reached a minimum thickness was one which was farthest from the region of supply, whether it was from one border of the geosyncline or the other. Also, according to the relative abundance of sediments derived from one side of the region of deposition or the other, the place where the deposits were at their minimum thickness would fluctuate towards or away from the margin of the region, being situated nearer to that side whence the smaller contribution of sediments came. Such a region might be termed the axis of the geosyncline during that period, but it would probably not be the region where the greatest depression of the floor of the geosyncline occurred during the same period. Examples of the application of these principles will appear in the sequel.

If there are obvious indications of contemporaneous submarine sliding in muds or sands, then the direction of sliding was towards the region of minimum sedimentation, and if this direction can now be determined, it affords a clue to the direction of the axis as defined above.

The distinction which can often be drawn from the study of ancient rocks between the behaviour of closely adjoining regions of the crust is of great importance, though its significance has been a subject of differences of opinion. Hall believed, for example, that the Appalachian region subsided through a great vertical distance on account of the weight of sediments swept into the area from an adjoining land. Dana, on the other hand, believed that lateral pressure caused the earth's crust to bend down, and thus made room for the accumulation of such sediments as were available. Yet others, while believing that subsidence originated independently of sedimentation, hold the view that continuing subsidence is assisted by the additional weight of the accumulated sediments.

# RAYMOND Percy Edward Raymond (1879–1952), American paleontologist and stratigrapher, was associated with Harvard University throughout the greater part of his constructive career, serving as curator of

invertebrate paleontology in the Museum of Comparative Zoology from 1912 to 1945 and simultaneously as a professor in the Department of Geological Sciences, retiring as Professor Emeritus at the end of that period. He is best known for his many contributions in paleontology, where trilobites were his first love, but he also had a lively interest in sediments and sedimentation. The following excerpt illustrates his characteristic pattern of thought, in which priority was always given to field observations rather than to data of any other kind. It was written at a time when most geologists assumed that "redbeds" were indicative of aridity at the time and place of their origin.

## THE SIGNIFICANCE OF RED COLOR IN SEDIMENTS *

Red color in rocks is generally due to the presence of a ferric compound of iron, and it has usually been assumed that it is the oxide, hematite ($Fe_2O_3$). It is a question, however, whether the coloring matter may not be in reality, a red hydroxide. In view of the importance of the deductions which follow from a correct evaluation of the meaning of red color, it seems worth while to review the rôle of iron in the sediments in the light of recent work on the chemistry of oxides and hydroxides of that metal.

With the exception of aluminum, iron is the most abundant and widely distributed metal in the rocks of the earth's crust, occurring chiefly in the complex silicates which are the most easily decomposed constituents of igneous rocks. It also occurs as the oxides, magnetite and ilmenite, which are not so easily attacked. Biotite, amphiboles, pyroxenes, olivine, and chlorite probably furnish the greater part of the iron which goes into solution.

### SOLUTION OF THE IRON

During the process of weathering, the complex silicates are broken down by the action of various acids and alkalies. The acids are partly of inorganic, partly of organic, nature, but very largely the result of organic processes. Carbonic acid is usually considered the most important single solvent. A small part of this is derived from the atmosphere, but much more from the decay of organic matter. It is well known that nearly all minerals are slightly soluble in water containing carbon dioxide, and such action alone would account in time for the freeing of considerable amounts of iron. The presence in decaying organic matter, however, of microorganisms such as bacteria, yeasts, and molds, results in the production of many organic acids, such as butyric, formic, lactic, acetic, citric, tartaric and propionic.

•  •  •  •  •

*From *American Journal of Science* [5] *13* (1927), 234–251.

As a result of the action of the various solvents in the soil, iron goes into solution in two forms; a large part of it as the bicarbonate and a lesser portion as organic compounds whose nature does not appear to be definitely known.

### FATE OF THE CARBONATE

Since the carbonate is soluble only in the presence of an excess of $CO_2$, such solutions are carried very short distances. On coming to the surface or otherwise losing carbon dioxide and returning to the presence of oxygen, the ferrous bicarbonate is immediately changed into the amorphous form of ferric hydroxide commonly called limonite. This material will, according to circumstances; (a) remain in the soil; (b) be deposited near the source; or (c) be transported in suspension to some other locality.

### FATE OF THE SOLUBLE ORGANIC COMPOUNDS

Very little is known about the organic compounds of iron, but it is known that some rivers carry an appreciable amount of the metal in solution. . . . The rivers containing an appreciable percentage of iron are those of fertile districts, and chiefly in warm regions. The rivers of the arid regions show only traces of iron.

.   .   .   .   .

Iron-depositing bacteria appear to live in fresh water only, but seem to be of universal distribution in that medium. Consequently the greater part of the iron in solution as an organic compound probably shares the fate of that carried as a bicarbonate, and is precipitated before it has traveled far. Some iron in solution does reach the sea, but apparently not in greater amounts than is necessary for the support of organic life there. In fact, the supply of available iron may to some extent control the amount of marine vegetation. The ferric hydroxide deposited through the action of bacteria may appear as a deposit composed chiefly of limonite, but is more often seen as a stain on grains of clastic rocks.

### ACCUMULATION OF FERRIC HYDROXIDE

The greatest concentration of ferric hydroxide is in the regolith, and it appears that climatic control is a factor in its accumulation there, for it is chiefly in tropical and semitropical regions that laterites and laterite-like materials occur. As Glinka[1] points out, it is in warm regions of "optimal moistening" that bacterial decay is so rapid as to balance the production of organic matter, leaving little residuum of humus to enter the soils. The growth of vegetation is so great that the water is held or transpired, and the soil does not become water-logged. Under these conditions the soil waters become alkaline (Robinson[2]), and leach out silica, leaving the hydroxides of iron and aluminum as the ultimate products of a very thorough decomposition of the rocks. Under favorable circumstances such decomposition goes on to considerable depths. The upper part of the regolith is red or orange-red, whereas at depths of from one to fifty feet the color gradually changes to yellow.

In moist temperate and arctic regions vegetation is also abundant, but in the cooler climate the action of putrefactive bacteria and other organisms is less rapid, and entirely inhibited for a part of the year. As a result, cellulose, which does not decay rapidly, tends to accumulate and remains as humus in the soil. In humid temperate climates, because of less evaporation, the soils are more moist than in the humid tropics. This results in poorer aeration and slower decomposition of the plant residues. Decomposition is of an anaerobic nature and leads to the formation of an acid type of soil water, which removes iron and aluminum rather than silica (Robinson). The downward movement of water in such a region produces a surficial zone of leaching from which the iron is constantly being removed. Robinson has called this the zone of eluviation. If the material is carried down to the permanent water table, carbonates of iron are apt to be formed in such regions, since the ground water is usually deficient in oxygen and rich in carbon dioxide.

If, however, the soil is porous and rather well oxygenated, ferric hydroxide is often formed in what Robinson has named the zone of illuviation, that is, the zone at which the fine-grained material carried down from above is dropped by the descending waters. At this horizon "hard-pan" cemented by red or yellow ferric hydroxide is often found. . . .

In arid and semi-arid regions, little decomposition takes place, so that little solution of iron can be accomplished. Observation shows that red and yellow are seldom seen in the soils of such localities, unless the country rock itself happens to be of those colors.

Black soils do, however, accumulate to some extent under semi-arid climates, since the vegetation grows rapidly during the wet season, and decay is checked in the dry months which follow. Under these conditions some leaching occurs, but evaporation is so great that the mois-

[1] *Die Typen der Bodenbildung,* Berlin, 1914.
[2] "Pedology as a branch of geology," *Geol. Mag. 61* (1924), 444–455.

ture is drawn upward, and a calcareous hard-pan is formed relatively near the surface. No red soil seems to be forming under these conditions.

· · · · ·

### Red and Yellow Colors

Unfortunately, knowledge of the chemistry of iron oxides and hydroxides is not as yet far enough advanced to give any satisfactory explanation as to why some formations containing much iron are red, whereas others are yellow. It has been the general assumption that the former were colored by hematite, and the latter by limonite, but I do not know that there is any definite proof that such is the case. The assumption has been based, of course, on the fact that there was formerly supposed to be a more or less continuous series of hydroxides from limonite, $Fe_2O_3 \cdot 3H_2O$, to turgite, $Fe_2O_3 \cdot \frac{1}{2}H_2O$, and then a passage to hematite, $Fe_2O_3$, with, theoretically, no water. The hydroxides containing from 6 or 7% to 28 or 30% of water are yellow, whereas turgite with 4 to 6% and hematite are red. The process of turning red was therefore supposed to be one of dehydration. It is true that with enough heat and enough pressure the yellow hydroxide can be turned red, but not at any temperatures or pressures encountered either at the surface of the earth or at any depths at which any of the red sediments have been buried. Observation alone shows the futility of appealing to deep burial, for in the Triassic sandstone of New Jersey, estimated to have a thickness of approximately three or four miles, the upper layers, never deeply buried nor acted upon by orogenic forces, are just as red as those at the base.

· · · · ·

It was long ago shown that yellow and red hydroxides of iron could be formed artificially, although never in crystalline form. Solutions of ferric chloride and ferric nitrate when treated with sodium, potassium or ammonium hydroxides, give precipitates of red colloidal ferric hydroxide. Solutions of ferrous salts when treated with alkaline hydroxides give precipitates of light bluish green ferrous hydroxide which upon oxidation changes to yellow ferric hydroxide. Yellow ferric hydroxide is also formed by oxidation and hydration of ferrous carbonate and in the rusting of metallic iron.

It does not appear that anyone has followed up the thought inherent in these facts, but I should like to put forward the suggestion that the coloring matter in sediments may be formed in much the same way as are the synthetic hydroxides. As is well known, ammonium hydroxide is formed in the putrefaction of organic matter; nitrifying bacteria work this into nitrites, and they are followed by another group of bacteria which change the nitrites into nitrates. In the meantime more ammonium hydroxide is being produced, so that, in the soil, it is entirely possible that ferric nitrate is produced, and then changed to red ferric hydroxide as is done in the test-tube. Under such conditions a part of the iron in solution would be precipitated as red material. Other and probably larger portions of the iron would be carried downward as the soluble bicarbonate and remain as such in the zone of ground water, to be later oxidized to the yellow limonite. If such action took place, one could understand both the layering of red and yellow hydroxides in the tropics, where the superficial soil-waters are alkaline, and the thinness of the zone of red hydroxides beneath the surface in temperate and cold, moist regions.

．　　．　　．　　．　　．

### Ferric Hydroxide in the Sediments

From what has been stated above, it appears that a *sine qua non* for the accumulation of considerable quantities of ferric hydroxide, either red or yellow, is the weathering of rocks through long periods of time under warm and moist conditions. The amount of such material on the continents to-day in tropical and subtropical regions is almost inconceivably vast, and a great deal of it is being transported and re-deposited. In the regolith the hydroxide occurs in part as a coating on other minerals, also as free particles of minute size, and apparently, in a colloidal condition.

When transported by streams, the larger part is at least temporarily deposited in alluvial fans or flood plains on the continent. When carried to the sea by rivers it is deposited wherever muds of the finest grain collect, that is, in estuaries, lagoons, and on the continental slopes. These are also the collecting places of the fine-grained, decaying organic matter, and of the resultant hydrocarbons and carbohydrates. The hydroxides of iron come therefore into contact with substances greedy for oxygen, in a medium, mud, which is notably deficient in that gas. Under such conditions it is believed that a reducing action goes on, and that the iron is reduced to a ferrous state. Observations indicate that such action does take place. . . . The red muds of the Tennessee do not give their color to the deposits of the lower Mississippi. There must, however, be considerable amounts of organic material if all the ferric hydroxide brought to the sea is to be reduced.

Where organic material is deficient in quantity, red deposits will be formed. There are at the present day, according to Murray and Hjort,[3] large areas where red clay is accumulating off the coasts of tropical eastern South America, western Africa, and China.

There is also a question as to just how great an extent the reduction of iron from the ferric to the ferrous condition is actually accomplished. Analyses of the blue clay, which is much more commonly found on continental slopes than the red, . . . show large amounts of ferric iron. Ferric hydroxide is not easily attacked, and it may be that in some instances the oxygen is not really removed, but that the color is masked by the organic matter.

### DEPOSITION ON THE CONTINENTS

Unfortunately there are no localities known to me where great amounts of red sediments are accumulating on land at the present time, a fact which may have an especial significance in the interpretation of the ancient deposits. This phase of deposition can therefore be discussed only briefly, and from a wholly theoretical standpoint. Ordinarily subaerial accumulations would be formed under the same climatic conditions as those which produced the regolith. It is possible, however, that the material might be carried far enough to enter the zone of another climate. It is still more probable that the residual material might be eroded and redeposited long after its formation, and under very different geographical and climatic conditions.

Since the red and yellow hydroxides are layered in the regolith, the red above the yellow, the denudation of such material naturally carries off more of the red than the yellow. The red color therefore predominates in the mixture, and the material transported is red. It is, therefore, necessary to speak of the latter color only in connection with deposition.

### EFFECT OF ARID CONDITIONS

If the red sands, silts, and clays were brought to and deposited in an arid region, where the streams spread out and lose themselves in their fans, the ultimate appearance would be governed by mechanical and not chemical conditions. Through the sorting action of the rivers there would be separation of the finer grains, which picked up by the winds would probably be transported considerable distances. The ultimate fate of such material would depend upon location, topography, and persistence in direction of the wind. The dust might be dispersed, or it might be accumulated in such a loess-like deposit as the Vernon

[3] *The Depths of the Ocean,* 1912.

red shale of the upper Silurian of western New York. The silt and coarser material, up to sizes of from 1 to 2 mm, would also be wind-blown, rounded, pitted, deprived of the red stain, and accumulated in dunes of the usual white or grayish white color. Locally, some portions of the accumulation might, if the dunes stayed long in one position, receive a second staining after the rounding had taken place.

### EFFECT OF COOL, MOIST CONDITIONS

As already stated, much humus accumulates in the soil when there is moisture enough to support vegetation and the climate is cool enough to check the action of bacteria over a considerable part of the year. Under such conditions leaching occurs, and also deoxidation, hence red sediments transported to such a region might have their color reduced to green or gray unless accumulation should be too rapid to allow plants to get a foothold. In such a region moisture could vary within large limits, as the grasses, sedges and mosses of semiarid arctic regions seem to leave nearly as large a residuum of humus in the soil as do the products of the slower-growing forests. The red stain is not, however, easily or quickly removed, as may be seen by anyone who has occasion to pass over the red fluvio-glacial soils of some parts of the Connecticut Valley. These soils have supported vegetation since glacial times, and have been more or less intensively cultivated for nearly 300 years, but many of them are still notably red.

### EFFECT OF WARM, MOIST CONDITIONS

This subject has already been sufficiently discussed when reviewing the conditions under which hydroxides of iron accumulate. In regions with such climates production of vegetable material is rapid, yet organic decay is equally favored by the continuous work of the numerous bacteria, fungi and other agents. As a result humus does not accumulate, and observation shows that even tropical forests exist on red soils which are not leached. Red sediments might therefore accumulate either slowly or rapidly under such conditions.

### EFFECT OF CONDITIONS OF SEASONAL, DEFICIENT RAINFALL

Under conditions of semi-aridity with the annual precipitation falling within limited periods, a sparce, or in places, even a luxuriant vegetation springs up, the greater part withering and dying as the dry season advances. Under such conditions, because dryness checks bacterial action, a small amount of humus collects in the soil, but whether enough to have any reducing action on red clastic deposits is not clear. If red sediments could be transported into such a region rapidly, they would undoubtedly remain red for the most part, unless the material brought in during the wet season were sufficient to overwhelm the established vegetation. In that case the plants would not readily regain a foothold, and the area would be transformed into a real desert. If the deposition were slow, a thin layer each year, there would probably be enough humus and production of acids by roots to remove a good deal of the red color.

## SUMMARY

Red residual deposits accumulate in tropical and sub-tropical regions where there is enough moisture to insure a good cover of vegetation. To accumulate a considerable quantity of such material requires a long period during which erosion is not particularly active. Débris removed from such a regolith may be deposited without loss of color in any region provided it accumulates rapidly enough. It is least apt to remain red in arid or other desert regions where there is little or no vegetation to hold the deposits in place, and in cold, moist regions where, due to abundance of humus, much leaching occurs. Somewhat more favorable for the retention of red color is a semi-arid region, but since plants do not quickly get a foothold in such a situation, a rapid influx of sediments would probably cause a more or less continuously barren surface, on which the wind would have full play. More favorable would be a cool, moist region with abundant vegetation, and sufficient rapidity of influx of sediments to prevent the accumulation of large quantities of humus. Last and best of the terrestrial locations are those with a warm, humid climate, where bacterial action is rapid and humus does not readily accumulate.

Red beds may be formed in the sea likewise if the influx of material is rapid enough to introduce more ferric iron than the organic matter present will reduce. That such has been the case at times is shown by the fact that some of the Palaeozoic red sandstones contain marine fossils near the base even though they may become non-marine, or at least unfossiliferous in the upper portion. Instances are the red Juniata sandstone of south-central Pennsylvania, the Bays sandstone of southwestern Virginia, and the Moccasin sandstone of eastern Tennessee.

Under conditions of rapid removal from the land the smallest of the red grains may be abundant enough to give a red color to a truly marine limestone formed some distance from shore. The Orthoceras limestone of Sweden is, in places, as at Kinnekulle, a deep cherry red, abundantly fossiliferous limestone. The coloring matter appears to be *terra rosa*, derived from the decomposition of Cambrian limestone in southeastern Sweden. In this country there are similar red limestones such as the Tellico and Moccasin of eastern Tennessee, which owe their color to particles of the finest size, washed out by marine action from the deposits nearer the shore.

When the ferric hydroxide is brought into the sea less rapidly, much of it may be reduced with the formation of ferrous carbonate and pyrite, which may later become oxidized, to form the yellow limonite. Thus it is possible to cross the red Upper Devonian non-marine strata of the eastern Catskills to the rusty yellow marine strata of equivalent age in the vicinity of Oneonta. The yellow of these rocks is, however, only surficial, and beneath the surface they are "blue," a color due, according to MacCarthy's recent and very important paper,[4] to a mixture of ferrous and ferric compounds with the former equal to or somewhat predominant over the latter.

The significance of red color in sediments appears to be the rapidity of accumulation. Since they are derived from a region long stable, red beds usually indicate movement of the earth's surface. The climatic conditions under which particular examples were deposited cannot be judged from the color alone but must be deduced from other lines of evidence.

# DOLE AND STABLER Richard Bryant Dole (1880–1917) and Herman Stabler (1879–1942), American hydrologists, were associated with the Water Resources Branch of the U. S. Geological Survey throughout the greater part of their active careers. The paper excerpted here presented the results of what appears to have been the first significant attempt to examine quantitatively the rate of erosion over a large area.

## THE RATE OF REGIONAL DENUDATION *

The accompanying tables [not reproduced here; see Addendum] present estimates of the rate of denudation in the United States. The figures show the rate at which the earth's crust is being moved as solid particles carried in suspension by streams and as matter carried in aqueous solution. . . .

The computations of denudation factors are based on figures representing the amount of mineral matter carried by streams, the size of the areas tributary to the streams, and the quantity of water discharged by the streams.

· · · · · ·

---

[4] "Colors produced by iron in minerals and the sediments," *Am. J. Sci. 12* [5] (1926), 17–36.
*From *U. S. Geological Survey Water Supply Paper 234*, (1909), pp. 78–93.

The depth in millionths of an inch per year covered by the material removed is found by dividing the tons per square mile per year by 0.1917 and the last three columns bear reciprocal relations to columns 10, 11, and their sum. Any attempt to estimate erosion in volumetric terms from determinations of dry suspended matter and dissolved solids involves the use of factors which are by no means absolute. The actual specific gravity of the mineral substance carried in streams in the United States is not greatly different from 2.6. This figure is practically identical with that commonly assumed for the specific gravity of the earth's crust and corresponds to a weight of 165 pounds per cubic foot. Each 165 pounds of substance found in water, therefore, represents the erosion of approximately 1 cubic foot of the crust of the earth, and estimates of ultimate rock losses based upon these figures are probably not in error more than 8 to 10 per cent. Common earth or loam, however, contains a large amount of air space, or voids, and dry earth is estimated as weighing 80 to 110 pounds per cubic foot. If an estimate of erosion be made upon this basis, the error for a large area will probably not be great, but may amount to 20 per cent or more when calculations are made for small areas. Finally, a third factor for calculation is based upon an attempt to determine the volume of river sediment or mud banks that a given weight of suspended matter may form. Investigators working upon different streams in the United States have obtained results indicating that a cubic foot of sediment may be produced by 50 to 125 pounds of dry material. The compactness of the mud is so variable that an estimate of this nature based upon an average of 90 pounds per cubic foot is likely to be in error by about 45 per cent. In view of the widely divergent values given for river sediment and for surface loam, the estimates for denudation expressed in millionths of an inch in depth from the entire drainage area and in years required for the erosion of 1 inch from the drainage area are based upon the assumption that 165 pounds of suspended or dissolved solids represent the removal of 1 cubic foot of the earth's crust.

· · · · · ·

The figures for dissolved solids practically represent material carried into the ocean; the figures for suspended solids, on the other hand, represent more properly material carried to tide water, because the decrease in stream velocity at that point occasions a gradual deposition of the matter transported in solid form. The tons per square mile per year removed from different basins show interesting comparisons. In respect to dissolved matter, the southern Pacific basin heads the list with 177 tons, the northern Atlantic basin being next with 130 tons.

The rate for Hudson Bay basin, 28 tons, is lowest; that for the Colorado and western Gulf of Mexico basins is somewhat higher. The denudation estimates for the southern Atlantic basin correspond very closely to those for the entire United States. The amounts are generally lowest for streams in the arid and semiarid regions, because large areas there contribute little or nothing to the run-off. The southern Pacific basin is an important exception to this general rule, presumably because of the extensive practice of irrigation in that area. The amounts are highest in regions of high rainfall, though usually the waters in those sections are not so highly mineralized as the waters of streams in arid regions.

Colorado River brings down the most suspended matter, delivering 387 tons per year for each square mile of its drainage basin. Though many small streams bring silt into the Great Lakes, sedimentation clears the water, and practically no suspended matter is transported by St. Lawrence River. In general much less suspended matter is carried by northern than by southern rivers, a phenomenon influenced probably more by the texture of the soil and the subsoil and the geologic character of the rocks than by stream velocity.

The detailed estimates throw considerable light upon the progress of erosion in different sections of the river valleys. The Mississippi, for instance, apparently discharges more material than is brought in by its tributaries, thus indicating that its lower valley is still being eroded. The lower Colorado, however, appears to be receiving deposits from both dissolved and suspended matter taken from its upland drainage area. The Rio Grande is similar to the Colorado in this respect.

The estimates reveal that the surface of the United States is being removed at the rate of thirteen ten-thousandths of an inch per year, or 1 inch in 760 years. Though this amount seems trivial when spread over the surface of the country, it becomes stupendous when considered as a total, for over 270,000,000 tons of dissolved matter and 513,000,000 tons of suspended matter are transported to tide water every year by the streams of the United States. This total of 783,000,000 tons represents more than 350,000,000 cubic yards of rock substance, or 610,000,000 cubic yards of surface soil. If this erosive action had been concentrated upon the Isthmus of Panama at the time of American occupation, it would have excavated the prism for an 85-foot level canal in about seventy-three days.

### ADDENDUM

In 1964, Sheldon Judson and Dale F. Ritter published a recalculation of the rates of regional denudation in the United States (*Journal of Geophysical Research, 69,* 3395–3401) using more adequate data than those available to Dole and Stabler. Their calculations were based on

| Drainage region | Denudation rate: inches per 1000 years | |
| --- | --- | --- |
| | Dole and Stabler (1909) | Judson and Ritter (1964) |
| Colorado | 2.3 | 6.5 |
| Pacific slopes, California | 1.3 | 3.6 |
| Western Gulf | 0.6 | 2.1 |
| Mississippi | 2.0 | 2.0 |
| South Atlantic and eastern Gulf | 1.4 | 1.6 |
| North Atlantic | 0.9 | 1.9 |
| Columbia | | 1.5 |
| United States as a whole | 1.3 | 2.6 |

the same inference that 165 pounds of eroded material is equal to the removal of one cubic foot of surface rocks, but their conclusions were notably different. They found "the over-all denudation rate for the United States to be twice that arrived at by Dole and Stabler." Assuming that the rates of erosion they reported are representative, they observed that "it would take 11 to 12 million years to move to the ocean a volume equivalent to that of the United States lying above sealevel. At this rate there has been enough time since the Cretaceous to destroy such a land mass six times."

A comparison between the regional denudation rates reported by Judson and Ritter and those reported by Dole and Stabler is shown in the accompanying table.

# ESKOLA
Pentii Eelis Eskola (1883-1964), Finnish geologist, studied at Helsinki University and the University of Freiburg where he received his Ph. D. degree in 1915. Joining the Helsinki faculty as a lecturer in 1916, he became Professor of Geology and Mineralogy in 1924 and Director of the Institute of Geology in 1926. In addition to these posts, which he occupied until his retirement a few years before his death, he was one of the most productive members of the Geologic Commission of Finland for more than thirty years.

## THE MINERAL FACIES OF ROCKS*

### IGNEOUS FACIES

F. Becke has in many publications laid stress on the intimate connection between the igneous and the metamorphic development of

*From *Norsk Geologisk Tidskrift 6,* pt. 1–2 (1920), 143–194. Excerpts are from pp. 177–189.

151

eruptivogeneous metamorphic rocks. Recently, in a lecture on different types of the metamorphism, given in April 1920 in Stockholm and Christiania, he traced the development of a cooling rock-mass, showing that there is gradual transition between the processes taking place before and those taking place after the complete consolidation of the magma. Thus the sharp distinction between the igneous and metamorphic phenomena is more theoretical than practical.

We call those rocks metamorphic which have originated by gradual replacement of the constituents of earlier rocks, with or without changes in the bulk composition. To the metamorphic rocks we oppose the primary rocks, i.e., all those that have crystallized at once from a large mass of solution, either aqueous or what is generally called magma, giving rise to the igneous rocks.

In accordance with the general law controlling chemical systems under given temperature and pressure, it follows that the mineralogical composition of an igneous rock will be the same as that of a metamorphic rock, provided that both have obtained their actual set of minerals under the same conditions.

At first glance it will seem that this theoretical postulate has no application in practice. Equilibrium cannot be arrived at unless the minerals already crystallized out are in continuous interaction with the rest magma and with each other and, above all, the crystallization may proceed at a constant temperature. Now, E. Baur[1] has set forth a hypothesis according to which the crystallization of the igneous rocks should have proceeded isothermically, the consolidation having been due to a gradual removal of the mineralizers. Acceptable as this hypothesis may be in certain cases, the cooling cannot be denied as a fact, and many features in the igneous rocks tell us that they have passed the fields of more than one chemical equilibrium. I believe indeed that petrographical evidence in this direction has not yet been sufficiently estimated. I shall name a drastic example from my own experience.[2]

A coarsely crystalline granodiorite, or quartz-monzonite, in the Namama region in Transbaikal, contains, in a eugranitic mass, crystals of hornblende in the ideal form, being the combination of (110), (001), and (101). This mineral is the most idiomorphic of the main constituents and must be regarded as the first one to crystallize out from the magma. Thereafter follow, in the series of idiomorphism, the plagioclase, the orthoclase, and last the quartz, in part in graphic intergrowth with the

---

[1] E. Baur, *Chemische Kosmographie,* Munich, 1903; also *Z. Physik. Chem. 42* (ca. 1903), 567.

[2] P. Eskola, "Igneous rocks of Sviatoy Noss in Transbaikal," *Öfvers. Finska Vet. Soc. Förhandl. 63,* Avd. A, No. 1 (1920).

orthoclase. The order of idiomorphism is remarkably distinct, and the whole structure tells of a quiet crystallization in an unagitated magma basin. No later metamorphic influence can be traced. Yet the hornblende was not the first mineral to separate, but was formed at the expense of other, still earlier, minerals. In the crystals of hornblende one finds corroded remnants of diopside, and all around them are numerous grains of iron ore, titanite, and epidote, all these having apparently been formed as by-products at the formation of the hornblende. This mineral is consequently, on the one hand, a uralite and, on the other hand, an apparent primary magmatic mineral. At the earlier stages of the crystallization there existed diopside and perhaps also olivine, for in some dark nodules in this rock one finds hornblende in granular aggregates that from their form seem to be pseudomorphs after olivine.

This is a single case, but I believe the conclusion may be generalized widely: It must be a common rule that, at the consolidation of magmas, minerals are formed and again resorbed, and in most cases we see no trace of them any more. The phenomena similar to that just named are of common occurrence, but as they are more often met with in rocks that show traces of stress influence, they have, often erroneously, been regarded as metamorphic.

Experimental work has in later times thrown much light on the mineral development in igneous rocks.[3] N. L. Bowen has, from these results combined with a rich geological experience, constructed a general view of the magmatic development.[4] In the process of differentiation the residual magma, from which minerals crystallizing at high temperatures are at first separated out, becomes successively enriched with substances lowering the crystallization temperature. A definite magma thus passes through all these stages which are, in some way, analogous to our facies.

Thus we often find, in igneous rocks, minerals belonging to different facies, the earlier of them having escaped resorption only in consequence of a rapid cooling.

On the other hand, we always see in the igneous rocks a tendency towards certain equilibria, apparently corresponding to the conditions during the last stage of consolidation. And when we know what mineral associations belong to the perfect equilibrium in each facies, we are able without any difficulty to state the facies under the conditions

[3] Among those works at the Geophysical Laboratory of the Carnegie Institution having special bearing on the formation and resorption of minerals during the process of consolidation are: N. L. Bowen, "The system diopside-forsterite-silica," *Am. J. Sci. 38* (1914), 207; and Olaf Andersen, "The System anorthite-forsterite-silica," *ibid. 39* (1915), 407.

[4] N. L. Bowen, *J. Geol. 23* (supplement to no. 8), 1915.

of which the rock has performed its crystallization. This is still further facilitated by the fact that perfect equilibria are not by any means rare in the igneous rocks. . . .

### The Hornblende-Gabbro Facies

Very commonly igneous rocks have arrived at equilibria in the amphibolite facies. A gabbroid magma there gives rise to a hornblende-gabbro. These rocks usually occur in the form of large batholiths which have intruded in the earth's crust in connection with orogenetic movements and now fill up anticlines of raised-up formations. They are especially common in the large pre-Cambrian areas in many lands. The crystallization in such "central" batholiths, in most cases, took place during the upward movement of the rock-masses. It seems uncertain, whether the crystallization, as Baur assumes, was due to a slow removal of the volatile compounds or to a slow cooling. The mechanical agitation caused by the movements during the crystallization no doubt also favoured the arrangement to the stable state. The fact is, in any case, that these rocks actually show mineral associations conforming to the rules of the amphibolite facies. In the Fennoscandian Archaean known to me, granites, granodiorites, hornblende-gabbros and hornblende-peridotites in such batholiths are, as to their mineral composition, nearly identical with those chemically identical metamorphic rocks between whose strata the batholiths have intruded.

### The Gabbro Facies

Quite an analogous parallellism as between amphibolites and hornblende-gabbros will be found prevailing between the hornfelses and those igneous rocks which have caused their contact-metamorphism. The eruptive masses here under consideration are, in most cases, laccolitic bodies and have intruded up to the higher levels of the earth's crust where the temperature was lower. Cooling may therefore have played the main rôle during the crystallization; we must expect traces from various conditions preserved, and in fact we find frequent deviation from the stable state. Aluminous pyroxenes may have been preserved as unstable relics instead of the stable diopside[5] and, in consequence of imperfect resorption, often due to armouring, olivine may occur in rocks with excessive silica. Many other examples could be named. Nevertheless, there are numbers of examples of such igneous rocks mineralogically almost identical with the corresponding hornfelses.

[5] The same deviations may, of course, also be found in metamorphic rocks. Note the fassaite, an aluminous pyroxene, at contacts of limestone!

Thus a normal norite, composed of plagioclase, diopsidic pyroxene, and hypersthene, may be mineralogically identical with a plagioclase-hypersthene-diopside-hornfels of class VI.

## The Helsinkite Facies

Primary igneous rocks having the mineral characters of the greenschist facies exist in the form of albite-epidote-rocks, the so-called helsinkites, of southern Finland, as described by A. Laitakari.[6] The helsinkites are medium-grained or coarse-grained rocks occurring in the Archaean in close connection with, and showing gradual transition into, the common pegmatitic and aplitic granites. They apparently represent phases of rock in which large quantities of water under high pressure have caused an extraordinarily large depression of the crystallization temperature. Other primary igneous albite-epidote-rocks, named epidote-syenites, have been described by E. Mäkinen from Österbotten in Finland,[7] and by myself from Sviatoy Noss in Transbaikal.[2]

## The Diabase Facies

Volcanic rocks show a mineral development similar to that of the pyrometamorphic rocks, or the sanidinite facies. The same development may also be met in such hypabyssal dike- and sill-rocks as many diabases.[8] The latter in fact may show the most perfect state of equilibrium in this facies; therefore I here call it provisionally the diabase facies.

Generally the volcanic rocks exhibit a very imperfect state of equilibrium. Some of their minerals have been formed at the intratelluric period under the conditions of the gabbro or hornblende-gabbro facies. They appear as phenocrysts in the lavas. Therefore the enstatite and augite, for example, commonly have crystallized as separate phases and do not form solid solutions, or enstatite-augite, which is the stable product formed by crystallization from melts under atmospheric pressure.

On the other hand, the natural quenching, which the lavas are subjected to, often causes the appearance of volcanic glass, a kind of unstable product only met with in the sanidinite and the diabase facies.

## The Igneous Eclogite Facies

All the Norwegian eclogites studied by me are of igneous origin. Concerning the eclogites in the Bergen region which occur in close con-

---

[6] A. Laitakari, "Einige Albitepidotgesteine von Südfinnland." *Bull. Comm. Geol. Finlande 51* (1918).

[7] E. Mäkinen, "Öfversikt av de prekambriska bildingarna i mellersta Österbotten," *Bull. Comm. Geol. Finlande 47* (1916).

[8] In Sweden and Finland many rocks have been called diabases that have a mineral development typical of the gabbro facies.

nection with the labradorite-rock, this conclusion was at first drawn by Th. Hiortdahl and M. Irgens.[9] Later C. F. Kolderup, by detailed geologic and petrographic investigation brought full evidence that the eclogites are a differentiated variety from the same magma as the labradorite-rocks. The latter belong to the series called the Bergen-Jotun-group of Caledonian eruptives by V. M. Goldschmidt.[10]

Another eclogite-bearing area which has provided material for my studies is that in the districts of Nordfjord, Söndmöre, and Nordmöre in the western coast-region of Norway. The main part of the rock crust here is gneiss, which has been regarded as pre-Cambrian. In it are embedded elongated masses of olivine-rock, many of them accompanied by eclogite schliers or bed-formed masses. Other lenticular, rounded, or irregular masses of eclogite are embedded immediately in gneiss. Labradorite-rocks occur at many places in evident connection with the olivine-rocks and eclogites.

A common evidence of the igneous origin of the Norwegian eclogites is their structure. The garnet is always free from inclusions, whereas the metamorphic garnet is usually filled up with quartz-grains. Mostly the garnet, having crystallized first, appears as rounded grains enclosed in the pyroxenes, but at several localities on Holsenö in the Bergen region a hypersthene-eclogite contains xenomorphic garnet filling the interstices between the pyroxenes.

When enclosed in labradorite-rocks or in gneiss the eclogites have consolidated earlier than their country-rock,[11] and the same also is true of eclogites connected with olivine-rocks.

Frequently the crystallization has begun in the eclogite facies, garnet and pyroxene having separated out, but has continued in the hornblende-gabbro facies, as already pointed out. The hornblende and feldspar then fill up the interstices between the anterior generation of minerals.

At the boundaries the eclogites enclosed in gneiss have a zone altered into amphibolite. The opposite alteration, from gabbro into eclogite which should have taken place if the current theory of the metamorphic genesis of the eclogite were true, has never been observed.

From other countries the literature contains descriptions of eclogites

[9]Th. Hiortdahl and M. Irgens, "Geologiske Undersogelser i Bergens Omegn," Universitets-program for andet halvarr, 1862.

[10]V. M. Goldschmidt, "Übersicht der Eruptivgesteine im Kaledonischen Gebirge zwischen Stavanger and Trondhjem," *Vidensk. Meddar dansk naturh. Foren* (1916), no. 2.

[11]Goldschmidt (n. 10 above, pp. 54, 129) states that the gabbros of the Bergen–Jotun group are also older than the labradorite rocks and remarks that this fact, being in disharmony with Bowen's theory of the magmatic development of rocks, cannot yet be explained in any way.

with truly crystalloblastic structure. There are eclogites in such series of crystalline schists which have been interpreted as sedimentogeneous, and the eclogitic micaschists seem to be sedimentogeneous themselves. From our experience in the other facies it would only seem probable that there should exist sedimentogeneous as well as eruptivogeneous eclogites. We must, however, bear in mind that foliation, or even an evidence of re-crystallization in an eclogite, is not a proof that the rock has formerly been a gabbro. The eclogite minerals may very well have re-crystallized in the same form.

Many occurrences regarded as metamorphic certainly need revision in this respect. This seems especially to be the case with those enclosed in eruptive gneisses. An earlier opinion, still current in the eighties of the last century, regarded the eclogites as igneous rocks, but when the theory of metamorphism was applied on the massifs of foliated "central gneiss," the eclogites enclosed in them must follow. Later they were regarded as very typical metamorphic rocks, and when the opinion turned to interpret the gneiss as igneous, now the eclogites did not follow. The students of eclogites in the subsequent period therefore had much trouble in finding out complicated explanations of the kind of metamorphism in the eclogites.

At any rate, we have, in the Norwegian eclogites, examples of primary crystallizations. There is another interesting mode of occurrence of igneous eclogite in the diamond-bearing kimberlites in South Africa and Australia. Besides diamonds and other minerals the blue ground and yellow ground contain fragments of rocks among which those of eclogite are most frequent.

There has been a considerable difference of opinion concerning the origin of the eclogite nodules. Some investigators have interpreted them as fragments of an eclogite formation in a great depth, brought up by the explosion-like eruptions of the kimberlite, while others have seen in them segregations from the kimberlite magma. As the chief argument in favour of the former opinion the fact has repeatedly been set forth that these nodules, in their mineral composition, are perfectly similar to true eclogites, and especially that they contain disthene, a mineral formerly only known from crystalline schists. It is psychologically interesting that this argument, which owes its existence only to a conservative tendency of mind, has been thought by some geologists more weighty than the following facts favouring the segregation theory: the extensive distribution and persistent characters of the nodules in the kimberlite pipes in South Africa and N. S. Wales, the non-occurrence of usual eclogite in the same regions, and, above all, the occurrence of diamonds in the nodules, even enclosed in the garnet. When the last-named fact forced R. Beck to accept the segregation theory,[12] he did not use the name eclogite but proposed a new term, griquaite, to designate these igneous aggregates.

Having found a perfect parallelism between the igneous and metamorphic rocks in all the other facies we have no difficulty in assuming an igneous eclogite and may regard the segregation theory as definitely proven.

In this paper I have not used the term griquaite for the igneous eclogites, though many reasons would make it desirable to have different designations for the two kinds of rocks. The term eclogite, however, has old traditions as a name of an igneous rock, and it may happen that a greater part of the eclogites will be once more regarded as igneous rocks. Provisionally I have used the old name commonly for all the eclogites. . . .

The crystallization temperatures of the eclogite rocks will be raised with the pressure. Eclogites occupy a volume about 15 percent smaller than that of corresponding gabbros, and the magma probably has a still larger volume. The volume of jadeitite (0.300; sp. gr. = 3.33) is as much as 22 percent smaller than that of the corresponding molecular mixture of albite and nephelite (sp. vol. = 0.383; sp. gr. = 2.61). When it has formerly been generally assumed, in physico-chemical petrology, that pressure has little influence on transformation points, this was only because such large changes in volume were not considered.

The critical minerals of the eclogite facies cannot be obtained from melts under atmospheric pressure, but the facts now set forth concerning the genesis of the eclogite would seem to evidence that they are stable in contact with magmas under very high pressures.

When brought upwards nearer the earth's surface, the eclogite-minerals become unstable. We actually find traces of alteration, either in the hornfels, the amphibolite, or in the greenschist facies. Considering the slow rate of gradual denudation by which deep-seated rocks generally have been brought up to the earth's surface, it would seem wonderful that such unstable things have surpassed the depth-zone of the amphibolite, so dangerous for their existence, as there the temperature was still high enough to make the velocity of transformations considerable. This wonderment leads us to a very interesting statement.

Unstable things are made lasting by means of quenching. Now we shall find that nature, wherever eclogites occur, has practiced a kind of quenching. The most effective method was that in the case of the

---

[12] R. Beck, "Untersuchungen über einige südafrikanische Diamantlagerstätten," *Z. dt. geol. Ges. 59* (1907), 275.

diamond-bearing pipes, where the eclogite nodules were thrown up to the earth's surface by violent explosions.

Other eclogites occur in Norway, Scotland, Erzgebirge, Fichtelgebirge and certain other districts in the Hercynian zone, in the Alps, Apennines, in Greece, and in West-American Cordillera (California). Jadeitites are known from Burmah, Tibet (?), Turkistan, Mexico (?) and the Alps. All the localities are in post-Cambrian folding-zones where deep-seated portions of the earth's crust have been brought up to high levels by orogenetic and isostatic movements and thereby been exposed to a quick denudation. This can be called a geological quenching.

Eclogites are not known from the Archaean areas of Finland, Sweden, or Northern America, or from other similar extensive old resistant shields. This is surprising, as it is just here that we have the deepest portions of the earth's crust laid bare. The relations will, however, be easily understood when we realize that here extensive continental areas have been elevated and subjected to denudation during enormous periods of time. Eclogites, if they ever existed there, could be converted into amphibolites. The garnet-amphibolites might be relict eclogites, but as they invariably bear almanditic garnet, it seems that more magnesian garnets are not likely to be preserved as relics, and we have no traces left of them.

From what was said above concerning the raise of the melting temperature of eclogites under pressure it would seem likely that there exists a zone in the deepest parts of the earth's crust where gabbroid material exists stable in the form of eclogite, at temperatures under which a gabbro would melt if the pressure were reduced. . . .

The melting point of a solid is raised by increasing pressure in direct proportion to the absolute temperature and the diminuation of the volume in melting, and in opposite proportion to the heat of fusion. If the melting points and the latent heats of the eclogite minerals were known, it would be possible with some approximation to calculate the pressures corresponding with various temperatures, under which the eclogite will just be retained in a solid form. It would be desirable, and perhaps it would not be impossible, to solve this problem experimentally. Perhaps the pure jadeite, having such a great change of volume by melting, could be most conveniently investigated.

So far, the theory of the eclogite-zone is merely a plan for future investigation. But it is very suggestive of further conclusions: if the critical minerals of the eclogite facies are such that they arrive at the earth's surface only under especially favourable conditions without being changed, there might very likely exist other high-pressure forms of material that never have been exposed because they are too quickly changeable when the pressure is reduced.

There are certain facts pointing towards the hypothesis that such minerals may exist. We have the isomorphic series of the jadeite minerals in which the pseudojadeite plays an important role. This is a silicate high in lime and alumina. Perhaps silicates still richer in lime, and perhaps even a pure soda-lime-pyroxene, having the same metal ratio as the labradorite feldspar, may exist as solids in great depths. If such a silicate could be spoken of as really existing, the problem of the labradorite-rocks would be much simplified.

The hypothesis under consideration is rich in suggestions concerning the state of the zones beneath the earth's crust. But it is better to wait until experimental research has thrown more light on these problems.

## ON THE PRINCIPLES OF METAMORPHIC DIFFERENTIATION *

### Introduction

Every student of metamorphic rocks is frequently confronted with the question: Is the composition of a rock the same as it was before the metamorphism, or has it been changed? In many cases considerable changes of rocks and migration of substances in them are well in evidence. Those changes listed under the term metasomatism have been studied from the physicochemical viewpoint[1] and many of them are now rather well understood. But in other cases of metasomatism as well as of other apparent metamorphic changes not yet specially classified the processes which have been at work and the laws by which these processes were controlled are still entirely unexplained. Often it is not at all possible to tell whether the composition of a metamorphic rock has been changed or not. All this creates a feeling of uncertainty in geological work, especially in the study of the Archaean.

During an attempt to interpret some main lines of the record of the Archaean rocks (Eskola[2]) I was therefore led to ask whether it might not be possible to outline some general physicochemical principles which would help towards an understanding of the changes of the composition, or the probable direction of such changes, in any particular case of rock metamorphism.

The sedimentary differentiation effected by the exogeneous geological

---

* From *Bulletin de la Commission Geologique de Finlande*, no. 97 (1932), 68–77.

[1] V. M. Goldschmitt, "On the metasomatic processes in silicate rocks," *Econ. Geol. 17* (1922), 105–123.

[2] P. E. Eskola, "Conditions during the oldest geological times as indicated by the Archean rocks," *Ann. Acad. Sci. Fennicae 36*, no. 4 (1932).

processes, such as weathering, transportation of materials, and sedimentation, is one of the chief subjects of geology and is fairly well understood. The study of magmatic differentiation has not yet reached the same advanced stage, but at least the general principles underlying the possible ways of this differentiation have been explained. Turning to the third great class of petrogenetic processes, listed under metamorphism, it may seem striking that a term like *metamorphic differentiation* is hardly to be found in geological literature.

Some consideration of phenomena known to every geologist who has worked in areas of highly metamorphic rocks, however, will be sufficient to convince one of the existence of processes to which this conception is applicable. As the first examples I shall mention a few among the most commonly known mixed rocks apparently differentiated by metamorphic processes: sheared mica-schist with numerous quartz veins; veined gneiss of the type called by Holmquist venite; garnetiferous gneiss, or mica-schist, in which the garnet may be richly concentrated in certain lenticular or band-shaped bodies. In some cases similar rock mixtures may have formed by means of an injection with granitic magma, but in other cases the process clearly belongs to the domain of metamorphism. No considerable change of composition has necessarily taken place in the above cases, only an internal differentiation. As a more uncommon but very extreme example may be mentioned banded chloromelanite eclogite alternating with mica-schist and being most probably of a sedimentary origin. Some of the bands, or schliers, of the eclogitic rock may consist almost entirely of garnet, and others entirely of chloromelanite, or jadeite. Thus the metamorphic differentiation may have led to the forming of chloromelanitites or jadeitites which are extremely alkaline rocks, but of a nature quite different from any usual alkaline igneous rock.

The reason why the conception of metamorphic differentiation was not used earlier was apparently because of several concomitant circumstances, such as the following: the metamorphic differentiation has rarely resulted in the forming of well-characterized rock masses of large dimensions; those most extremely differentiated though small bodies, which represent the most striking instances of metamorphic differentiation, are often difficult to interpret as to their mode of origin; changes of composition due to external transfer of substances into or from the rock masses frequently obscure true internal metamorphic differentiation; the metamorphic processes also exhibit the opposite tendency towards a homogenization of composite masses,[1] and the metamorphic processes generally are complicated and as yet little understood. One of the most striking instances of metamorphic differentiation is the forming of concretions. Although this phenomenon belongs most characteristically to the domain of metamorphism, this fact is, however, mostly forgotten because it takes place in little altered sediments.

### THE CLASSIFICATION OF METAMORPHIC CHANGES OF COMPOSITION

Changes of the composition of rocks may have occurred in some of the following ways:

1) Differentiation within a rock mass, due to
   a) the growth of crystals or aggregates of crystals (the concretion principle),
   b) the concentration of the least soluble substances (the principle of enrichment in the stablest constituents), or
   c) the extraction and redeposition of the most soluble substances (the solution principle);
2) Transfer of substances into and from a rock mass, effecting
   a) addition,
   b) metasomatism, or
   c) extraction of substances.

The two chief kinds of changes here distinguished are usually intimately connected, as transport of substances arouses internal differentiation as well. Differentiation in a broader sense, meaning the forming of new kinds of rocks and mineral deposits in general, is moreover the most outstanding feature of all metamorphic changes of composition.

All metamorphic changes involving crystallization of minerals are controlled by the law of mass action.[1] The migration of pore solutions is presupposed to account for the addition and extraction of substances. The pore solutions must move in the rock, or at least those substances which participate in the chemical reactions must do so, by means of diffusion or otherwise. From the energetic viewpoint, this migration of substances may be caused either by exogeneous, or by endogeneous agencies. The migration is exogeneous, when a rock-mass is soaked through by liquids pressed into the rock by external forces, such as (1) intrusive magmatic solutions, (2) solutions moved by crustal deformations, or (3) ground-water currents. The migration is endogeneous, if it is due only to a concentration gradient which results from the reactions themselves. The latter case is best illustrated by the growth of an individual crystal. The concentration of the crystallizing substances within a sphere around it decreases, and more substance moves by means of diffusion towards the crystal. Related to this is the forming of reaction zones, or reaction walls, at the contacts between two non-compatible mineral masses. The forming of walls of some thickness implies a certain amount of diffusion, and the thickness is a measure of the extent of this diffusion.

The exogeneous changes largely cover the changes due to the transfer of substances into and from the rock mass, headed under (2) in the above classification. Even differentiation within an originally homogeneous rock mass may, however, be caused only by exogeneous agencies, without any interchange of substances derived from the outside, for example, when crustal movements effect an internal transfer of substances along joint planes or shearing zones. Related to this is the case when a sheared rock mass during crustal movements is soaked with water which gives rise to a recrystallization and internal transfer along its main paths in the rock (case 1 c).

Addition, extraction, and metasomatic interchanges are mostly intimately connected with each other. In a rock impregnated with pyrites the elements of the latter have been added in solutions which caused a metasomatic replacement (e.g. silicification, sericitization, or magnesia metasomatism) of the invaded rock. In most cases of injection with granitic magmas the injected rocks have also been altered metasomatically.

The general principles and the classification of metasomatism will not be discussed in this paper. Some aspects of the problems of metasomatism, however, will be touched upon in connection with internal differentiation.

### THE CONCRETION PRINCIPLE

The ideal example of metamorphic differentiation by the concretion principle is seen in the forming of an individual crystal. Look at a porphyroblast of almandite, staurolite, or cordierite, in a mica-schist or gneiss! Where such crystals have grown as large as 30 cm long, like the crystals of cordierite on Kurksaari in the Orijärvi field, they may well be spoken of as small differentiated masses in the rock, and smaller crystals are of course not materially different. Big crystals grow at the expense of their smaller neighbours according to the general principle of the decrease of free energy. The process involves a diffusion of substance towards the growing crystal, and its concentration is therefore diminished within a sphere around the crystal, as strikingly illustrated, for example, by crystals of almandite surrounded by a bleached zone in the rock. This is the sphere deprived of all its iron, which has wandered into the garnet.

Now an aggregate of crystals may under certain conditions act like an individual crystal, behaving as though it exerted an attraction to the substances of which it is composed. We may take as a first example a calcareous concretion in silt, such as the Imatra stones.[2] Assuming them to be epigenetic concretions, the crystallization of calcite in them is understood to be due to a reduced solubility at their surface.

The same seems to be true of many phosphate, marcasite, or flint concretions. The mechanism of the precipitating action is not always easily understood, but the general principle seems to be the same as in the case of a growing individual crystal.

The forming of concretions is most strikingly demonstrated in porous sediments, but it apparently occurs also in siliceous rocks at the metamorphism. Several kinds of "spots," or aggregates of mineral grains, may be referred to this class. Mostly, however, individual crystals form instead of aggregates in metamorphic rocks.

The occurrence of phenomena to which the concretion principle is applicable makes it probable that, in general, chemical differences between two rocks which meet one another along a contact surface will become more accentuated by the metamorphism. Plenty of examples of this are seen in the highly metamorphosed Archaean rocks whose metamorphism approaches palingenesis. Where, for instance, a basaltic dike has once cut a granite and both have become metamorphosed, the basalt into an amphibolite and the granite into a gneiss, it is not unusual to find a lighter contact zone in the gneiss.

Apparent as the accentuation of chemical differences may be, the differentiation thus performed is at any rate rather limited, and no great changes in the composition of the primarily different rock bodies can be inferred.

In the case of varved schists, originally varved sediments, the concretion principle would imply the accentuation of the varve structure by metamorphism. The more siliceous, coarser, and lighter (sandy) layers would have become still richer in quartz, just as flint concretions in some Archaean shales have developed into pure white quartz nodules. The more aluminous, finer-grained, and darker (clayey) layers, again, would have been enriched in aluminous minerals. Such an enrichment is in fact apparent in the Ladogian varved schists of Eastern Finland in the form of porphyroblasts of staurolite, andalusite, or cordierite, developed along the upper margin of the darker layers.[2] Usually the porphyroblasts have been later pseudomorphosed into chlorite and micas, a change which may be referred to as an instance of the principle of enrichment in the stablest constituent discussed below.

Metamorphic differentiation of this kind seems to be most notable in rather highly metamorphosed schists. So far we have no means of estimating its results quantitatively, but they do not seem to be great.

## THE PRINCIPLE OF ENRICHMENT IN
## THE STABLEST CONSTITUENTS

The study of metamorphic rocks reveals the occurrence of still another kind of differentiation which cannot be referred to the concretion principle but may well be deduced from physicochemical considerations. When a new set of mineral constituents comes into existence by recrystallization, and among the newly formed minerals is one whose solubility in the pore liquid is exceptionally small, it will crystallize out, and the pore liquid becomes impoverished in the compounds of this mineral. Solutions percolating the rock mass will bring more of these compounds from adjacent layers, especially from those in which that particular mineral cannot form, being incompatible with the assemblages of minerals. Thus a rock may become enriched even by a mineral whose compounds are not originally present in large amounts. The changes following this principle may therefore be expected to act either in the same direction or in a direction opposite to that of the concretion principle.

An example of this principle was encountered above in the pseudomorphs of micas and chlorite after andalusite, staurolite, or cordierite. It means an addition of potash which is most probably derived from the close vicinity and from adjacent layers in the same rock mass.

More generally and on a large scale this metamorphic differentiation has been inferred by Väyrynen[3] in the case of highly aluminous sedimentogeneous schists which have been changed into sericite schists by an addition of potash during the metamorphism. They have originally contained excessive alumina present in the form of kaolinite. From the viewpoint of the aluminous layer such a change is an instance of metasomatism, as potash must be carried to it from outside sources, and it may either have been expelled from crystallizing intrusive magmas or simply been carried in those solutions which, slowly moving, generally exist in the rocks. But, in a complex including rock masses of different composition, it is quite possible and very probable that the change has taken place under static conditions by means of diffusion in the pore solutions due to the concentration gradient. A necessary condition is that potash is originally present in a minimum concentration[1] to induce the crystallization of sericite. Hereby the potash concentration decreases below that in the adjacent layers and migrates from these to the place of deposition. Considering the nonhomoge-

[3] Heikki Väyrynen, "Über den Chemismus der finnischen Kaolinvorkommen verglichen mit Verwitterungssedimenten." *Bull. Comm. Geol. Finlande* no. 87 (1929).

neous complex as a whole, the differentiation is thus endogeneous in the sense defined above.

A metamorphic differentiation of this kind is probably rather common, although it is difficult to distinguish it from metasomatism effected by addition of substances from intrusive magmas or from solutions moved under kinetic conditions. The concentration of almandite in schlieric portions of some mica-schists and paragneisses may probably be referred to this group of phenomena.

The same would seem to be true of the garnet schliers as well as of the chloromelanitite or jadeitite bands in the eclogitic rocks mentioned above.

I will abstain from mentioning further examples of rocks to which this principle might be applicable, as they have not yet been studied well enough from the present viewpoint. I wish, however, briefly to mention in this connection a hypothesis which has played an important rôle in the Archaean geology of Fennoscandia, viz., the hypothesis of magnesia metasomatism. A more detailed discussion and references to the literature may be found in my recent paper.[2]

Stated briefly, the fact underlying this hypothesis is the widespread though on the whole sporadic distribution of cordierite-anthophyllite rocks, cordierite- and anthophyllite-bearing quartzites (so-called ore-quartzites) and cordierite mica-schists, commonly associated with sulphide ores, in the leptite areas. The hypothesis is that these magnesia-rich rocks are products of a metasomatism which has resulted in a replacement of the feldspars by magnesium silicate, silica, and sulphides, carried from granitic magmas. As Tilley and Flett have pointed out, it is somewhat difficult to believe that the residual liquid of granitic magma could contain any considerable amounts of magnesia. I have therefore posed the question whether the transfer of magnesia into the leptitic rock could not be accounted for by applying the principle of enrichment in the least soluble constituents, besides a metasomatism caused by an addition of silica, sulphides, and volatiles. The large amounts of solutions soaking into the leptites would, of course, also carry some amounts of magnesia which, due to the poor solubility of magnesium metasilicate, could replace the alkalies and lime of the feldspars and crystallize as anthophyllite and cordierite, while the iron content of the solutions was mainly deposited in the sulphides. This explanation seems to offer the most probable solution of the problem of magnesia metasomatism.

The interesting results of Magnusson[4] concerning the relations be-

[4] Nils H. Magnusson, "Langbans malmtrakt," *Sveriges Geol. Undersökn.* [Ca] no. 23 (1930).

166

tween the leptites and skarn masses in the Långban ore field in Sweden seem further to illustrate the above conclusion. Next to the leptite towards the skarn there is a zone of cordierite- and andalusite-bearing transitional rock, occasionally containing gedrite, followed by a "sköl" containing considerable mica and passing over into the skarn composed of lime, iron, and magnesia silicates. Alkalies, chiefly potash, have been carried from the transitional rock towards the skarn and been deposited in the sköl as micas, while magnesia and iron oxides have migrated in the opposite direction and been deposited in the transitional rock. The migration and interchange of materials is explained by Magnusson as a result of a regional metamorphism or thermometamorphism. He also explains most of the skarn masses in the same way, as products of interaction between existing carbonate and silicate rocks, and therefore calls them "reaction skarns."

It might seem strange that magnesia has moved farther into the leptite from the skarn than lime, as lime silicates are believed to be more soluble. The principle of the control of the least soluble minerals removes the difficulty.

This principle is probably applicable in numerous cases of metasomatic replacements that have occurred by the interaction of the substances of existing rocks at their contacts.

### The Solution Principle

I have recently advanced the idea that granitic magma may form by means of a differential fusion of silicate rocks in the deep zones of the earth's crust.[5] Especially in the geosynclinal zones during orogenic periods the magma thus originating can be mobilized and collected to form intrusive masses, but remains of it are left forming veins in the passages along which the granitic residual solutions had moved. All this is fairly well illustrated by the veined gneisses. The veins are commonly composed of pegmatite-like quartz-feldspar-mica mixtures, and their materials may have moved longer or shorter distances, but in many wide-veined gneiss areas there is ample evidence that the veins have been derived from the country-rock.[6] The silicate solutions from which the veins have crystallized, though relatively water-rich, may well be spoken of as magma, and the process as palingenesis, though not exactly in the sense originally defined by Sederholm.[7] But the proc-

[5] P. E. Eskola, "On the origin of granitic magmas," *Mineral. Petrog. Mitt. 42,* no. 5/6 (1932), 455–481. [See pp. 169–177 of this volume.]

[6] P. J. Holmquist, "Typen und Nomenklatur der Adergesteine." *Geol. Fören. Stockholm Förh. 43* (1921).

[7] J. J. Sederholm, "Om granit och gneis," *Bull. Comm. Geol. Finlande* no. 23 (1907).

ess also tallies with all the characteristics commonly associated with the conception of metamorphism, especially if its extreme nature is emphasized by the prefix ultra-, as Holmquist has done. Thus the forming of venites exhibits an extreme case of metamorphic differentiation. As probably all the processes controlled by the solution principle, it is exogeneous, the solutions having been mobilized mainly by orogenic forces.

It has often been assumed that the crystallization relations of silicate solutions would be greatly modified by the presence of water. While experimental studies are not yet able to illustrate this question, we are referred to the study of natural rocks for information. As to the composition, the veins of the venites belong to the granites, and there is no, at least no great, effect of water to be seen.

How is the composition of the residual solutions modified on further cooling and dilution? The answer to this question is to be read from the metamorphic rocks. A differentiation due to the mobilization of substances dissolved by the water circulating in the rocks is clearly recorded by the quartz veins.

In their mode of occurrence, forms, and position in the rocks, the quartz veins bear a very marked resemblance to the pegmatitic veins of the veined gneisses. Transitional types between the granitic or pegmatitic veins of the migmatites and the quartz veins also occur, the amount of quartz increasing gradually. But, remarkably enough, these transitional types are comparatively rare. On cooling, the residual granitic magma apparently becomes rapidly deprived of most of the silicates, and silica is left almost alone in solution.

In metamorphic basic rocks, such as spilites or greenschists, we find somewhat different products deposited as veins from the migrating solutions. Pegmatite-like veins in these usually consist of albite, besides calcite and quartz, and many accessory silicate minerals. In the Archæan areas where most of the masses of amphibolites and other basic rocks are small, the composition of their veins and joint-fillings is not markedly different, and quartz is the most common constituent of the veins even in ultrabasic rocks. This probably means that silica has migrated from adjacent rocks.

In acidic and intermediate rocks, silica—and in basic rocks calcium carbonate—thus prove to be the most soluble substances under the conditions of the later stages of metamorphism. The metamorphic differentiation therefore consists mainly in the migration and recrystallization of these compounds in the form of veins which, considered as rocks, are extremely differentiated, almost monomineralic.

The extraction of the most soluble compounds naturally involves a corresponding impoverishment of the residual solid rock in these substances. In the metamorphism at great depths and high temperatures, the substances thus extracted are of a granitic composition, and the remainder should therefore become relatively enriched in those compounds which were originally present in excess of this compostion. The excess of alumina in primarily clayey sediments should increase as well, as also the excess of quartz in quartzitic schists. As I have pointed out elsewhere,[5] this expectation is verified by the frequent occurrence of such extreme schists in the most highly crystalline complexes of the Archæan. In its effect this differentiation is similar to that according to the concretion principle, and both of them are probably active at the same time.

In the same way the extraction of silica during the metamorphism at lower temperatures might be expected to bring forth an impoverishment in quartz. This, however, can only rarely be verified by observation, apparently owing to the very large amounts of quartz present in all kinds of rocks.

# THE ORIGIN OF GRANITIC MAGMAS *

## INTRODUCTION

One of the most prominent features of pre-Cambrian areas is the extensive occurrence of granitic rocks. Furthermore a glance at a geological map of Fennoscandia or any other geologically well explored area shows that granites are more common in the older pre-Cambrian formations than in its younger divisions. In its most ancient portions, like the so called granite gneiss region of Eastern Fennoscandia, they are almost universal. We know, furthermore, that granites in all mountain zones are generally found to be the more extensively developed the deeper the mountains have been eroded. Therefore probably all the students of old mountain chains and pre-Cambrian areas will agree . . . that granites have become more and more common as erosion has exposed deeper horizontal sections of the earth's crust.

On the other hand, we know from the results of geophysics that the earth globe, on the whole, is gravitatively stratified, its inner core being built up of comparatively heavy materials surrounded by successively lighter spheres. The study of the earth's interior has led to the well-known conceptions of a metal core, a transitional sphere, a basic silicate

*From *Mineralogische und Petrographische Mitteilungen* (Leipzig) *42*, pts. 5/6 (1932), 455–481.

sphere, or the sima sphere, and a more acidic, or granitic, silicate shell, the sial. It is not necessary here to discuss the geophysical (chiefly seismological) or geochemical data upon which these conceptions have been based. I only wish to point out that some petrological facts are also not understandable unless we assume the existence of a basic silicate sphere under the granitic shell. Such a fact is the occurrence of plateau basalts erupted as immense masses from the depths under the earth's crust. Being different from all other igneous rocks in so far as they are not differentiated in the same sense as other rocks, the plateau basalts would seem to be derived immediately from the sima sphere and thus afford us samples of the sima material.

We have thus two seemingly contradictory facts which must be accounted for by every theory of the origin of granites, namely, the downwardly increasing amounts of granites in the earth's crust, and the downward increase of basicity in the globe. These contradictions would seem irreconcilable to the pre-Cambrian geologists. Being confident of their experience as to the downward increase of granites they might doubt the existence of the sima. Nobody has ever seen the sima, although it should be exposed somewhere, if, as the geophysicists argue, the sial sphere is no more than about 50 kilometres thick, or even thinner, perhaps only 25 kilometres, while it seems probable that the total amount of erosion in many parts of old mountain chains, for example, in the Archaean of Fennoscandia, may exceed 50 kilometres.

While pondering possible ways of reconciling this contradiction in the course of a few recent years, I have become more and more impressed with the idea that granitic magmas must have been formed mainly in connection with orogenic movements by the pressing out or squeezing of the lowest melting materials, partly from more basic rocks not yet entirely solidified and partly from rocks partially re-fused in the deep regions of the geosynclines. . . .

.　　.　　.　　.　　.

. . . Among the oldest rocks there are quite large masses of volcanic rocks, originally basalts, now metabasalts, or amphibolites. This means that in those early times as well as later basaltic magma existed or was produced in or immediately below the lithosphere to feed the large-scale basalt eruptions. Furthermore we must assume that the crystalline-liquid phase boundary can never have been anything like a definite surface, but rather was a thick intermediate zone. This must be so, because the melting temperature of a rock is no definite point but an interval of an amplitude of several hundred degrees (see below).

## The Importance of Squeezing in Differentiation

Taking for granted that the primary mode of origin of granites was crystallization differentiation, there remains the question whether the separation of the crystallized and liquid portions was mainly effected by a sinking down of the earliest crystals or by a squeezing of the residual magma from a crystal mesh. Differentiation by crystal settling has often been assumed to play the most important rôle, although within recent years even some of the cases which had been regarded as classical examples of gravitative adjustment are now explained in other ways, as for instance the Sudbury and Bushveld masses and Tertiary granites of Britain which were recently otherwise explained by *Holmes*.[1]

Furthermore, gravitative adjustment in composite igneous masses is generally illustrated in laccolithic, or sheet-shaped, bodies whose intrusion was not directly connected with mountain folding or overthrust on a big scale, while it is far more rarely, if at all, to be observed in overthrust phacoliths and still less so in the so-called batholithic bodies which represent the commonest kind of granitic intrusions in ancient mountain zones, the true home of granites.

Most striking is the lack of evidence of crystal settling in the Archaean formations which may generally be referred to as roots of ancient mountain chains. Neither from the inconspicuous vertical sections existing in the low Archaean countries nor from the spatial relations which may be deduced from geological maps or stereograms has there ever been found any evidence of settling on the floors of magma chambers. On the contrary, as mentioned at the beginning, the relations on a large scale prove very conclusively that granites, not basic rocks, increase in amount downwards. Examination of the contacts between basic rocks and granites showing cognate relations one to the other, reveals a picture of acid magma soaked out from crystalline rocks, rather than that of crystals accumulated on the floor of a liquid chamber.

A gravitative control has nevertheless been in operation: the granitic magma, being lighter than the surrounding rocks, had a tendency to rise. In the Archaean granite masses the traces of movements, i.e. the parallel and linear textures, are mostly directed upwards, proving that the magma has moved in that direction. In the surrounding schistose rocks the folding axes in the nearest vicinity of granite masses are usually steeply inclined or nearly vertical, the granites occupying the axial culminations. This mode of intrusion has lead Wegmann to compare the intrusive granite masses with salt domes, or diapires.

[1] A. Holmes, "The problem of the association of acid and basic rocks in central complexes," *Geol. Mag. 68* (1931), 241–255.

In other cases, as in the Variscan granites of Central Europe and also in the case of the pre-Cambrian rapakivi masses of Fennoscandia, the movement has been horizontal, apparently guided by existing joints. The magma itself was passive and was set in motion by different forces the most important ones of which were connected with orogenesis, that great group of earth movements whose innermost cause is still so little understood. Another important factor is gravitation, which seems to operate by making liquids move rather than causing crystals to sink or rise. This may generally depend upon the fact that the greater part of the masses moving by orogenesis are solid rather than liquid.

.    .    .    .    .

### The Origin of Granitic Magmas through Differentiation in the Deep Zones of the Lithosphere During Orogenesis

Let us suppose that the upper part of the sima sphere is crystallized (the lithosphere) and the lower part of it liquid (the magma sphere). There must be a transition zone between the two spheres in which an interstitial liquid portion (pore solution) gradually increases in amount and becomes more and more concentrated with silica and silicates until, at a certain depth and sufficiently high temperature, the crystals disappear and the whole consists of isotropic viscous magma. We do not know where and in which sphere this boundary would be encountered. The existence of such a magma-like pore solution in the deeper parts of the lithosphere would, however, seem granted, even if the earth's crystalline shell were thick enouth to continue downwards to the peridotitic sphere, regardless of whether the deepest parts of the lithosphere consist of gabbro or eclogite facies. The complete recrystallization of the metamorphic rocks of the deep zones and the thorough metasomatic alterations that we know occur, clearly tell about solutions percolating through the rock masses.

Basaltic lavas, according to experimental data, begin to crystallize at about 1300° whereas the last granitic residual magma crystallizes somewhere around 600°. From the geothermic gradient, the transitional zone containing both crystals and magma should therefore be more than 23 kilometres thick, should the phase boundary be within the basaltic sphere. Supposing that the plateau basalt lavas were poured off from the uppermost part of the magma sphere without crystals, the composition of the transition zone would grade from that of the plateau basalts to that of some intermediate igneous rock.

Now, if a rock containing such a pore solution in the deep zones of the lithosphere were dragged along by orogenic movements and rolled out (ausgewalzt) in a manner of which there are illustrations in all mountain zones and in the Archaean areas, there certainly would occur a squeezing out of a residual magma, just as water may be squeezed out from a moist sponge. The composition of that residual magma would vary according to the temperature, but it would always be more closely related to granites than the material. Its amount would increase as the temperature rises, either by the geothermic gradient when the rocks are pressed down into greater depth, or by mechanical or chemical sources of heat. The acid magma thus produced could be moved along shearing planes or zones of weakness in the rock, and form migmatites in other places, or it could be collected into larger magma basins. Being lighter than the surrounding rocks, the magma, kept in motion by the orogenic pressure, would always tend to rise, in other words, to intrude into the upper parts of the earth's crust. The sial crust therefore should have grown gradually thicker during the geologic periods. On its way upwards, coming to cooler regions, the magma would partly crystallize, and the residual magma would be continually driven through the crystalline masses, changing in composition until it reached the composition of typical granitic magmas.

From the geologists present when I read the first manuscript of this paper for the "Réunion" mentioned above, came no opposition to the thesis of the origin of granitic magmas by a differential re-fusion of older rocks, whereas the suggestion of granitic magmas derived from crystalline sima materials under orogenic movements aroused some objections. To Professor A. Holmes it seemed improbable that granites could have been derived from a basaltic material so poor in those chemical elements that constitute the rarer minerals of the granites. This statement gives me a reason to add a few remarks. It is quite true that basalts—and the sima, if it has the same composition as the basalts—contain only small quantities of the granitic elements, yet they contain enough to form a certain amount of low-melting magma which can be squeezed out if the rock is powerfully rolled out. Small as the amount of this portion is, we must assume that the amount of sima under the sial is so much greater, and the sima masses mobilized in every geosyncline during an orogenic cycle should be large enough to produce granites on a big scale. And even basic rocks contain small amounts of the rarer elements usually concentrated in granites, for example, boron or zirconium.

Furthermore, granites could not be formed by re-fusion of older material before the existence of something to be re-fused. In other words, the earliest and most primary method of formation of granites must have been differentiation of a primary non-differentiated silicate mantle, an original sima, which was somewhat more acid than the plateau basalts at present. The first differentiation probably was connected with crustal movements just as much as differentiation in later times was.

Finally, as pointed out above, we do not know whether the composition of the earth's crust at its boundary against the magma zone would be at all that of the plateau basalts, which is pictured as a representative of the sima only because we know of nothing else from autopsy. According to a hypothesis for which I have brought evidence earlier and which has been accepted by many petrologists, among others by Holmes, silicates under the high pressure in the lower parts of the earth's crust probably exist in the eclogite facies. I have pointed out also that there may possibly exist still other high-pressure minerals which are less enduring than the eclogite minerals and therefore become entirely changed with no traces left when brought up to the surface. The plateau basalt lava erupted would be re-fused eclogite.

The eclogite hypothesis has not, however, been considered at all in this connection. The only assumption upon which the present theory has been based is that the increase of temperature in the earth's crust, indicated by the geothermic gradient, is sufficient at a certain depth to exceed the crystallization temperature of the low-crystallizing granitic magmas. This seems a reasonably safe assumption notwithstanding what the minerals may be. . . .

·    ·    ·    ·    ·

### The Origin of Granitic Magmas through Differential Anatexis during Orogenesis

Many geologists have looked for an explanation of the origin of the granites in the assumption of a re-fusion of acid sedimentogeneous rocks like mica-schists, sandstones, or para-gneisses, or other, older rocks. But this hypothesis has been discredited because it was not consistent with what we know nowadays about the physical chemistry of rocks. In many cases the re-fusion temperature would be very much higher than the original crystallization temperature of an igneous rock. We may only remember that quartz, when once crystallized, is a refractory mineral, although it may crystallize from hydrothermal solutions at low temperatures. In the same way the granites or granitic pegmatites, although they melt at lower temperatures than basalts, apparently cannot be brought into re-fusion at the same temperature at which they had originally crystallized. The same is the case with all those mineral associations which have originated by crystallization from diluted aqueous, hydrothermal, or pneumatolytic solutions. This different behaviour of crystallization and re-melting is due to the loss of volatile substances.

Furthermore, as especially emphasized by Bowen, the excessive heat necessary for the re-fusion of large rock masses would not generally be available in the earth's crust.

There can, however, hardly be any objection against the assumption of a partial re-fusion of rocks. The amount of water required to lower sufficiently the re-fusion temperature is present in most rocks, more especially in sediments and weathered volcanics, but also in the deep-seated rocks. A partial re-fusion should take place as soon as the temperature rises above that point at which the last residual magma crystallized. There would be formed a liquid portion which would be identical in composition with the last crystallizing part of a magma of the composition of the orginal rock, plus some ichor. It would be more or less like a granitic magma. Crystallization and re-fusion are reversible phenomena so long as the melt once formed is not removed. Granitic magmas therefore may originate by a differential re-fusion or anatexis of any silicate rocks containing the components of a granite.

This conclusion has far-reaching consequences for the development of the geosynclinal zones: rocks formed on the earth's surface are folded down into great depths where temperature is high enough to give rise to a certain amount of palingenic magma in the interstices of the mineral grains. Being lighter than the rock in whose pores it is at first enclosed, this melt portion tends to rise, and actually does so, as soon as the orogenic movements mobilize it. The potash-rich magmatic solutions soak through the overlying rock-masses and, in accordance with the laws of mass-action, alter them metasomatically. This is the granitization. The ichor squeezed out in some place seeks its way along the shearing planes and other planes of small resistance. It may move shorter or longer distances. There may be formed veined gneisses and other kinds of migmatites so widely spread in the Archaean, or they may concentrate into larger basins giving rise to masses of comparatively pure granites. The source of the ichors that have given rise to the widespread Hangö granite of southern Finland may be largely looked for in a partial re-fusion of leptitic rocks once formed as sediments and pyroclastics on the earth's surface and later pressed down into the roots of the Svecofennides.

As pointed out above, the idea that granitic magmas may originate by re-fusion of older rocks is by no means new and, at present, perhaps most geologists, among them more especially those who have themselves worked in pre-Cambrian areas or in ancient mountain zones, are adherents to such views. Far less clearly seen, on the other hand, is that the re-fusion of older rocks must have been only partial and that, in general, only a small portion of the older rock-mass can have been re-fused, perhaps with the exception of some rather exceptional cases where older granites having the composition of the lowest-melting silicate mixtures have been remelted entirely.

Both differentiation (preferably by means of squeezing out from partly crystallized rocks) and palingenesis must have been active in the formation of the earth's outer silicate shell and its arrangement mainly according to the densities. In the most ancient geologic development, differentiation should have been the more primary and more important factor while, during later orogenic periods, palingenesis may have played a more important rôle. . . .

. . . . .

### THE "EARLIEST HISTORY" OF THE EARTH

Most of the conclusions and statements offered in this paper presuppose that the earth was once entirely liquid. Personally I am not quite convinced that this supposition is true. If the earth was formed by accumulation of solid materials and only its inner parts heated up afterwards, palingenesis should, of course, have been the primary, and through the ages the most important, method of producing magmas. Otherwise the above conclusions would not necessarily be modified in any essential features.

The literature of the last few years is rich in theories concerning the origin of the earth, mostly proposed by geophysicists or astrophysicists. They do not seem to have added much solid knowledge that is of interest to the geologist. Geologic history with its 1600 millions of years is only the last part of the earth's much longer history as a planet. During the earliest times of which the Archaean formations bear witness the physical conditions seem to have been much the same as today. Of certain interest in connection with the granite problems is, however, the apparently wide distribution in the Archaean of acid supracrustal rocks, the leptites, which from many indications are connected with hypabyssal and abyssal granitic rocks by gradual transitions. Is this an indication of a thinner crust?

One consequence of the existence of a thinner crust upon a more mobile magma sphere would be that the Archaean mountain ranges should have been much lower and the mountain roots shallower than at present. This may be a point worth considering for the students of the Archaean.

SUMMARY

The gravitative stratification of the outer crust of the earth has probably come into existence mainly by crystallization differentiation and squeezing out of the residual magma on the one hand, and partial refusion and squeezing from older rocks on the other. Granitic magmas might be, to use a metaphor that may sound somewhat vulgar, characterized as the sweat that oozes out from the body of mother earth during the convulsions of orogeny. The sial crust has thus grown gradually thicker during the geological ages and is still growing.

MEAD  Warren Judson Mead (1883–1960), American engineering geologist, received his baccalaureate degree in 1906 and his doctorate in 1926 from the University of Wisconsin. In the meantime he had been a member of the faculty there, attaining the rank of professor in 1916, and had engaged in various field studies for the U. S. Geological Survey, the E. J. Longyear Company, the Panama Canal Commission, and other organizations concerned with geological problems encountered in engineering projects. He left Wisconsin in 1934 to become Professor of Geology and Chairman of the Department of Geology in the Massachusetts Institute of Technology, where he continued his teaching career until retirement as Professor Emeritus in 1954. During this time he frequently served as consultant to the U. S. Army Corps of Engineers and various private corporations, generally with regard to proposed dam and tunnel sites. He was a leader among American geologists in the trend toward quantitative rather than merely qualitative treatment of geological problems.

## THE GEOLOGIC ROLE OF DILATANCY *

Hard, spherical grains, such as shot, shaken down in a container, tend to arrange in a condition of maximum-density packing. If the grains are spherical and of uniform size, each grain is in contact with twelve neighboring grains. This arrangement has a minimum of voids, 25.9 per cent. It is obviously impossible to change the shape without increasing the volume of this aggregate (assuming that the grains are not deformed), as any differential movement between the grains involves a change in the system of packing, which of necessity requires increase of voids and consequently of volume. . . .

. . . . . .

*From *Journal of Geology 33* (1925), 685–698.

## Dilatancy in the Deformation of Solid Rocks

It is convenient to refer to the hard grains as the solid phase and to the material between the grains as the fluid phase. Using these terms, then, the experimental work seems to demonstrate two general principles. (1) When the fluid phase is sufficient only to fill the voids with the grains in a condition of maximum-density packing, deformation of the mass requires increase in volume. (2) When the available fluid phase is sufficient to fill the voids with the grains arranged in minimum-density packing, the mass may be deformed to any extent without increase in volume.

The writer believes that this conception can safely and profitably be carried over to a consideration of the mechanics of deformation of the solid rocks. Rocks in general may be regarded as granular aggregates. To the extent that they are porous, the pores represent the volume of a fluid phase, but the amount of fluid phase is, with the exception of a few special cases, too small to play much part in determining the manner of deformation. A sandstone, if cemented sufficiently to merit the term, has less porosity than sand. The small proportion of a fluid phase causes all solid rocks at or near the surface to yield to deformation by fracture, with increase in volume. This fracturing of rocks clearly involves dilatation, and the net volume of the fractured mass has been increased by the total volume of the openings produced.

That the deformation of brittle materials involves an increase in volume *prior* to their failure has been generally recognized. Bucher[1] has discussed this matter in a consideration of the mechanical interpretation of joints, and quotes Chwolson, who gives a formula connecting the modulus of volume increase with Young's modulus and Poisson's ratio. He also quotes the work of Kahlbaum and Seidler, and of Lea and Thomas, as giving experimental evidence for increase in volume accompanying deformation under one-sided compression. That this increase in volume occasioned by deformative stresses imparts a greatly increased rigidity to the rock when under great containing pressures appears very probable. Bucher offers no explanation of how this increase in volume is accomplished, whether by change in the physical nature of the material itself, or by the development of voids.

When rocks are deformed under certain conditions involving high confining pressures and a proper rate of application of deforming stresses, they yield to deformation by plastic flow with the development of schistose textures characteristic of rock flowage. This manner of yielding to deformation does not involve a general fracturing of the rock, and probably does not require increase in volume. If the analogy of

[1] Walter H. Bucher, *J. Geol. 29* (1921), 1.

the requirements for plastic deformation of an unconsolidated granular mass be carried over to the case of rock flowage of a solid rock, it is necessary to conceive of the latter as consisting of a solid phase of hard grains and of a fluid phase surrounding these grains of a sufficient amount to permit the movement of the hard grains without occasioning dilatation of the mass by their interference. The solid phase is represented by the harder, more resistant minerals. The fluid phase is represented by those constituents of the rock which are relatively mobile, as evidenced by their rearrangement to schistose structures through processes of crystallization and recrystallization. This involves a complete atomic or molecular rearrangement of that portion of the rock.

Solid rocks in general, then, may be considered as granular aggregates consisting of a solid phase and a *potentially* fluid phase, which is caused to function as a fluid phase under certain conditions of composition, pressure, temperature, and rate of deformation. . . .

·   ·   ·   ·   ·

## DILATANCY AND ORIGIN OF MAGMAS

If the conclusion be accepted that deformation of a rock by flowage requires that the rate of deformation be slow enough to permit the potentially fluid phase of the rock to function as a fluid, and that deformation at a more rapid rate must of necessity produce failure by fracture, it follows that great and comparatively rapid deformations of the earth's crust may extend far below the surface and well into the zone normally characterized by rock flowage. If this is at a depth where the rocks are at a temperature above their melting-point but are kept solid by pressure, the result of fracture dilatation would be immediate liquefaction of the rock in that zone to an extent measured by the increase in volume. This fluid rock migrating by way of the fracture zone to regions of lower pressure would remain fluid and contain sufficient excess heat to fuse a certain amount of rock in its path. The presence and movement of this fluid material would considerably upset the dynamic stability of the whole and result in the development of magma and magmatic activities of greater or lesser extent, depending on the magnitude of the original deformation.

·   ·   ·   ·   ·

## SUMMARY

Incoherent, granular masses, such as sand, in a condition approaching maximum-density packing, are dilated by deformation. In a condition of open packing they deform without dilatation. Prevention of free dilatation by enclosing pressures induces failure by fracture or shear when the mass is deformed, and with the development of joints and faults along thin zones of dilatation.

Deformation of a potentially dilatant mass causes *decrease* in pressure of the fluid portion, and therefore fluids in rocks—water, oil, gas—move toward regions of dilatation.

The mechanics of response to deformation of incoherent granular masses is applied by analogy to solid rocks by conceiving of them as having a solid and a *potentially* fluid phase. When the latter functions as a fluid, the rock yields to deformation by flowing, otherwise by fracture.

Dilatation occasioned by deeply penetrating zones of fracture initiates magmas. Cooling magmas become potentially dilatant when the solid phase develops beyond a certain proportion. The fluid phase alone is then mobile and forms dikes and veins in the surrounding rock and in the granular mass itself. The flow of the fluid phase into cooler parts causes reheating of those parts.

# FERSMAN
Akeksandr Yevgen'yevich Fersman (1883–1945), Russian mineralogist and geochemist, attended Novorossisk University in Odessa from 1901 to 1903 and the University of Moscow from 1904 to 1907, where, after spending two years in Paris and Heidelberg, he continued as a member of the faculty until 1912. From then until the start of the First World War he was Curator of the Mineralogical Museum in St. Petersburg (later, Leningrad). During that war he was a member of the Committees on Natural Resources and on the Study of Natural Productive Forces of the Soviet Academy of Sciences. For the next several years he was engaged in field studies of the ore deposits in the Urals, the Trans-Baikal Region, Northern Mongolia, and the Crimea. His field work eventually provided the basis for the industrial development of the Kolya Peninsula and the exploitation of valuable mineral deposits in various parts of the Soviet Union. He had attained the rank of Academician in 1919, and the later years of his life were devoted largely to administrative duties in the Academy of Sciences and the writing of books and articles on geochemistry and ore prospecting.

## A GEOCHEMICAL GENETIC CLASSIFICATION OF PEGMATITES *

Processes of formation of pegmatites proceed in three interconnected stages: magmatic, pegmatoid, and hydrothermal. These in turn can be

*From "O geokhimicheskoi geneticheskoi klassifikatsii granitnykh pegmatitov," originally published as a monograph by the Akademiia Nauk of the USSR in 1930, with a condensation in German in *Tschermaks mineralogische und petrographische Mitteilungen*

divided into ten temperature stages. The regular succession of crystallization of minerals in the various phases of the process results in pegmatites that have characteristic mineral assemblages and that can be divided into three series: a pure lineage, contact pegmatites, and migmatitic pegmatites.

At present we can define granitic pegmatites as products of crystallization of magmatic residual granitic solutions which separate from granitic rock during cooling of a magma. Morphologically they are characterized by precipitation of mineral associations in a regular sequence, by appreciable dimensions of the individual crystals, and by clearly contemporaneous crystallization of the various minerals. Chemically they are distinguished by greater or lesser enrichment in certain volatile components and especially by strong enrichment in dispersed elements of residual crystallization.

This definition is given in place of a purely formal and morphological characterization; in it the pegmatitic process is considered to be a constituent part of a unified physicochemical process of cooling of the granitic magma, corresponding to crystallization processes beginning with the magmatic stage and continuing through the hydrothermal stage. *Mutatis mutandis* this definition can be extended also to pegmatites of other magmas.

According to Niggli and Vogt, we can divide the process of cooling of a magma into three stages:

1. At the highest temperatures is a magmatic solution from which volatile components are given off in a definite sequence; individual solids crystallize successively, and after settling out of minerals that are in excess, regular mineral complexes precipitate eutectically. This stage corresponds to the coexistence of three phases and is traced on a phase diagram to an upper critical point Q where the composition of the melt and the composition of the gas phase become the same.

The probable temperatures of this stage, for residual granitic crystallization, lie between 800° and 600° (i.e. approximately down to the point of transition between high-temperature and low-temperature quartz).

At this stage we distinguish two quite clearly expressed phases of crystallization of granite, which the writer calls B, epimagmatic, and C, pegmatitic. They are characterized by distinctive and very characteristic minerals.

2. At approximately 600°, i.e. at about the transition point between

---

*41*, (1931), 64–83, and reprinted in Russian in *Izbrannye Trudy*, tom 1 (*Selected works*, vol. 1), Akademiia Nauk SSSR (Academy of Sciences of the USSR), Moscow, 1952, pp. 66–80. Translated from the *Izbrannye Trudy* version by John B. Southard.

Figure 4. Formation of residual granite magmas (pegmatites, pneumatolites, and hydrolites)

| Residual pegmatites | Types | | Phases | Temp. in °C | Types | Pneumatolites and hydrolites |
|---|---|---|---|---|---|---|
| | | | | 800 | | |
| | | B | Epimagmatic | | | |
| Ordinary pegmatites | 1{ | | | 700 | | |
| (Allanite-monazite pegmatites) | | C | Pegmatitic | | | |
| Pegmatites with rare elements | 2{ | | | 600 | | |
| Tourmaline and muscovite pegmatites | 3 | D | | | 1 | Molybdenite veins |
| | | | Pegmatoid | | | |
| Fluorine-beryllium pegmatites | 4{ | E | | | 2}— | Cassiterite veins |
| | | | | 500 | | |
| Lithium pegmatites (with Sn) | 5{ | F | | | 3} | Wolframite veins |
| | | | Superstitial | | | |
| Manganese-phosphatic pegmatites | 6 | G | | | | |
| | | | | 400 | }4 }× | Scheelite-gold veins |
| Cryolite pegmatites | 7 | H | High temperature | | | |
| Fluoro-carbonate pegmatites | 8 | | | | 5— | Copper veins |
| Sulfide pegmatites | 9{ | | | 300 | } 6— | Zinc-lead veins |
| | | I | Medium temperature | | | |
| Zeolite pegmatites | 10{ | | | 200 | | |
| | | K | Low temperature | | 7 | Cobalt-nickel veins |
| | | | | 100–150 | } 8— | Antimony-mercury veins |
| | | L | Hypergene | | | |
| | | | | 0 | | |

Figure 5. Genetic lineages of the pure series of granitic pegmatites

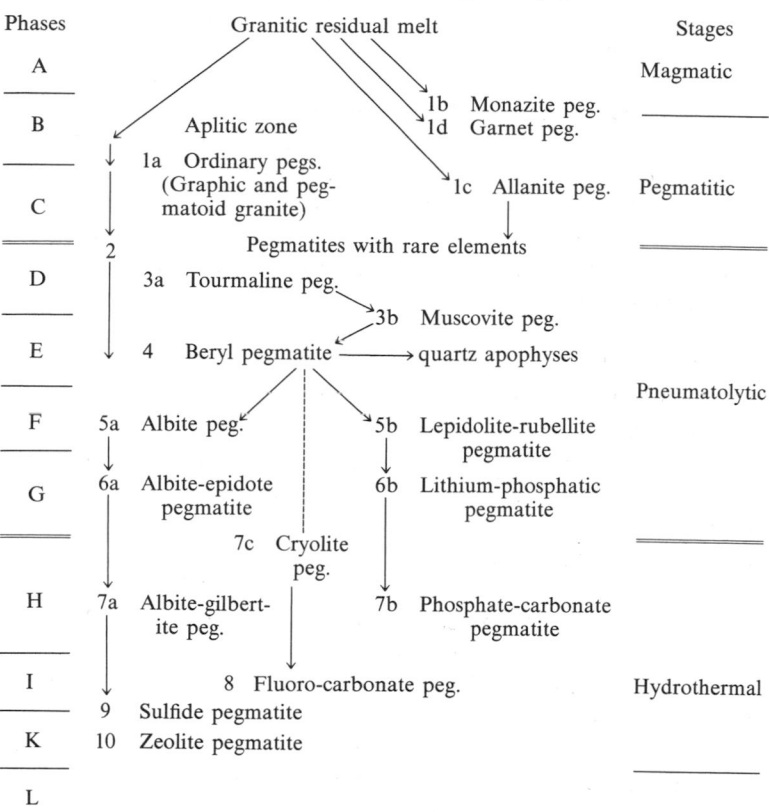

high quartz and low quartz (coinciding in general with the cessation of crystallization of rocks of graphic granite type), the main pneumato-lytic–pegmatitic stage begins, which continues down to a second critical point H, the critical temperature of water; this stage can be divided into four phases which geochemically differ quite sharply from one another. These four phases are characterized by clearly expressed replacement processes, corresponding, however, to definite points of the crystallization pattern, and they divide the field (at approximately 500°) particularly well into two larger parts, with the boundary between phases E and F sometimes characterized by retrograde boiling processes.

3. The third stage begins at the critical point of water H, and includes a series of hydrothermal processes that follow regularly from the course of crystallization of pegmatitic solutions as a whole. The writer calls them "post-pegmatitic."

As already indicated, the boundaries between these three stages—magmatic, pegmatoid, and hydrothermal—are marked by two critical points: the upper is easily distinguished, because it corresponds approximately to the transition between high and low quartz, and thus lies between 573° and 639°. For the usual rather high pressures in the process of pegmatite formation this point can be taken to be 600°. It is very important that this point can be clearly determined morphologically in the pegmatite itself, even at individual stages of its crystallization, by using a number of new criteria indicated by the writer. The second boundary point H corresponds approximately to 370°–430° but in the pegmatite itself it is marked only by a number of morphological features that are not always unambiguous and without indisputable and objective character. This causes difficulties in determining the boundaries of the processes corresponding to the writer's phases F–G–H.

Thus we arrive at a temperature scale in which ten definite temperature phases are distinguished; within them the various pegmatites must be arranged in a regular way. We are speaking of the occurrence of those phenomena which would clearly determine such a classification for all pegmatites and which would permit unified scales and measures for all pegmatites.

When the two points indicated above are established for the paragenesis of some pegmatite, its entire mineral complex is arranged geochemically in a uniform scale, and thus the same scale can be used for all pegmatites of various deposits.

This work, done by careful analysis of twenty of the most important granitic pegmatite deposits, gave results that are shown graphically by the method assumed by the writer in Table 9 for about twenty of the most important minerals.

The entire group of more than 250 minerals that are characteristic of granitic pegmatites can be regularly arranged in such a scheme. A number of these minerals (more than 50) which must be called typomorphic are distinguished; they form quite interesting and regular series, in part already indicated by Scharitser, Kunitz, and Jakob, and combined by the writer into a single evolutionary series of granitic pegmatites. It should be emphasized that the regularity of such pegmatite associations in the geochemical analysis of over 300 pegmatites is far more common than could have been believed at first.

Geochemical laws of migration of elements, quite distinctive and even of general character, can be established from analysis of the mineral associations, because the crystallization paths of pegmatitic solutions are determined, strictly, by the rather constant composition of the granitic residual solutions and are complicated only by changes in

## TABLE 9

| Phases | A Magmatic | B Epimagmatic | C Pegmatitic | D Pegmatoid | E | F Supercritical | G | H Hydrothermal | I | K | L Hypergene |
|---|---|---|---|---|---|---|---|---|---|---|---|
| Temperature in deg. C | | 800 | 700 | 600 | | 500 | | 400 | 300 | 200 | 100 |
| Biotite | | | | X | | | | | | | |
| Monazite | | | | | | | | | | | |
| Plagioclase | | | | | | | | | | | |
| Allanite | | | | | | | | | | | |
| Microcline & orthoclase | | | | | X | | | | | | |
| Nb, Ta, & Ti compounds | | | | | | | | | | | |
| Zircon compounds | | | | | | | | | | | |
| Apatite | | | | | | | | | | | |
| Tourmaline | | | | | | | | | | | |
| Potassium-alumina micas | | | | | | | | | | | |
| Quartz | | | | X | | | | | | | |
| Beryl | | | | | | | | | | | |
| Topaz | | | | | | | | | | | |
| Albite | | | | | | | | | | | |
| Lepidolite | | | | | | | | | | | |
| Mn, Fe, Na, Li phosphates | | | | | | | | | | | |
| Cryolite | | | | | | | | | | | |
| Gilbertite | | | | | | | | | | | |
| Fe, Cu, Zn sulfides | | | | | | | | | | | |
| Flourite | | | | | | | | | | | |
| Zeolites | | | | | | | | | | | |

the composition of the accessory minerals. Thus arises a quite interesting pattern of the process of formation of granitic pegmatites, and thereby also their classification is outlined. A definite type of pegmatite (for example, muscovite pegmatite) is considered not as some wholly independent entity but as a constituent part of a unified process.

Thus, we cannot classify pegmatites sharply, because properly speaking a more or less well-expressed crystallization of individual parts of the entire series determines each type; types with complex character or types corresponding to two or three parts of the entire series can be formed.

Thus arises a picture of the formation of granitic pegmatites, with pneumatolites (in part ore veins) entering into the same temperature scale as *parallel processes*. . . .

In conclusion, a short description of the most important pegmatite types will be given; in this, it should not be forgotten that the classification is artificially imposed upon a unified series.

### Pure Lineage

I. By the term "pegmatites of pure lineage" we mean pegmatites in which there is no important interaction with the wall rocks and which can be considered to be closed systems, whose crystallization proceeded regularly along definite pegmatite-crystallization paths.

*Type 1. Protopegmatites*

(a) *Ordinary pegmatites,* containing some tourmaline, garnet, and green apatite, often called coarse-grained granitic veins. Pegmatitic texture is weakly expressed (for the most part phase B pegmatites up to the formation of graphic texture). Narrow selvages with fine-grained aplitic texture are not uncommon. Lath-like biotite is characteristic. There are no rare elements.

(b) *Garnet pegmatites,* differing from Type (a) by enrichment in almandine (containing a greater or lesser quantity of spessartite), with the principal crystal form {112}, often with {110}, more rarely only {110}.

(c) *Monazite pegmatites,* with aggregations of biotite (lepidomelane), some monazite, zircon; often transitional to Type 2.

(d) *Allanite pegmatites,* related by a gradual transition to allanite granites. Often relatively melanocratic, with high content of lepidomelane; also contain some hornblende, zircon, rarely pyrite, chalcopyrite. Allanite as primary crystals elongated along the crystal axis.

*Type 2.  Pegmatites with Rare Elements*

These pegmatites are widespread, and are distinguished by diversity of mineralization; they are rich in minerals and elements of the groups Ta (Nb), Ti, Y, U, Th, Zr, Hf, P, and others.

Crystallization commonly begins with the aplitic zone (phase B), then follows the main zone of graphic texture (phase C), gradually becoming coarser-grained and grading into a pegmatoid (coarse-grained granitic) aggregate of microcline perthite and quartz. Crystallization of "dark minerals" is usually restricted to the closing stages of crystallization of graphic granite. Consequently, whereas at the beginning of crystallization this type is quite closely related to the formation of the host rock itself, at the end of the process it grades into phase D rocks; large masses of feldspar and quartz are deposited, giving this type great economic importance. In phase C (not later!) much biotite and lepidomelane; later a little muscovite crystallizes.

*Type 3.  Boron-Fluorine Pegmatites*

(a) *Tourmaline pegmatites,* with short columnar crystals of black tourmaline, small quantities of apatite and garnet. They are transitional into earlier stages to ordinary pegmatites and into later stages to muscovite pegmatites.

(b) *Muscovite pegmatites,* of great industrial importance; muscovite is formed by hydrolysis of feldspathic material (tabular muscovite with rhombic outline). Some tourmaline, apatite, garnet (in the muscovite), beryl, and a little biotite before and at the beginning of formation of the muscovite.

*Type 4.  Topaz-Beryl Pegmatites*

This most important group is characterized principally not by the diversity of mineral associations, but, corresponding to phase E, by the frequent presence of voids in which minerals continue to grow unhindered, reaching superb development.

Characteristic are: topaz, beryl (aquamarine), muscovite in the form of isolated free crystals, microcline perthite (sometimes amazonite), and orthoclase perthite. Tourmaline (dark blue or greenish black), cassiterite, malacon, lepidolite, and rosettes of albite are observed in small quantities on the free druses in the voids as phase F formations.

*Type 5.  Sodium-Lithium Pegmatites*
(*Phase F and beginning of Phase G*).

The boundary between phases E and F is usually marked by a sharp break in the unified process; a quite clearly expressed transformation and replacement of minerals formed earlier occurs here.

### Type 6. Lithium-Sodium-Phosphatic Pegmatites

Very diverse pegmatites belong to phase G, which represents the end of the pneumatolytic products. If the pegmatitic solution becomes free of phosphoric acid and carbonic acid relatively early, there remains in this phase only an alkaline residual solution, which usually dissolves quartz and causes further albitization of the pegmatite as early as phase F. In case of breakdown of perthites, Ca molecules are set free also, and there arises an important group, called type 6c by the writer, consisting of albite, epidote, accessory chlorite, and iron glance.

On the other hand, in case of complete development of the pegmatite a series of iron phosphates with Li, Na, Mg, F, OH arises, whose presence gives this type very distinctive character.

### Type 7. Cryolite Pegmatites

The beginning of high-hydrothermal activity and the entire region around the critical point H govern rather complex associations, as could have been expected. These associations can be traced to phosphatic pegmatites of type 6 albite-epidote pegmatites (albite-gilbertite association). However, characteristic phase G pegmatites correspond to the so-called cryolite type, which is very rarely found independently and is sometimes represented in various pegmatites (mostly type 4) as isolated mineral formations.

### Type 8. Fluorine-Carbonate Pegmatites

Very rare. Composed of various minerals—products of the last remnants of the pegmatitic solutions (parisite, calcite, magnesite, beryl, and so on).

### Type 9. Sulfide Pegmatites

Generally rare, but in some regions (for example, in southwestern Africa) quite widespread, with the sulfides commonly represented by chalcopyrite, or chalcosite, sphalerite, and galena. Doubt is often cast upon the primary nature of the sulfides.

### Type 10. Zeolite Pegmatites

Quite rare, usually found in connection with contact phenomena.

### Type 11. Fillings of Miarolitic Cavities

II. Primary fillings of miarolitic cavities form an entirely special type, displaying a rather clearly expressed connection with granitic rocks. Their associations most often correspond to phases F–G–H.

CONTAMINATED LINEAGE OF PEGMATITIC PROCESSES

III. *Pegmatites with an excess of volatile components*—pneumatolites—are formed by primary enrichment (often caused by high confining pressure) or by secondary enrichment in volatile components, which affects the process in the most diverse ways and leads to three contaminated types:

*Type 12—With Sulfides of Zn, Cu, Pb, and Fe;*

*Type 13—With Large Quantities of Sn, W, and Bi;*

*Type 14—With Excess of Water (Strong and Premature Hydrolysis of the Feldspars).*

IV. *Contact pegmatites* arise from a certain selective assimilation of the elements of the host rocks, which geochemically leads to enrichment in Ca, Mg, Fe, and Al. Physicochemical analysis on the basis of the mineralogical phase rule introduced by Goldschmidt allows us to arrange systematically all the possible combinations formed by these phenomena into individual series, and reduce them to six types which are characterized in the tables in the following way:

*Type 15—Pegmatites with Magnetite—Fe,*

*Type 16—Pegmatites with Diopside and Titanite—Ca, Mg,*

*Type 17—Pegmatites with Plagioclase and Tourmaline—Ca, Fe,*

*Type 18—Pegmatites with Cordierite and Biotite—Mg (+Fe),*

*Type 19—Pegmatites with Scapolite and Zeolites—Ca,*

*Type 20—Alumina Pegmatites—Al.*

It is noteworthy that the assimilated elements separate as diverse minerals even in the first phases (B–C); because of this the residual pegmatitic melt returns relatively rapidly to the usual path of crystallization, re-establishing its pure lineage. In this auto-purification process we see the basic difference between contact pegmatites and migmatitic pegmatites.

189

V. *Migmatitic pegmatites.* Where intense interaction takes place between residual pegmatitic melts and wall rocks, mixed melts are formed; crystallization of these does not follow pure lineages but produces completely new associations which in space and time lead genetically to new regularly organized mineral formations.

For the most part these are pegmatitic residual melts that are quite strongly overheated at considerable pressure; in this case there is an exchange migration of elements, and three zones are formed: endocontact, exocontact, and a mixed zone between.

To this series belong two groups of pegmatites. One of them forms the well known injection migmatites and arterites of Sederholm; they can be explained by complete saturation of the primary rocks by the pegmatitic melts. The second group is formed by desilication of the pegmatites during their intrusion into basic or ultrabasic rock series. In the latter case albitites, plagioclasites, plumasites, and marundites are formed which in general have lost the character and paragenesis of the usual granitic pegmatites and are distinguished by enrichment in plagioclases (including basic plagioclases), spinel, corundum, margarite, and sillimanite.

VI. *Pegmatites of special type.* A further series of pegmatites is formed by pegmatitic residual melts of special constitution, whose genesis is still not clear (cerite pegmatites), or which are formed under completely special, unique paragenetic conditions (contact with ore deposits, etc.). In the same series the writer tentatively places graphitic pegmatites, which in a genetic sense are probably nonhomogeneous formations and in need of a complete geochemical revision.

VII. *Primary and secondary pegmatites.* Genetically, we can divide pegmatites into two groups; all the pegmatites described above can be considered to be primary, but secondary pegmatites can also be formed by secondary melting of various rocks in connection with temporary rise in temperature (palingenesis).

Secondary granitic pegmatites are also formed during silication of pegmatites of basic and alkalic rocks—for example, by assimilation of $SiO_2$ by nepheline syenite pegmatites.

In both cases, secondary pegmatites are characterized by complete absence of elements that are typical of granitic pegmatites.

## BRIEF CONCLUSIONS

The geochemical genetic classification of pegmatites presented above gives us important indications for the understanding of various pegmatites, and is valuable not only theoretically but also from a practical viewpoint. The following main conclusions and consequences can be drawn from the foregoing.

1. Pegmatites should be considered to be residual magmatic melts that change in a regular way as a result of gradual crystallization on the one hand and the escape of volatile componenets by distillation on the other. A definite evolutionary course of crystallization, leading from a magmatic liquid region through a fluid pegmatoid-pneumatolytic stage to hydrothermal formations, thus becomes clear.

2. The region of crystallization of granitic pegmatites lies approximately between 800° and 100° and falls into ten phases the positions of which are determined by two definite points, at approximately 600° and 400°.

3. The pegmatitic process can be considered to be an unbroken crystallization process; however, due to retrograde distillation, replacement phenomena, rejuvenation, and so on, it does not correspond to the evolutionary stages of Bowen's reaction series.

4. Because of the characteristic crystallization of definite minerals, there arises in the course of the individual phases of the continuous process, the possibility of classifying and systematizing pegmatites, with ten principal types corresponding in broad features with the individual phases of the process.

5. We can establish three principal series of pegmatites: (A) a pure lineage, to which belong pegmatites of granitic residual solutions, not altered by the action of wall rocks; (B) a contact lineage, in which the wall rocks are in part assimilated by the granitic-pegmatite magma, but the main crystallization path is not changed; (C) a migmatitic lineage arising from a strong interaction between the wall rocks and the residual solutions and leading to new forms of equilibrium and mineral associations.

6. Pegmatites can serve as objects of analysis in a genetic sense, in space, and in time, and form more or less regular mineral associations of zonal nature.

7. The interpretation of pegmatites as a continuous, unified, evolutionary sequence of granitic residual solutions enriched in volatile components was given theoretically by Niggli and Vogt, but had already been noted mineralogically by Scharitser, who expressed these ideas forty-five years ago, taking as a basis the analysis of a series of pegmatites from Schüttellhofen.

8. *Mutatis mutandis* the methods of geochemical analysis of granitic pegmatites can be extended to pegmatites of other magmas, making it

possible to create a genetically and geochemically verified classification even for the group of pegmatites that is second in importance—nepheline syenite pegmatites.

# MATSUYAMA

Motonori Matsuyama (1884–1958), Japanese geophysicist, was associated with Kyoto University throughout most of his life, first as a student, graduating in 1911, and then as a teacher, retiring from his professorship in 1949, when he became President of Yamaguchi University. His investigation of the remanent magnetization of volcanic rocks from Japan and Korea provided the first adequately supported information concerning the reversal of the earth's magnetic field in Quaternary time.

In the following excerpt from his 1929 paper errors in spelling and grammar have been corrected. In the heading of that paper, the author's name is given as "Matuyama" and this spelling of his name appears in many subsequent references to him and his work. The Japanese character to be transliterated is the same as that in the frequently used word, "tsunami," and the author's name should be pronounced with the "tsu" sound no matter how it is spelled.

## ON THE DIRECTION OF MAGNETIZATION OF BASALT*

Early in April 1926 a specimen of basalt from Genbudô, Tazima, a celebrated basalt cave, was collected for the purpose of examining its magnetic properties. Its orientation was carefully measured in its natural position before it was removed. When this block was tested by bringing it near to a freely suspended magnetic needle, its magnetic north pole was found to be directed to the south and above the horizontal direction. This is nearly opposite to the present earth's magnetic field at the locality. In May of the same year, four specimens of basalt were collected from Yakuno, Tanba, with similar care. When tested, their magnetic axes were found to have an easterly declination of some 20° and a downward inclination of some 50°.

Since the time of Melloni [1859] it is believed that lava gets its magnetism in cooling in the direction of the earth's magnetic field. . . . The above-mentioned places are not a great distance from each other and have nearly the same magnetic field. These basalts are described as the lavas of probably Quaternary eruptions.

*From *Proceedings of the Imperial Academy of Japan* 5 (1929), 203–205.

Since that time 139 specimens of basalt have been collected from 36 places in Honsyû, Kyûsyû, Tyôsen, and Manchuria, of which 38 specimens have already been examined more accurately. . . . The specimen was enclosed and fixed in a spherical surface in such a way that its orientation could be read from outside. Distribution of the normal component of magnetic force on the surface of the sphere due to the enclosed basalt was determined by means of a magnetometer, and the direction of magnetic axis and the intensity of magnetization were determined by the method of harmonic analysis.

To see the degree of reliability, four specimens from Genbudô were examined. As the result their magnetic axes were found to have a mean westerly declination of 150° and a mean upward inclination of 49°, the largest deviations being 12° in the former and 14° in the latter.

Care was also paid to the tilting of the crust after the basalt sheet was laid out. At Fushun, Manchuria, the specimens were taken from a dolerite sheet which was conformably under and overlaid by a shale strata dipping 25° to the north with a nearly eastwesterly strike. Hence due corrections were made for the measured direction of magnetic axes of these specimens.

. . . The earth's magnetic field in the related area has a westerly declination varying from 4°.5 to 6°.5 and a downward inclination from 40°.5 to 60°. Since much larger variations of angles are concerned here, the mean direction was considered to prevail over this area.

. . . A peculiar arrangement can easily be noticed. There is a group of specimens, including that from Yakuno, whose directions of magnetization fall around the present earth's field. A number of other specimens, including that from Genbudô, forms another group almost exactly antipodal to the former. . . .

The age of eruption of the collected basalts is not always clearly known. Among the specimens of the first group those from the northwestern Kyûsyû are described to be of post-Tertiary and that from Tansen, Tyôsen, is believed to be of Quaternary period. None of them is known to be older than the beginning of the Quaternary; they might be younger. In the second group, the basalt of Genbudô is considered to be also of Quaternary eruption. One of the specimens from Kissyû, Tyôsen, is reported to be of Pleistocene while the other is definitely older, since it is surrounded and a part covered by the first. Thus we may consider that in the earlier part of the Quaternary period the earth's magnetic field in the area under consideration was probably in the state represented by the second group, which gradually changed to the state represented by the first group.

There are three examined specimens of basalt known as of Tertiary eruption. Two from Fushun, Manchuria, had a mean westerly declination of 168° and a downward inclination of 77°. They are described to be of the Miocene period. A specimen from Zaitokusan, Tyôsen, is reported to form the base of the Sitihôzan group, unconformably covering the probable Oligocene group, and may be of Miocene. When examined this specimen had an easterly declination of 35° and an upward inclination of 70°. Thus there is also a roughly antipodal relation.

According to Mercanton,[1] the earth's magnetic field was probably in a greatly different or nearly opposite state during the Permocarboniferous and Tertiary ages from what it is at present. From my results it would appear that, in the area under study, the earth's magnetic field has reversed its direction during the Miocene, and again during the Quaternary period, in comparatively shorter intervals of time.

# CLOOS
Hans Cloos (1886–1951), German geologist, was trained at the University of Freiburg and after receiving his Ph.D. degree spent several years in southwest Africa as a mining geologist and in Indonesia as a petroleum geologist. During the First World War he was a military geologist in France but was soon released from the army because of poor health. In 1919 he was appointed Professor of Geology at the University of Breslau and in 1925 he became Chairman of the Department of Geology at the University of Bonn, a post he filled with great distinction for twenty-six years, in spite of great misfortunes during the Hitler regime and the Second World War. He was a pioneer in the study of "granite tectonics" and contributed much to knowledge of the structure of the earth's crust, frequently directing attention to the significance of minor structural features that accompany major dislocations. His style of scientific writing was "classical in conciseness and beautiful in expression although, unfortunately, difficult to translate" (Robert Balk).

## THE BATHOLITH PROBLEM *

In accordance with the ideas of Ed. Suess, we will consider primarily as batholiths only those plutonic rock massifs which cut through and displace the adjacent strata and which appear to continue into the depths without a foreign substructure. This eliminates concordant laccoliths and also the large gneiss-granite laccoliths. The point of difficulty lies precisely in the concept that the granite has worked itself up from

[1] P. L. Mercanton, *Compt. Rend. 182* (1926), 859–861, 1231–1232.
*From *Fortschritte der Geologie und Paleontologie 1* (1923), 3–14, 72–77. Translated by Judith Frondel.

"eternal depths" at the expense of the surrounding rocks and that these have disappeared forever and have been replaced by the granite.

Especially in the logical sequence which Daly has expounded, the batholith concept has indeed the undeniable merit of being both broadly inclusive and simple; it satisfactorily ties together an abundance of individual data in a single, homogeneous, clear-cut generalization. . . . [It] greatly simplifies the solution of the problems encountered by structural geologists and vulcanologists who are obliged to unravel mountain-structures; for them the posing of problems ceases when the granite contact is reached. All the complicated structure and stratigraphy of the folded and faulted mountains is cut off at the granite. The material proceeds further, but in a remarkably simplified form; it has been condensed and unified into granite. . . . Even more than this, the batholith concept binds the largest portion of the earth's crust directly to its great depths; it provides a vertical connection from top to bottom more effective and remarkable than the conduits and vents of volcanoes. . . .

The first . . . explanation [of batholith emplacement] was by fusion, advanced by the French investigators. Like hot volcanic magmas the granite was supposed to have made fluid all the adjacent rocks, assimilated them, and thus cleared the way for itself. Here, one can separate a more temperate viewpoint, according to which magmas were present at the beginning and increased upward in time and space, from an extreme viewpoint which attributed the origin of the magmas and magma chambers solely to the action of hot gases on the solid crust of the earth. We must, however, discard both of these hypotheses because of countless geological observations that stand in opposition to them. The contacts between granite and the adjacent rocks are not, in truth, fused borders but are the product of a predominantly mechanical disturbance. This fact accords consistently with the hypothesis of magmatic stoping of Barrell and Daly. The granite does not melt the adjacent rocks but breaks them apart and the fragments from the roof fall into the melt where, since they are denser, they sink. Thus the magma eventually takes the place of the removed fragments. The sunken fragments may be, but are not necessarily, melted in the depths of the magma chamber. This active work of the granite is compared with the "overhead stoping" of a miner in tunnels. . . . In this form the batholith concept enjoys today a fairly general acceptance, but one cannot fail to note in most investigators a certain uneasiness in their practice, a certain careful, reserved manner of expression.

Obviously the critical point lies in the fragments, those innumerable small agents of exchange of place and material. There is no doubt that they actually can be observed in large numbers at almost all contacts and that on the adjacent rocks there is no lack of attack by the granite, which prepares and loosens new fragments. Daly has done much uncommonly careful and ingenious work to prove that the fragments are actually heavy enough to sink in the still viscous and only slightly lighter granite magma. It is difficult to prove theoretically that they must sink. . . . I do not care to go into a discussion of the calculations . . . [but the results] do not seem to me to be convincing.

How does it stand, then, with the one sure expedient of the geologist, field observation? Because of the importance of the fragment question, I devoted a monograph, years ago, to well-disclosed examples. It was apparent that tectonic and exogeneous forces participated in the genesis of the fragments in the granite. . . . [They] were exactly along previously determined lines of regional tectonics. Frequently such joints are discovered by the attached precursors of the granite. . . .

Another point of view: If large granite bodies do in fact broaden, or at least do not narrow, downward, then more and larger masses must occur in the more deeply eroded parts than in the higher parts of such mountains . . . [as those in] the southern part of the Bohemian massif. . . . [There] one indeed finds numerous but only very small intrusions of granite; everything else is gneiss. And in the granite region of Linz and between Linz and Passau these intrusions diminish and one finds instead large areas of gneiss. These gneisses are indeed for the most part granite-gneiss, mostly granite which was compressed and deformed at the time of origin. Many have not even developed a true parallel fabric. But . . . their occurrence is not that of batholiths. They are rather granites of a "first generation." They arose at a distinctly earlier time, at the close of folding, and filled spaces which were opened for them by the folding. Accordingly they conform to the strata of the adjacent rocks without cutting through them. . . . There is no space question or batholith problem in these older concordant granite-gneisses.

·  ·  ·  ·  ·  ·

The true batholith breaks through its roof and pushes upward, higher here and less high there; it is distinguished by complete independence from the roof strata as well as from those bounding it on its sides. Here, also, the microstructure gives a completely divergent picture. It shows how the granite conforms step by step to its roof, how it rises and falls with it, how it arches up in domes of beautiful curvature and regularity. . . .

Doming is a phenomenon which, though it has been emphasized

specifically with regard to many batholiths, seems not to be in agreement, in my opinion, with the batholith theory. It is reported everywhere that the granite not only cuts through its roof but also distends it and builds a regular arch under it. The amount of doming is . . . mostly between several hundred and a thousand meters. It seems to me that therein lies a contradiction. There seems to be no reason at all why the granite, which makes place for itself by the destruction of its roof, must or can lift it up at the same time. Even granting this possibility, the unusually regular form of this arch and its restriction to the granite and its immediate surroundings still remain unintelligible. It contradicts the imagination to the highest degree that such an uplift can emanate from a medium which lacks a floor and therefore an abutment. . . . How is it conceivable that the magma on the one hand was so fluid that innumerable slightly denser blocks sank into it and on the other hand was sufficiently viscous to support a heavy roof which was already fractured, bent, and loosened in every way? This is probably the weakest point in the batholith theory and has been accepted as such by almost all investigators. Help may be found in the proposition that many granites have actually broken through to the surface, but such much-sought "areal eruptions" have never been observed, at least in connection with batholiths. On the contrary, almost all granite massifs give proof of the indestructibility of their roofs.

All this and a series of further doubts have long since shattered my confidence in the universal validity of the batholith concept. . . . We are faced with the fact that at the moment there is no large batholith that has been thoroughly investigated which does not entertain in some way a doubt concerning its batholith nature.

Therefore we have the task of finding some process which explains the characteristic variety of features of so-called batholiths by a different and mechanically simple maneuver which does not contradict the numerous field observations.

$$\cdot \quad \cdot \quad \cdot \quad \cdot \quad \cdot$$

Some generalizations:

1. The large, previously investigated plutonic massifs have won their place in the surrounding crust not by destruction of it (either mechanical or by physico-chemical solution), but by displacement of it. The massif-structure signifies, therefore, neither a change of state of previously existing rocks (by melting and re-solidification), nor a simple exchange of material between shallower and deeper parts of the crust (by opening and place-exchange), but an addition of new material

transported from the depths. The space for this addition was gained by displacement, above, to the sides, and in part below.

2. Such a process of formation has commonly been accepted for small and concordant massifs, called laccoliths. It can be extended to discordant and very much larger massifs and embraces a part, probably a very large part, of the so-called batholiths.

3. The discordant relationship, with the borders of such massifs truncating the stratification of the roof and walls, does not have its origin in some unusual, cross-cutting, destroying power of the granite, but in the fact (accidental for the granite, since it lies outside of it) that the path which it found and followed had already been cut discordantly through the adjacent rocks.

4. The similarity to laccoliths goes further, inasmuch as many of these massifs are connected to their magma chambers only by narrow, mostly vein-like, conduits, from which they broaden laterally into foreign and older formations.

5. The decision as to whether there is a concordant laccolith or a discordant and apparently batholith-like massif is obviously to be found in the adjacent rocks. If the magmas find flat broadening strata-joints, they will prefer these; . . . if, on the other hand, they enter previously folded structures, they must, and can to a certain degree, use cleavage joints. . . .

•    •    •    •    •

## General Conclusions

Geologists should not infer that all discordant intrusive bodies involve widespread assimilation of foreign material by the magmas. Assimilation plays a part, but in many cases it is an accompanying process, not the major one. Although blocks fall into the magma and sink in it, only a small part of the massif's space is obtained in that way. The rock resulting from the solidification of the magma has clearly preserved, in the main, the characteristics of the deep magma.

No large magma chambers, high in the upper crust, favorable for vertical, gravity-controlled exchange of material, are available for the important processes of differentiation in rock-formation. The diverging portions of the plutonic masses influence the progress of density layering in the earth's upper crust in only an inhibited and limited manner.

On the other hand, magmatic activity at greater depths contributes to both vertical and horizontal exchange of material in an important manner.

In general, the emergence of extensive magma-masses at the earth's surface should not be considered. The lack of true "areal eruptions," as demanded by the batholith theory, forbids such an explanation.

To the extent that this generalization leads to correct conclusions, most of the granite in the upper portions of the earth's crust will be reinterpreted as some other kind of older rock. The relative amount of granite is oddly less than was formerly believed; indeed, in places —despite large granite areas—it is so small as almost to disappear. In most regions, rocks formerly identified as granite are now considered to be gneiss, and Paleozoic crystalline rocks are seldom placed among the granites.

．　．　．　．　．

### Practical Conclusions

In recent years it has been demonstrated through so-called granite-tectonic research that geologic science need no longer halt at granite. Tectonics can be carried by means of the compass into regions which formerly were accessible only by means of chemistry and the microscope.

. . . We may hope that similarly geological and mining practices need not halt at granite. Where the crust is not entirely destroyed or replaced by granite, but continues beneath it, the ore deposits of the crust can also continue under the granite. . . . We have one example near Passau where today, in the Bavarian graphite mine, treasures are brought forth from beneath granite.

# VENING-MEINESZ Felix Andries Vening-Meinesz

(1887–1966), Dutch geophysicist, received an engineering degree in 1910 and the Ph. D. degree in 1915 from the Technical University in Delft, Netherlands. He was a member of the Netherlands Geodetic Commission from 1911 to 1927. During most of his productive career he was Professor of Geodesy and Geophysics at the University of Utrecht and Professor of Geodesy at his Alma Mater. He was the pioneer in determining gravity in ocean basins by means of instruments mounted in submarines, and the data secured on his many long undersea traverses enabled him to write a new chapter in tectonic geology.

## CONVECTION-CURRENTS IN THE EARTH*

In a previous paper the writer has drawn attention to the fact that the hypothesis of convection-currents in the subcrustal layer under the

*From *Koninklijke Nederlandse Akademie van Wetenschappen Proceedings 50* (1947), 237–245.

eastern half of the Indian Archipelago may give a good explanation of the deep-focus and the intermediate earthquakes in this area. He presented this hypothesis as early as 1932[1] for explaining the sinking down of the deep basins which are clearly connected with the great folding processes in the neighbouring tectonic belts but which probably have originated with a great time-lag of many millions of years after the folding. In the Banda arc the last great folding period is put by Umbgrove[2] in Tertiary $f2$, i.e. some twenty million years ago, while the sinking of the Banda basin, although difficult to determine exactly by direct evidence, is probably much more recent. Direct evidence that this area has provided erosion products to the surrounding tectonic belt and that it, therefore, must have been above sealevel, dates further back but, as Molengraaff already pointed out and as Umbgrove also is inclined to assume, it seems likely that the principal part of the sinking of the basin is simultaneous with the rising of the adjacent tectonic belt which took place in the pleistocene, i.e. only some 1 or 2 million years ago. Molengraaff explained, for example, that in Timor, the miocene folding is intersected by the present coast-line of the deep basins and that it must, therefore, be anterior to the sinking. His opinion about the simultaneity of the rising and sinking movements is widely accepted. It agrees with the explanation of both movements by the hypothesis of a convection-current in the subcrustal layer which at the same time must bring about a rising above the rising current and a sinking above the sinking one.

This hypothesis may also explain the evident connection of these crustal movements with the folding phenomenon and the great time-lag between both. During the folding-period the Earth's crust may be supposed to have down-buckled along the tectonic belt, thus forming a considerable crustal bulge at the lower boundary of the crust, which according to the negative anomalies and the topography in this belt and assuming a density difference with the substratum of 0.6 must have a cross-section of 1500–2000 km$^2$. It must have pushed away the subcrustal material. As this last material is poorer in radioactive constituents than the crust, we may expect a slow heating up of this area by the excess of radioactive radiation caused by the concentration of crustal material along the belt.

This heating up must have disturbed the equilibrium in the substratum. If we assume with most geophysicists that the Earth is cooling notwithstanding the amount of radioactive minerals present in the outer layers, the substratum must have shown a downward temperature-gra-

[1] F. A. Vening Meinesz, J. H. F. Umbgrove, Ph. H. Kuenen, *Gravity Expeditions at Sea*, vol. II, Publ. Netherl. Geod. Comm., Waltman, Delft, p. 135.
  [2] *Ibid.*, pp. 140ff.

dient tending to bring about instability as it causes layers of lower temperature to overlie higher temperature layers. The writer, however, agrees with Jeffreys in supposing that these layers have some strength or, in other words, that below a certain limit, stresses only bring about elastical deformations; the stresses have, therefore, to exceed this limit before flow can take place. According to the smallness of the deviations from isostatic equilibrium of 10–15 mgal the writer supposes this limit to lie between 25 and 50 kg/cm². If only the vertical temperature-gradient caused by the cooling of the Earth is present, this strength must prevent any convection-current to originate and it has, therefore, a stabilising effect. If, however, at the same time, a temperature gradient in a horizontal sense is present, the normal density equilibrium in horizontal layers is disturbed. If this gradient is sufficient the resulting stresses will overcome the strength-limit of the substratum and a current must set in which, because of the vertical temperature-gradient, takes the character of a convection-current.

We must expect this heating of the subcrustal layer below the tectonic belt to a temperature sufficient to start the above phenomenon, to be a slow process and so it does not seem unlikely that we can thus explain the time-lag of many millions of years between the folding in the tectonic belt and the coming about of the convection-current. It is important to investigate this numerically to see whether this is possible.

We shall begin by assuming that the whole crustal root consists of granite. This leads to a density difference from the substratum of about 0.6 (peridotite = 3.23, dunite = 3.29) as we assumed above when mentioning the cross section of 1500–2000 km². For our deductions we shall adopt a cross section of 1700 km².

For the radioactive heat-production we shall use the figures for different types of rocks given by Gutenberg in Table 22 on page 155 of *Internal Constitution of the Earth* and the figures of Table 18–2 on page 270 of *Handbook of Physical Constants* by Birch, Schairer and Spicer. The mean figure for granite given by Gutenberg is $7.8 \times 10^{-13}$ cal/cm³ sec and by the second table $5.6 \times 10^{-6}$ cal/gm yr, which gives $4.8 \times 10^{-13}$ cal/cm³ sec. The mean figure is $6.3 \times 10^{-13}$ cal/cm³ sec. Taking the mean for peridotite and dunite in Gutenberg's table, we find $1.5 \times 10^{-13}$ cal/cm³ sec and the *Handbook* gives for ultra-basic rocks $0.9 \times 10^{-6}$ cal/gm yr = $0.9 \times 10^{-13}$ cal/cm³ sec; the mean is $1.2 \times 10^{-13}$ cal/cm³ sec. The excess heat developed in the root is the difference and so we obtain $5.1 \times 10^{-13}$ cal/cm³ sec. For the whole root of 1700 km² cross section this gives 9 cal/sec cm (the cm dimension at right angles to the cross section).

This figure has been derived for a root consisting entirely of granite.

This is, however, unlikely. If the root has been formed by the downward buckling of the crust, as it has been supposed, we must expect deep crustal layers to be present and it is usually assumed that these layers are not granitic but more basic. Since, according to the assumed mode of originating of the root, these layers may be expected to form the outer shell of it and as we may suppose the root to have partially melted away because of the higher temperature these materials must have been subjected to when they were pushed downwards, it would of course be possible that a great part of this outer shell has disappeared. The explanation of the more acid type of volcanism in the nearby inner Banda-arc by the flowing off of the molten material of the root, as, for example, by Anderson[3], would seem to point to the granitic central part of the root being now exposed to the melting, and this would appear to confirm our last supposition.

We cannot, however, come to any certainty about this point and so it is no doubt possible that the root partially consists of deeper rocks than granite. It is simple to see that if for these rocks the difference of the heat-production from that of the sub-crustal material would be proportional to the difference of the density from that of this same subcrustal layer, our result for the excess of the heat-production of the root would remain the same. The figures for the heat-production given by Gutenberg and others, however, deviate from this proportionality in the sense that the heat-production in the crust diminishes probably quicker with depth. Resuming, we must recognize that the above mentioned figure of 9 cal/sec cm for the root may be too high and so we shall reduce it to 7.5 cal/sec cm.

Adopting this figure, the problem has to be solved what temperature distribution in the subcrustal material is caused by this source of heat after a lapse of time of some 18 million years. For this solution we have to apply the formula of heat-conduction for the two-dimensional case represented by our problem. This is given by the differential equation for the temperature $\theta$:

$$a \, \Delta\theta = \frac{\partial\theta}{\partial t}, \tag{1A}$$

where $\Delta\theta$ expressed in polar coordinates $r$, $\varphi$ is

$$\Delta\theta = \frac{\partial^2\theta}{\partial r^2} + \frac{1}{r}\frac{\partial\theta}{\partial r} + \frac{1}{r^2}\frac{\partial^2\theta}{\partial\varphi^2}, \tag{1B}$$

[3] W. Q. Kennedy and E. M. Anderson, "Crustal layers and the origin of magmas," *Bull. Volcan. Soc.* II, vol. III, 1938.

and

$$a = \frac{\lambda}{c\rho};$$ (1C)

$\lambda$ = coeff. of thermal conductivity,
$c$ = heat-capacity,
$\rho$ = density.

The quantities $\lambda$, $c$, and $\rho$ all refer to the subcrustal material.

We shall simplify our problem by the suppositions that the root has a circular cross section with a radius $r_0$ and that the heat-production is concentrated in the centre. We shall furthermore assume that the phenomenon is cylindrically symmetric. As the fundamental law of heat-conduction given by (1A) is linear in $\theta$, our phenomenon is not affected by the normal cooling of the Earth and so from this point of view there is no objection to adopting this assumption.

The presence of the surface of the Earth at a distance of about 49 km (thickness of the crust = 30 km + distance of centre below the lower crustal boundary = ±19 km) must, however, affect it and so we have to prove that this effect is negligible. It is simple to do this. The effect of the boundary can be taken account of by assuming the presence of a sink of heat of the same amount as the heat-source in the root and at the same distance of 49 km above the Earth's surface. This sink is therefore at a distance of 98 km from the source. We shall, however, find that the effect of the sink at this distance is negligible and so we can maintain our supposition of cylindrical symmetry.

According to this supposition formulas (1A) and (1B) become

$$a\left(\frac{\partial^2\theta}{\partial r^2} + \frac{1}{r}\frac{\partial\theta}{\partial r}\right) = \frac{\partial\theta}{\partial t}$$ (2)

The solution of this equation is an exponential integral, which we shall as usual indicate by the symbol $Ei$:

$$\theta = \frac{q}{4\pi\lambda}\left[-Ei\left(-\frac{r^2}{4at}\right)\right] \qquad \left(Eix = \int_{\infty}^{-x}\frac{e^{-u}}{u}\,du\right)$$ (3)

where $q$ is the heat-production in cal/cm³ sec.

We introduce

$q$ = 7.5 cal/cm³ sec.
$\lambda$ = 0.01 (see *Handbook*, p. 254).
$c$ = 0.20 (see *Handbook*, p. 235).
$\rho$ = 3.27.

This leads to
$$a = 0.015.$$

We compute $\theta$ for $a$ time $t = 18$ million years $= 5.67 \times 10^{14}$ sec.

Using for $Ei\,(-x)$ the table in Jahnke and Emde, *Funktionnentafeln* pp. 21, 22, we find the following values for $\theta$. For the radius $r_0$ of the root we introduce 23 km which corresponds to the supposed cross section of the root of 1700 km$^2$.

| $r$ (km) | $x = r^2/4at$ | $-Ei(-x)$ | $\theta$ |
|---|---|---|---|
| 23 | 0.1555 | 1.432 | $+85°.4$ |
| 40 | 0.470 | 0.599 | $+35°.8$ |
| 60 | 1.058 | 0.200 | $+12°.0$ |
| 80 | 1.880 | 0.0506 | $+ 3°.0$ |
| 100 | 2.940 | 0.0141 | $+ 0°.8$ |

It is remarkable to see that a temperature of 85° at the surface of the root requires such a long lapse of time to come into being. It is also interesting to find that the heat after this long interval practically did not come beyond some 100 km. We see here our supposition confirmed that the effect of a heat-sink at this distance is negligible.

For making a rough estimate of the magnitude of the stresses caused by this temperature distribution we compute the rise of the surface of the substratum brought about by the expansion while neglecting the elastical deformations caused by the resulting stresses. For this rough estimate we adopt a rectangular cross section for the root of a height of 37 km and a breadth of 46 km (see Fig. 1), and we assume in the column of the substratum bordering the root a temperature of 85°.4 over 37 km height and below this a falling off of the temperature as given by the above table, i.e. at 17 km below the point C a temperature of 35°.8, at 37 km below it a temperature of 12°, etc. We adopt a volumetric thermal expansion of the substratum of $3 \times 10^{-5}$ and we assume that the adjustment of the hydrostatic equilibrium of these layers leads to the entire expansion appearing at the surface. We then find a rise there of 146 meters which for a density of 3.27 represents an anomaly of 14 mgal and an excess pressure of 45 kg/cm$^2$. This is exactly the order of magnitude we may presume for the strength-limit of the subcrustal layers, and so we see that the great time-lag of 18,000,000 years before the starting of the convection-current could well be explained. When the strength-limit is exceeded by further heating, the subcrustal matter would flow off from the neighbourhood of the root and this would disturb the equilibrium in the column below it; a rising current

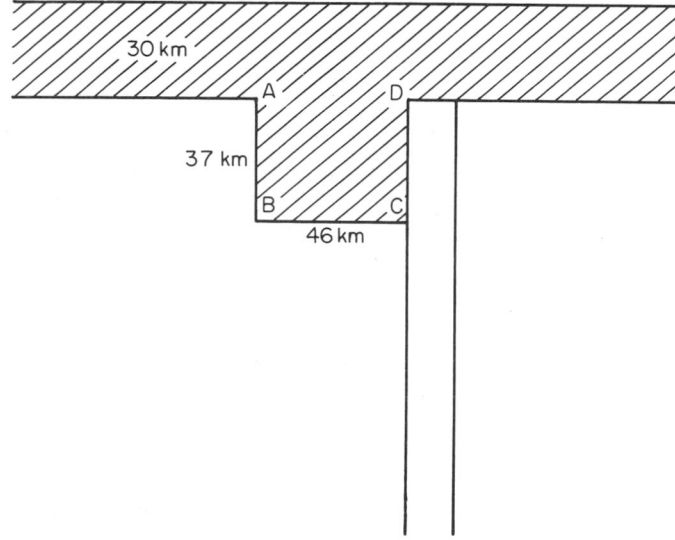

Fig. 1.

would set in here while a sinking one would originate in the area which had become loaded by this flow while the pressure difference in the deeper layer would bring about a flow contrary to the one at the surface. The convection-current would thus be started and as it begins by bringing about an increase of the temperature-difference between the rising and sinking columns it would accelerate till after some time a maximum difference would be reached; this would probably occur after about a quarter of a complete turn. The speed will then decerease again till the current has about made half of a complete turn, i.e. when it has brought the higher temperature matter on top and the lower temperature matter below; the rising and sinking columns will then have assumed the same mean temperature, and the equilibrium is restored. The heat conduction will more or less alter this picture and the amount of movement needed for restoring the equilibrium but it does not change the principle of the phenomenon.

If we assume that up to now about a quarter of a complete revolution has been made, and supposing in accordance with the dimensions of the Banda basin and the depth of about 400 km of the deep earthquakes in this area that the current takes place inside a cross section of about 500 km height and 500 km breadth, we find that in 2,000,000 years it must have travelled a distance of about 200 km and so the mean velocity must have been about 10 cm per year. During this interval, which is only one ninth of the interval involved in the above problem, the cooling cannot have got much further than to a depth of about 40 km, i.e. to a fifth of the depth of the upper horizontal part of the current. It does not seem likely that this can have seriously affected the course of events.

For obtaining an estimate of the sinking of the surface above the sinking column we have to assume the temperature distribution in the subcrustal layer before the current started and outside the area heated by the root. Referring to the curve given by Gutenberg in *Internal Constitution of the Earth,* page 162, we think that Fig. 2 gives an acceptable estimate. We may probably adopt the temperature at the lower boundary of the rigid crust at about 700°, which would mean a gradient in the crust varying from 30°/km at the surface to 10°/km at the bottom.

If we assume that during the history of the Earth the subcrustal layer has been turned over several times by convection-currents, the temperature-curve in this layer has to show, as Gutenberg remarks, a much smaller gradient of, for instance, 1°/km; from 100 km–500 km depth he assumes a temperature of 1500–1800°. In the upper layer, however, where it touches the crust, a cooling curve must have formed since the last convection-current took place, which might have occurred after the Eocene folding period in the tectonic belt. This has been represented by the curve of Fig. 2.

From this curve we may estimate the mean temperature of the up-

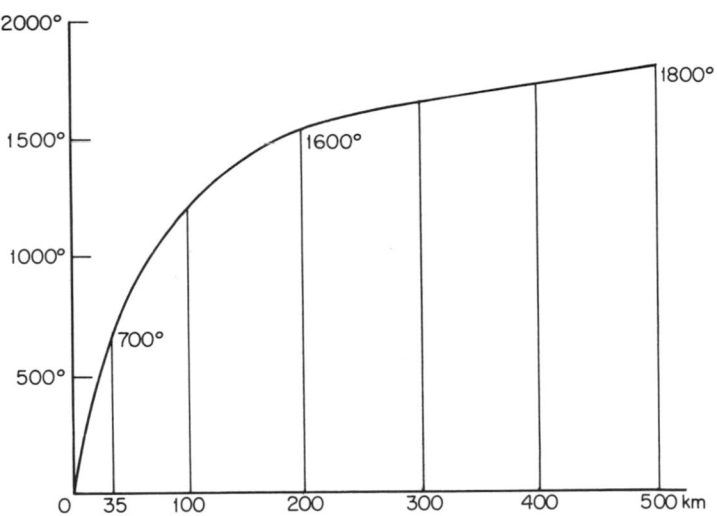

Fig. 2. Temperature curve in the upper 500 km.

per 200 km of the subcrustal layer at some 1200°, and after a quarter revolution of the current this mean temperature must have reigned in the greatest part of the sinking column, increased, however, by a certain amount because of the heat-conduction from the surrounding matter. As a result we may make the rough estimate that over the lower half of this column the mean temperature will be about 500° below the normal one. Adopting again a thermal expansion coefficient of $3 \times 10^{-5}$ this amounts to a shortening of the column of 3.8 km.

We may assume that about half of this shortening will appear at the surface and the other half at the bottom of the column, thus causing the pressure gradient needed for the horizontal parts of the currents at the surface and at the bottom, the first being directed towards the sinking column and the second away from it. This rough assumption is in harmony with the formulas for a steady convection-current; in another paper the writer hopes to enlarge on these deductions. We come to the conclusion that we may expect a sinking of the surface over the sinking column of about 2 km.

The reverse must be true for the rising column, and so we may estimate the rising of the surface here at this same value. We neglect here the rising at the start caused by the radio-active effect of the root as derived above. The result would thus be a difference between the two areas of about 4 km. This difference is in good harmony with the actual topography of the Banda arc area and, in fact, of the whole eastern half of the archipelago but there is an obvious disagreement in the fact that the mean level of the whole region has not remained the same when the deep basins originated but that it has been lowered over 1.5 or 2 km. This point had already been raised by MacGillavry in 1930; he drew attention to the difficulty of explaining this lowering of the mean level, while we might rather expect that the thickening of the sialic crust by the orogenic phenomena would bring about a rising of this mean level.

Our hypothesis of convection-currents in the subcrustal layer can give a simple explanation of this difficulty and it can at the same time make clear that this area as a whole must show an excess of gravity as the anomaly-field of the East Indies shows it to be the case. The explanation is that the presence of convection-currents brings about an increased cooling of the Earth in this area. This is clear as the sinking current brings matter of lower temperature downwards which absorbs heat from the surrounding matter while the excess heat brought to the surface by the rising current is for a large part lost to the Earth by an increased radiation at the surface. Admitting this excess of cooling up to a depth slightly larger than that to which the currents go, it follows that the density is correspondently larger than normal while the shrinking must lower the surface. If the whole area consisted of rising and sinking columns and if the excess heat of the rising column was entirely radiated into space we should thus obtain a mean lowering of the surface of half the shrinking of 3.8 km derived before for the sinking column, i.e. about 2 km. This figure may be too large but it is certainly possible that it would attain the amount of 1.5 km which is present. It is also possible that part of this amount has been caused by older current-systems. In that case this part of the lowering would, however, already have been present during the last folding in tertiary $f$ 2.

The discussion of the gravity field may be postponed to a future paper. The writer wishes here only to add a short remark which follows from the last deductions. If we are right in attributing the low level of the mean topography in the eastern half of the East Indies—and, in fact, in the whole area east of Asia where we find tectonic basins—to an abnormal cooling here of the Earth up to a depth of some 600–800 km, this must mean a disturbance of the thermal equilibrium of the Earth of a much greater size than that caused directly by the presence of the crustal root as derived before. The question then arises whether this would not be likely to start a correspondently greater type of convection-current, made possible by the presence to a much greater depth of a slight temperature gradient of the order of 1°/km or less caused by the cooling.

This current-system rising under a broad borderzone of the continent and sinking under the adjoining oceanic zone would thus have continental dimensions and might even be supposed to involve the whole thickness of the mantle up to a depth of 2900 km. It might be imagined to bring about the major cycles of orogeny well known in the geological history of the Earth.[4] During each cycle the current would only make about one half of a revolution in the same way as it has been explained for the smaller type of current dealt with above. After each cycle the temperature gradient must have disappeared, and it takes a long period of rest before the cooling has brought it again into being.

There is much to be said in favour of this explanation of the orogenic cycles. It explains their occurring more or less periodically with a variable period. It likewise explains the regressions in the beginning of an orogenic period and the slow change to transgressions in the end of this period and during the long period of rest between the cycles; these regressions are connected with the rise of the surface over the borderzones of the continents when a rising current originates there,

[4] See also David Griggs, "A theory of mountain-building," *Am. J. Sci. 237* (1939), 611–650.

while the transgressions come into being when the current is slowly dying out.

If these speculations may be allowed, we should come to the conclusion that the initial disturbance of the thermal equilibrium needed for bringing about these large cycles would be caused by the smaller types of current-system here discussed which themselves are started as a direct consequence of the folding together of the Earth's crust. We thus would see here a chain of events of steadily increasing size started in the beginning by a small surface effect of the Earth and leading eventually to a big current-system having its main cause in the cooling of the Earth which provides it with the energy required.

# BRYAN

Kirk Bryan (1888–1950), American geologist, was a member of the U. S. Geological Survey, which he joined in 1912 as a Geologic Aid in the Ground Water Division, becoming Senior Geologist in 1926, the same year that he began his teaching career as an Assistant Professor at Harvard University where he became Professor of Physiography in 1943. His chief contributions to geology dealt with the geomorphology and erosion cycle of arid and semi-arid regions, ground water resources, glacial and periglacial phenomena, the interrelation between geomorphology and archaeology, and military geology, in which he became interested while serving with the American Expeditionary Forces during the First World War. Subsequent to his sudden and untimely death, August 31, 1950, while engaged in field work in Wyoming, his former students and colleagues established as a memorial the Kirk Bryan Award of the Geological Society of America.

Bryan's concept of the pediment as an end-product in the cycle of erosion in arid or semi-arid regions was widely accepted by geomorphologists, and this landform has now been identified in many such regions throughout the world. Only a few of the astutely coined terms he proposed for "the new subscience of cryopedology" have thus far come into general use, and "permafrost" is still in the vocabulary of many geologists despite his devastating criticism of it, but Bryan himself would probably be the first to recommend patience.

## MOUNTAIN PEDIMENTS *

In general, the mountains of the Papago country rise from plains which are similar in form to the alluvial plains that commonly front mountains of an arid region, but large parts of the plains are without

* From "The Papago Country, Arizona," *U. S. Geological Survey Water Supply Paper 499* (1925).

alluvial cover and are composed of solid rock. These plains constitute a land form that is distinct and requires a name. "Mountain pediment" has been chosen as the name for such a plain of combined erosion and transportation at the foot of a desert mountain range. The plain ordinarily surrounds and slopes up to the foot of the mountains, so that at a distance the mountains seem to be merely ragged projections above a broad triangular mass—the pediment or gable of a low-pitched roof. This metaphor was first used by McGee but applied to only one of many plains of this type that he described. The same metaphor was also used by Weed in describing the Little Belt Mountains of Montana, which are surrounded by gravel-capped plains of erosion that, though developed in a region much less arid, resemble the plains cut on rock in the Papago country. "Mountain pediment" as a term replaces "subaerial platform" and in part "suballuvial bench" as defined by Lawson. It appears preferable because it is less awkward and because it expresses the intimate relation of the plain to the mountain without unnecessary implications as to origin.

The normal mountain pediment has a smoothly sloping surface, more or less covered by alluvium and broken only by scattered hills which rise abruptly from its surface, and in many of which are prolongations of the intercanyon ridges of the mountains. . . .

The angle of slope of pediments ranges from about 50 feet to 200 feet to the mile. It is noticeable, however, that in any one mountain range the slope of the pediment is steeper opposite the smaller canyons and very much flatter opposite the large canyons. The parts opposite the intercanyon portions of the mountain front are steeper than the parts opposite canyons, and they commonly slope not only outward from the mountains but toward the stream channels, which emerge from the canyon mouths.

Exceptions to this general condition occur, for at the mouths of certain canyons the pediments have steep slopes, especially in the direction of the axes of the streams. This exception seems to be due to especially resistant boulders which have been brought down by the stream and dropped at the canyon mouth, causing the stream to spread and lose its carrying power. The boulders, until they weather into fragments small enough to be moved, protect and preserve a slope steeper than is normal to the pediment.

.     .     .     .     .

The formation of pediments in the Papago country has been very generally interrupted by a new cycle of erosion, and the processes may now be observed only in localities of small extent. These processes will be briefly stated. At the base of a mountain front débris is swept outward by ephemeral streams which head in the mountain canyons and by small rills which originate through the concentration of rain wash at the base of the mountain slope. These streams are not permanent or even intermittent; they operate only during or immediately after a rain.

At the base of a mountain slope the fine débris washed down by rains is moved forward by little rills toward the larger streams. As the supply of débris is small these rills are not fully loaded and are effective erosive agents, tending to reduce the height of interstream areas. The grade of the rills and of the smaller streams is steeper than that of the larger streams, because all are underloaded by about the same proportion, and therefore the larger volumes of water transport their loads on the lower gradients. As a result of this relation of stream grades, the pediment, cut and molded by these streams has a lower slope opposite the larger canyons than opposite the smaller canyons. Also, the parts of the pediment opposite the intercanyon ridges have a steeper slope away from the mountain and in addition slope toward the adjacent streams.

The pediment is greatly increased in extent by lateral migration of the streams at and below the mouths of the canyons. The irregularities of the pediment are removed, the higher places being eroded and the lower filled with débris and protected. The lower parts of the canyons are also widened by undermining the slopes of the intervening spurs. When the spurs become narrow they are cut through by slope recession on both sides, and hills are left standing as outliers on the pediment. These solitary hills are worn away with extreme slowness. Their erosion depends entirely on the gradual disaggregation of the rock which composes them and on the movement of the débris over the pediment during rains. The hills retain the same steep slopes as the original mountain but grow gradually smaller until the last remnants are masses of boulders or single rocks projecting above the general level.

The development of the pediment is therefore due to erosion, which may be summed up under three heads—(1) lateral planation by the streams issuing from the canyons, (2) rill cutting at the foot of mountain slopes, (3) weathering of outliers and unreduced remnants, with transportation of the débris by rills. These processes can not operate below a level determined by the grade necessary to transport débris away from the mountains. All inequalities below this level will be filled up just as those above it are eroded. Thus the pediment is a slope of transportation and is usually covered with a veneer from 18 inches to 5 feet thick of débris in transit.

As transportation of relatively fine material by water is the essential factor in the formation of the pediment, in contradistinction to the erosion of mountain slopes, which is largely controlled by the movement of large boulders, it is obvious that the pediment grows most rapidly along the major streams. In every indentation in the mountain front and in places where streams emerge from the canyons onto the plains the rate of formation of the pediment is rapid, and consequently extensions of the pediment into the mountains are common. These extensions consist of branching valleys, many of which are 2 miles or more in width and reach far into the interior of the mountain mass. The erosion of the mountains at the headwaters of many streams is much faster than in the lower portions of the same streams, for there is obviously more water pouring down the mountain slopes of the larger mountain masses, and feeble streams are incapable of much planation. Consequently the headwater slopes may recede more rapidly than the side walls of valleys. The extension of the pediment may thus divide the original mountain into groups of detached hills separated by relatively broad surfaces cut on rock, as in the Sacaton Mountains. . . .

## CRYOPEDOLOGY—THE STUDY OF FROZEN GROUND AND INTENSIVE FROST-ACTION WITH SUGGESTIONS ON NOMENCLATURE*

### INTRODUCTION

Study of the action of frost, particularly in the Arctic and in areas having a periglacial climate during the Ice Age, goes on apace. However, discussion of the problems involved is handicapped and confused by the awkwardness and inadequacy of available terms. The present paper is concerned with the propriety of introducing some order into the terminology by the adoption of new terms and the modification of certain older ones. All future needs cannot be anticipated but the proposals here made should give a measure of relief.

.  .  .  .  .

### THE GENERAL PROCESSES

In our textbooks, discussion of weathering and erosion is largely confined to types of activity current in temperate climates. The relatively modest role of frost-action in temperate climates can be described with

*From *American Journal of Science* 244 (1946), 622–642.

ordinary English words. "Frost" has, according to Webster, several meanings: (1) the act of freezing, applied chiefly to water; (2) the state of the air which occasions freezing; (3) frozen dew or hoarfrost; (4) metaphorically, coldness of temperament, etc. The first two senses are those commonly in use in geological discussions. The word is also a verb, "to frost," in which the meaning is more confused: (1) to frost or freeze vegetation; (2) to cover with hoarfrost and hence (3) to produce a "frosted" or matte surface on cake, metals, or other substances. In order to describe the action induced by freezing and thawing, geological writers have been forced to compound the terms "frost-action" and "frost-work." Webster does not define "frost-action" but the meaning of "frost-work" is given as the pattern of ice crystals on a windowpane or other surface.

Thus the general use by geologists of "frost-action," "frost-work," "frost-splitting," "frost-split," "frost-riving," "frost-riven," "frost-heave," and "frost-heaved" is not completely supported by dictionary definitions. However, these terms are all perfectly derived verbal nouns and adjectives of self-evident meaning. There is, however, no way of deriving from these verbal expressions corresponding nouns for the products of the varieties of action that they imply. All that can be done is to use expressions such as "materials produced by frost-action," or "frost-split fragments" or "frost-heaved ground." Experience shows that such roundabout expressions are awkward and inadequate. Several terms have been introduced for particular frost-born products but no satisfactory general terms of wide connotation have yet been brought forward.

## The New Sub-Science—Cryopedology

The present wave of interest in the Arctic, stemming from the recent war, involves studies in both pure and applied science. This new drive will advance knowledge in a field which heretofore has been investigated for its own sake or for application to the problems of the Pleistocene. The construction of roads, airfields, and other facilities gives rise to problems new to American engineers and construction men. The extensive experience and studies by the Russians in Siberia have been summarized in the excellent manual by Muller.[1] New studies have recently been undertaken in Alaska by the U. S. Geological Survey and by the U. S. Engineers. This economic interest reinforces and adds a drive which means progress in the study of intensive frost-action and permanently frozen ground.

[1] S. W. Muller, *Military Intelligence Division, U. S. Army, Strategic Engineering Study No. 62, 1945.*

It appears that a new sub-science is being created and that it deserves a name. "Cryopedology" is proposed . . . as a suitable name, being derived from krúos, κρύος, icy cold, pedon, πέζον, ground or soil, and logos, λόγος, knowledge. The Greek root "cryo" is familiar in the words cryolite and cryogenic and "pedon" in Pedology, or Soil Science.

·   ·   ·   ·   ·

In the remainder of this paper the various processes and phenomena of Cryopedology are reviewed and a set of terms is proposed. The terms should be general in import and allow the retention of local and special terms. So far as new varieties are discoverable, new names may hereafter prove necessary. Local words with local connotations are so useful, particularly in reports of an economic import, that many of these terms should be retained as synonyms. The new terms are compounded so far as possible from familiar roots already established in English usage. They will, therefore, be readily converted into other European languages.

### Need for General Terms

Frost-action as a term involves a variety of processes and implied results. There are the phenomena of freezing. . . . The onset of low temperatures freezes the water in the pores of the ground but there is little resulting expansion. In a body of ground provided with capillary pores and connected to unfrozen water-bearing ground, ice continues to crystallize in layers and masses. Expansion of the frozen layer ensues and results in thrusts in all directions. As the direction of easiest relief of strain is upward, expansion of the ground in that direction is notable and is usually called frost-heave. However, the upward expansion is frequently highly concentrated at spots having the best capillary connections to the best water-supply. There is no common expression for the lateral thrust resulting from expansion although horizontal as contrasted with vertical frost-thrust would sufficiently carry the meaning. . . .

However, the thawing of frozen ground induces new movements. The frozen ground usually contains ice to a volume much greater than the volume of pore space. On melting, the grains are separated from each other by films of water and the mass lacks coherence. There results differential and mass flow. Our present knowledge is insufficient to describe all the intricacies of this flow. The objective of many students is to analyze the movements completely. It is certain, however, that if the melt-water can escape, much fine-grained material is carried off. Further, the body of melted ground is rearranged by differential movement and, if a gradient exists, there is also a mass flow down-slope.

These movements may be arrested by a new freezing cycle, and obviously the number of alternations from freezing to melting and their duration and intensity affect the movements. Further, every cold period is accompanied by evaporation of water and ice. The surface of the ground becomes loose and pulverulent. This dry layer also modifies movements on later melting.

The mass movement down-slope was named by Andersson[2] "solifluction" (from *solum*, soil, and *fluere*, to flow). His term, not being strictly limited to flow under conditions of freeze and thaw, has been extended to cover soil flow under other conditions. Salomon-Calvin[3], who restricts solifluction to motion over a base of permanently frozen ground, points out that those who use solifluction as synonymous with "soil flow" need another expression for the process described by Andersson. This new term is here suggested.

Furthermore, the movements of material under severe freezing and thawing are not confined to simple mass flow but are more complex. Fine-grained materials are winnowed out so that the surface layer is coarser than the base. Also, the coarse and fine components of the surface layer move differentially so as to produce the much studied and highly varied "soil structures."

. . . . .

What can be proved easily is that the surface layer, 1 to 3 feet thick and in places as much as 10 feet thick, has been disturbed and that some of its components have been translated down-slope. The nomenclature here proposed emphasizes the disturbance rather than the fact or the method of down-slope movement.

In summation, the easily ascertained effects of intensive frost-action can be assigned to two groups of related processes: (1) the break-up of rock by freezing of water, a familiar process; (2) the differential and down-slope movement of the surface layer. The latter process, although it has been the subject of many studies over the past thirty years and in spite of the pursuit of these studies at an accelerated rate, is still not well understood. Most of the difficulties in nomenclature are in this field of effort. . . .

[2] J. A. Andersson, *J. Geol. 14* (1906), 91–112.
[3] Wilhem Salomon, Heidelberger Akadamie der Wissenschaften, *Sitzberg. Jahrgang,* 1929 (Berlin and Leipzig).

## Terms for Frost-Splitting

The break-up of rock by freezing normally requires repeated freezing with intervals of thawing and results in the production of rock spalls and also in the comminution of rock into small grains. These phenomena are referred to as "frost-splitting" or "frost-riving," and the fragments are said to be "frost-split" or "frost-riven." These are good English expressions and unobjectionable. They are paralleled by the German, *Frostsprengung* and *Spaltenfrost*. The slim crystals of ice which form at right angles to the ground surface are called needle ice, and in German, *Pipkrake*. However, no word is available for the product of frost-splitting either as individual pieces or as a mass. . . .

In compounding a new term, the obvious root is derived from Latin *gelo, gelare*, to freeze, and *gelu*, frost. There are many derivations in English, most of which refer to the formation of a jelly from a liquid, as gelatine, gelatinize, and so on. However, "gelation" means to cool from a molten state and "regelation" is familiar as the process of re-freezing of ice under pressure. The Latin, *congelare*, to freeze, is familiar in the word congeal, derived through the French, and the prefix *con* blurs the sound of *gel* (*i*) so that the compound becomes distinctive.

Thus for frost-splitting the word *congelifraction* is proposed from *congelare* to freeze and *fractare*, to break. There is then available the noun "congelifract" for the individual fragment produced. If the congelifracts are large, the body or heap of fragments, or "spalls," is a rubble of congelifraction. But there are many kinds of rubble, and precision is necessary if one is to distinguish between heaps of rubble produced by simple gravitational accumulation in a warm desert, and the rubbles of talus in a cool mountain area where most of the rock spalls are "congelifracts." Further, the comminution of rock into mineral grains by frost-action produces a distinct type of sand and finer fragments. Both large and small congelifracts would form bodies of material to be designated by the term "congelifractate."

## Terms for Movement under Frost-Action

As previously pointed out, the term solifluction is no longer strictly confined to flow under freeze and thaw.[4] A. Heim[5], for instance has introduced "subsolifluction" for the flow and sliding of soft materials under sublacustrine and submarine conditions.

[4]C. F. S. Sharpe, *Landslides and Related Phenomena*, Columbia University Press, 1938.
[5]Arnold Heim, *Neues Jahrb. Mineral. Geol. Palaentol. 2* (1908), 136–157.

However, some authors . . . not only use solifluction for the process but also for the product. Such usage may be justified in French grammar, but is not to be excused in English. Nor can the spelling "solifluxion" common in the writings of English authors be strongly defended. . . .

· · · · ·

It is obvious that a word is needed for the process and for the result. A recent coinage by Edelman, Florshutz and Jeswiet (1936) is "cryoturbation" which has been adopted by Cailleux (1942). The word is derived from the Greek κρύος = icy cold or frost and τυρβάζω = to trouble, confuse, or stir up. The root "cryo" is familiar but there are no derivatives of the verb, although its equivalent, the cognate Latin *turbare,* is represented in turbine and other words.

An equivalent word can be compounded from the Latin *congelare,* to freeze, with *turbare,* to stir up, to produce "congeliturbation." The product of the process of congeliturbation is a congeliturbate. That all varieties of ground moved by frost-action are moved differentially seems established. Thus, all are stirred up or disturbed. Therefore, congeliturbation and congeliturbate should include all varieties of process and all resulting materials.

· · · · ·

The down-slope movement of the congeliturbate produces a drag on materials below, resulting in "drag folds" involving the underlying material and the congeliturbate. Such plications are referred to by some English authors as the "underplight" (Dines *et al.* 1940). However, the neutral and descriptive term "plication" seems adequate and is also applicable to those instances in which the "drag" phenomena involve only the congeliturbate.

The movement of fine-grained materials, mostly the finer products of congelifraction, to the surface is a significant part of congeliturbation. It is essential to the theories of formation of soil structures set forth by Eakin (1916), Högbom (1913), Gripp and Simon (1933–34), and others. This fine material is washed down-slope in the yearly period of melting in streams or sheets of water or it may flow as mud. Taber (1943), Poser (1931), and others make much of this process. Insofar as the material flows as mud the process is included in solifluction. The English terms, "sludging" for the process and "slud" for the material, are neither euphonious nor necessary as such material can be referred to as a congeliturbate transported by solifluction or by sheet-wash as the facts indicate.

## TERMS ASSOCIATED WITH PERMANENTLY FROZEN GROUND

. . . The terms "perennially frozen ground" and "perpetually frozen ground" are . . . awkward; the equivalent German and Russian is equally difficult. . . . Muller, in his useful review and analysis of Russian studies of the Arctic, has sought the obvious convenience of a single word for permanently frozen ground by coining "permafrost."

"Permafrost" has the merit of being euphonious, but it is an etymological monstrosity, made by contracting "permanent" (through French from Latin, *permanere*) and combining it with the English word "frost," none of whose meanings refer to the ground. It sounds like a trade name for a refrigerator, and "permaform" and "permalift" actually exist as the trade names of types of brassieres. There is also a glue named "permacel." These slight crimes might be forgiven, but it is impossible to make a verb or a verbal noun from "permafrost," as "permafrosting" and "permafrosted" imply that a permanent surface or coating has been applied. Hence the act of producing permanently frozen ground cannot be expressed. Further, the term cannot be easily converted into other European languages.

These various objections can be met by a new term which, being compounded from Latin roots already established in English usage, would convey a meaning on its face. Such a word is "pergelisol" from *per* = throughout or continuing + *geli* = *gelare*, to freeze + sol, from *solum*, the soil or ground. In this term the use of the prefix "per" blurs the resemblance to gelatine and other derivatives of *gelare* with the connotation of jelly.

The several modifications and attributes of the permanently frozen ground pointed out by Muller can then be easily made: "subgelisol," "supragelisol," and "dry pergelisol."

One of the great problems of the Arctic is the time and manner of formation of the pergelisol. To what extent is the area now occupied strictly in accordance with modern climate? Johnstone (1930) has recorded frozen ground at depths of 30 feet below the surface and thus obviously below the depth of present-day freeze and thaw. It must be fossil. The question is thus raised as to what extent part of the pergelisol may be residual from the colder climate of the Pleistocene? The great areas of congeliturbates in periglacial areas imply that pergelisol was also present. Thus future discussion will involve again and again the process of formation of pergelisol. It is suggested that the term "pergelation" be adopted, a word strictly analogous to "regelation," already a familiar term in glaciology. Muller[1] uses "aggradation of permafrost" in the sense of pergelation as here proposed. For the thawing of pergelisol by natural or artificial means he uses "degradation of the permafrost" an idea which can easily be carried by de-pergelation.

Above the pergelisol lies a layer which thaws each summer and freezes each winter to a degree dependent on the march of temperature and the duration of the seasons. In this layer "frost-action" takes place, and hence Muller calls it the "active layer." As thawing cannot occur without previous freezing, it is useless to argue as to which produces the greatest part of the activity involved. The annual thawing of this layer is its prime characteristic and it is consistent that the terminology emphasize this distinction from the pergelisol. In thawing there is usually produced more water than the volume of pore space so that the layer becomes soft and tends to flow. It may therefore be termed the "mollisol" from L. *mollere,* to make softer, pliable, to melt, and sol = *solum.* The root of this word is familiar in "emollient" and other words. The act of thawing and softening may, if desirable, be known as "mollition."

The softening of the mollisol is its major characteristic although in well-drained ground where dry pergelisol occurs, melting produces no apparent softening. Whether such areas are large is not known and thus it is at present impossible to evaluate dry pergelisol. However, softening, or "mollition," is the common activity and sets in motion the forces which result in congeliturbation. A fossil mollisol is a congeliturbate.

Muller points out that cool or short summers or very cold, long winters lead to failure to melt all the ground frozen the winter before. There thus intervenes between the mollisol and the pergelisol a layer of frozen ground which may persist for one or several years. For this layer he uses the Russian term "pereletok." Offhand there is no objection to adopting this Russian word but the pronunciation, which can be expressed more or less accurately by "pjerelyétok," is difficult. However, by the use of the prefix *inter,* among, between or amid, one can coin "intergelisol," which gives a term that will sufficiently express the likeness of this material to pergelisol and also its situation between the top of the pergelisol and the mollisol.

Muller also introduces the Siberian word "talik" for bodies of unfrozen ground above, within, or below the pergelisol. This word has the merit of shortness and has only the handicap that it cannot easily be made into a verb. It appears that for various causes these areas of unfrozen ground are formed and again are refrozen. The production of "talik" is an idea that will doubtless be discussed and for which a

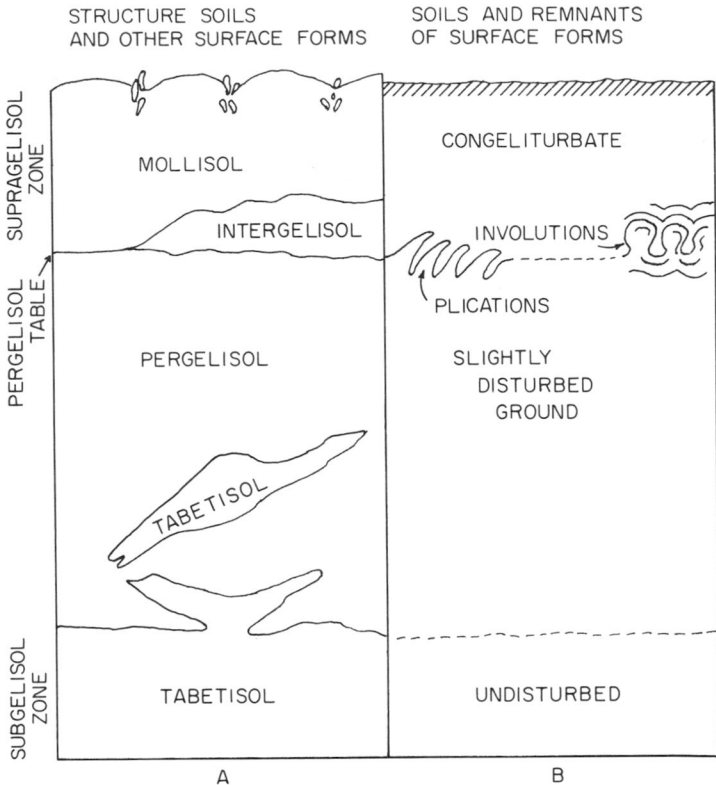

Fig. 4. Diagram showing terminology proposed: A. characteristic parts of the ground in areas of permanently frozen ground; B. characteristic parts of the ground in periglacial areas.

term appears to be desirable. The new term "tabetisol" is here suggested from L. *tabescere,* to melt, and sol = *solum.* The root is present in English in "tabes," a wasting disease, and "tabetic," wasting, which is symptomatic of tabes. The production of tabetisol would be expressed by the verb to "tabificate" and the verbal noun "tabification."

The proposed terminology is parallel for present-day areas of intensive frost-action and for areas where this process was current in the past. The terminology is summarized in Fig. 4.

## WIDESPREAD EROSION BY FROST-ACTION

The idea that landscape can be molded by frost-action and that widespread and extensive reduction of elevation may occur in areas where frost-action is the dominant process is an old one. . . .

·   ·   ·   ·   ·

. . . In Arctic and high mountain lands, reduction of the land may be largely due to intensive frost-action and concurrent action. Furthermore, similar processes were once at work in the periglacial region. . . . The land forms are not analyzable under the normal "Cycle of Erosion" of Davis. A new term seems necessary, and an appropriate coinage would be "cryoplanation," from κρύος, icy cold or ice, and plane, through French from L. *planus*, Greek, πλάτος, broad. The term would be parallel to peneplanation although without implication that the process had reached or nearly reached completion. We would, however, be able to say that an area is or has been subject to the "Cycle of Cryoplanation" in contrast to areas subject to the "Pluvial-fluvial Cycle."

# BUCHER
Walter Hermann Bucher (1888–1965), American geologist, was born in Akron, Ohio, and received his Ph.D. degree from the University of Heidelberg, Germany, in 1911. He began his teaching career at the University of Cincinnati, Ohio, in 1913, becoming Professor of Geology in 1925. In 1940 he was appointed Professor of Structural Geology at Columbia University and continued his teaching and research there until his retirement as professor emeritus in 1956. His investigations of cryptovolcanic structures and his contributions to the solution of orogenic problems were notable factors in the progress of twentieth-century geology. The paper reprinted here was part of a symposium organized by the American Geophysical Union in 1940.

## THE MOUNTAIN-BUILDING CYCLE *

The preceding papers have set forth characteristic aspects of tectonophysics, that is, the concerted effort to understand the structural details of the Earth's crust and the physical condition of the Earth as a whole in terms of the modern physics of materials. On the geophysical side, this effort comprises two main lines of work: (a) the determination of the present physical condition of the Earth's surface and its body as a whole, through measurements of as many variables as possible at as many points on the Earth as possible; (b) experimental determination in the laboratory of the laws of deformation of the materials and the necessary constants involved.

On the side of geology, tectonophysics demands a critical, accurate description of structural detail as well as of the structural features of the Earth in their larger relations. Compared to the geophysicist, the geologist is at a great disadvantage. Whereas the former observes a present condition or behavior, the latter must decipher the overlapping

*From *American Geophysical Union Transactions of 1940,* pp. 163–166.

and fragmentary records of successive stages of behavior. While the former measures the time-dimensions by means of radio signal, stop-watch, or clock, the latter has only a few relatively crude, indirect methods by which to determine the incidence in time, measured by tens of millions of years, of successive structural events.

Yet it is largely the geologist who must furnish the essential data which define the nature of the physical processes that have produced the present structure of the Earth's crust. The goal of his efforts must be a picture accurate enough to permit the mental construction of a model Earth from which not only the present distribution of physical properties, including the distribution of major stresses and strains, may be deduced, but the long sequence of former states of which the present tectonics of the Earth's crust are the visible record. Every informed geologist knows that the sum total of knowledge sufficiently accurate for that purpose is as yet wholly inadequate, even as far as the essential structural features of a relatively well-known country like the United States are concerned. We must be content, therefore, for a long time to come with thinking in terms of partial hypotheses that must be checked constantly against the growing stock of accurate information.

The topic assigned to the speaker, "the mountain-building cycle," occupies the center of all thinking concerning the dynamics of the Earth's crust. It refers specifically to the cyclic recurrence of tangential movements accompanied by more or less intense deformation along the long and relatively narrow orogenic zones which are a unique feature on the face of the Earth. It is the purpose of this comment to point out emphatically that any attempt to find an explanation for this cyclic phenomenon, in order to be successful, must take into account what goes on outside the orogenic belts. The "cycle of mountain-building" is but one aspect of a greater cyclic process that affects all parts of the Earth's crust.

We turn, accordingly, from the spectacular phenomena of the orogenic belts to the large surfaces that lie between them. There another cycle is clearly recognizable. It consists of alternating transgressions and regressions of the sea. Grabau has assembled a large amount of stratigraphic data that seem to bear out the inference that, in spite of divergent local conditions, the broader phases of this cycle are essentially world-wide (pulsation-hypothesis). The epochs of regression outside the orogenic belts coincide with regression and orogenic movements within them. Similarly, periods of transgression outside coincide with transgression of the sea and absence of orogenic movements inside the orogenic belts. The "mountain-building cycle" is thus but a part of the diastrophic cycle of the Earth's crust.

The transgressions and regressions of the sea result from changes in two variables, namely, (a) the volume of water in the oceans, and (b) the dimensions of the space that lies below sea-level. As far as the speaker knows, there is no reason to assume that the volume of water in the oceans has undergone changes of significant magnitude, at least during the time-intervals involved in the cycles of transgression and regression with which we are concerned in this discussion. For the purposes of this argument we shall, therefore, assume that the volume of water remained practically constant.

The amount of space that lies below sea-level depends on the relative position of sea-level. This can be changed in two ways: (a) by deposition of sediments below sea-level; (b) by crustal deformation. While it is impossible, at present, to arrive at any convincing estimate of changes in sea-level produced by sedimentation below sea-level during a given time-interval, a consideration of the geological facts leads to the conclusion that the changes of sea-level due to sedimentation are of a smaller order of magnitude than those produced by crustal deformation and may therefore be neglected in a qualitative analysis of the nature of marine transgressions and regressions. The facts are as follows:

Whenever, in the accessible geologic record, the sea transgressed over parts of the interior of a continental mass, the continental surface did not merely become submerged as, for example, that of North America would be, if its whole surface were lowered uniformly say 1,000 feet. Instead, lowering centered over one or several areas forming basins of sedimentation. In the typical cases, sedimentation even in the central parts of the basins took place in relatively shallow water, generally hardly more than one or a very few hundreds of feet in depth. But sediments have accumulated in such basins, in the course of three or four geologic periods to thicknesses of one to several thousand feet depth. This shows conclusively that the *surface of the basins was actively lowered not only with reference to sea-level, but to the surrounding lines of swells*. The nature of this shortening of the Earth's radius beneath the basins is one of the fundamental problems of crustal deformation.

The lines of swells that separate the basins do not rise with reference to sea-level while the basins sink. In typical cases they receive sediments also, at least during the advanced stages of transgression, so that on them the sedimentary record is fragmentary, representing only a part of the sediments in the basins and that partly at least in reduced thicknesses. *The lines of swells between the basins are,* therefore, *merely belts of lesser lowering with reference to sea-level,* but nevertheless of actual lowering. American geologists are familiar with these relations along the lines of swells that characterize the structure of the eastern half of the United States, such as that of the Jessamine and Nashville domes, and the Mississippi arch and Ozark domes. The Paris and Aquitanian basins of Mesozoic-Cenozoic age in western Europe are especially instructive. They represent portions of the but recently peneplaned surfaces of the Late Paleozoic orogenic belts. The contrast between the peneplaned strongly linear belts of folding that emerge in the "swells" of Brittany, the Plateau Central, and the Rhenish uplift on the one hand and the nonlinear broad basins that cut across them, on the other, is shown strikingly on the geological map of France. It should be studied carefully by anyone concerned with the problem of crustal deformation.

During times of regression, the roles are reversed. While both, basins and swells, rise with reference to sea-level, it is the *swells* that *rise differentially with reference to the basins*. The result is that they rise above sea-level and, in the typical case, have hundreds of feet of sediments removed from them by erosion. In the basins, on the other hand, there may be only a slight stratigraphic hiatus followed by rapid sedimentation. The Late Middle Devonian and the Late Mississippian deformations in the eastern half of the United States, which were followed by the transgressions of the Upper Devonian Black Shales and the Pottsville, respectively, are familiar examples.

In the swells, these epochs of regression represent true deformation, accompanied by steepening of dips across which later sediments come to lie with regional unconformity. They coincide with epochs of folding in the orogenic belts. To the speaker, the conclusion seems inevitable that outside as well as within the orogenic belts, active compression prevails in those phases of the diastrophic cycle which are represented by epochs of folding and thrusting in the orogenic belts. The opposite phase during which in the orogenic belts, in the most typical cases, thick series of limestones or radiolarites or very fine-grained marine shales accumulate in complete conformity, that is, in absence of any evidence of tangential movements, obviously is the exact counterpart of that which causes essentially continuous sedimentation in the basins.

In both the transgressional and the regressional phase, the difference between the behavior of the crust inside and outside the orogenic belts seems to be quantitative rather than qualitative (Fig. 1). In the same time-interval, the surface of the Earth is depressed deeper along the elongated mobile belts than in the more or less equidimensional basins; and in the orogenic phase uplift and deformation are greater along the sharply defined orogenic belts than along the ill-defined lines of swells between the basins.

These relations have been tested with some care only in Europe and

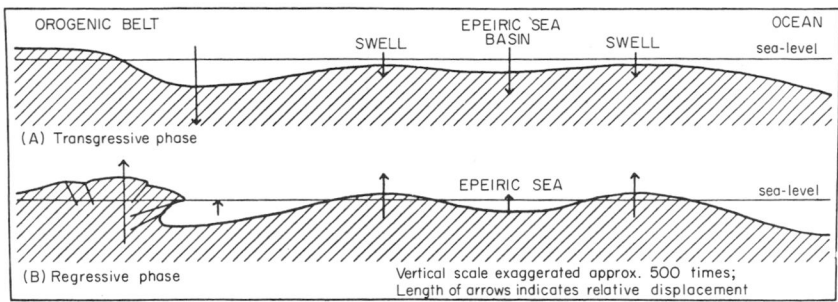

Fig. 1. The diastrophic cycle.

North America. Even there, studies in sufficient detail are available only for a few basins and swells. It is but hypothesis when we assume these conditions to be typical of all land-masses. Yet as far as the writer knows, similar conditions seem to prevail in the other continents. Without concrete evidence of essentially different conditions elsewhere, no other hypothesis seems acceptable at the present.

The little that is known so far concerning the larger features of the topography of the ocean-floors points to similar structural conditions. On the floor of the Atlantic, the best-mapped of the oceans, the mosaic of basins separated by lines of swells is a conspicuous feature. The contrast between them and the West Indian orogenic belt, with its island-chains and submarine welts and furrows, is as striking as any seen on land. Everything suggests that the processes which operate on the exposed parts of the Earth's crust act also on the twice larger area of the ocean-floors.

This raises a significant question. How can the non-orogenic phases of the diastrophic cycle, which comprise the larger part of geologic time, be times of marine transgression if in their course the structural basins on the ocean-floors, which are more numerous and much larger than those on the continental surfaces, are deepened relative to the surrounding swells like those on land?

The speaker believes the most probable answer to be, that the relative vertical distance between the continental and oceanic surfaces decreases during the non-orogenic phase and increases during the orogenic phase. This is expressed in Fig. 2 by arrows which indicate relative movement.

The answer may, however, be simpler. The volume of the ocean-basins need be increased by the lowering of the floors of the numerous structural basins beneath the oceans only if the framework of the intervening swells remains fixed in its vertical distance from the center of

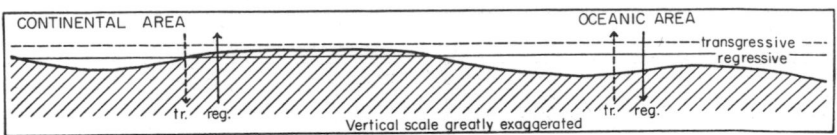

Fig. 2. Apparent change in relative position of continental and oceanic areas during transgressive (tr.) and regressive (reg.) phases of diastrophic cycle.

the Earth. It is possible, however, that basins are merely lowered differentially with reference to the Earth's surface of which every point is actually being lowered as the result of a general shrinkage. The volumetric changes involved in a slight shortening of the radius of a sphere are so great that it is entirely possible that a local increase in depth is more than offset by loss in total area.

For the purposes of this symposium it is not desirable to follow this trend of thought. It is hoped that the main thesis has been brought out clearly. The diastrophic cycle is a matter of the whole Earth's crust, of which the cycle of "mountain-building" is only the most spectacular expression.

The speaker is convinced that this cycle, in its most general terms, may be defined as follows. It consists of alternating non-orogenic and orogenic phases. The non-orogenic phase is characterized on the continents by sinking of parts of the Earth's surface below their former position (with reference to the center of the Earth), this sinking being least along the lines of swells, greater in the centers of the basins, and greatest along elongated belts within the orogenic zones. The orogenic phase consists of a rising of parts of the Earth's surface above their former position (with reference to the center of the Earth), this rising being least, or zero, or possibly even negative, in the centers of basins, greater along the lines of swells, and greatest within the orogenic zones where it is accompanied by more or less conspicuous tangential movements and resulting deformations.

It is the task of the structural geologist to test the correctness and generality of this picture and to refine it in its details. Insofar as he has confidence in the validity of this picture, the geophysicist then will bring his ingenuity to bear on the problem of its possible meaning in terms of the physics of materials.

# PENCK   Walther Penck (1888–1923), Austrian geomorphologist, completed his formal education at the universities of Heidelberg and Vienna and in 1912 became geologist to the Dirreción General de Minas in Buenos Aires.

During the First World War he served for a short time with the German army in Alsace and in 1915 he was appointed Professor of Mineralogy and Geology in the University of Constantinople (Istanbul). Returning to Germany in 1918, he accepted a professorial appointment in the University of Leipzig but devoted most of his time to field work in the mountainous regions of Central Europe and to the preparation of the results of his widely ranging studies for publication. Several of his manuscripts were published after his untimely death from cancer at the age of thirty-five by his father, the famous geographer, Albrecht Penck.

The Pencks, father and son, were sharply critical of the "American School" of physiographers, under the leadership of William Morris Davis, with their emphasis upon the cycle of erosion and its successive stages in their "morphological analyses." Such critiques as the one excerpted here eventually had a profound influence upon all geomorphologists, regardless of nationality, and have done much to guide their field observations and sharpen their thinking concerning the origin of landforms.

## THE CYCLE OF EROSION *

What has found its way into morphological literature as the cycle of erosion is what Davis expressly defined as a special case of the general principle, one which was particularly suitable to demonstrate and to explain the ordered development of denudational forms. It is postulated that a block is rapidly uplifted; that, during this process, no denudation takes place; but that on the contrary, it sets in only after the completion of the uplift, working upon the block which is from that time forward conceived to be at rest. The forms on this block then pass through successive stages which, with increase of the interval of time since they possessed their supposedly original form, i e. with increase of developmental age, are characterised by decrease in the gradient of their slopes.

They are arranged in a *series of forms,* which is exclusively the work of denudation and ends with the peneplane, the peneplain.[1] If a fresh uplift now occurs, the steady development, dependent solely upon the working of denudation, is interrupted; it begins afresh, e.g. the peneplane is dissected. A new cycle has begun; the traces of the first are per-

---

*From *Abhandlungen der Kgl. Sächsischen Akademia der Wissenschafften, Math.-Phys. Klasse* (Leipzig) 72 (1920), 65–102.

The version used here is that of "Morphological Analysis of Land Forms" by Walther Penck, translated by Hella Czech and Katherine C. Boswell (New York: St. Martin's Press, 1953). The excerpts are from pp. 7–16 and are reprinted with the permission of Macmillan Co. Ltd., London.

[1]["Peneplane" is used by the translators for *Rumpffläche,* "peneplain" for *Fastebene,* which Penck equates with *Endrumpffläche,* his "endpeneplane."]

ceived in the uplifted, older forms of denudation. Thus it has become usual to deduce a number of crustal movements, having a discontinuous jerky course, from the arrangement by which more or less sharp breaks of gradient separate less steep forms above from steeper ones below.

. . . Both Davis himself and his followers have made and still make the tacit assumption that uplift and denudation are successive processes, whatever part of the earth is being considered; and investigation of the natural forms and their development has been and is being made with the same assumptions as underlie the special case distinguished above. There is, therefore, a contrast between the original formulation of the conception of a cycle of erosion and its application. Davis, in his definition, had in mind the variable conditions not only of denudation, but of the endogenetic processes;[2] in the application—so far as we can see, without exception—use is made only of the special case, with its fixed and definite, but of course arbitrarily chosen, endogenetic assumption. And criticism, with its justified reproach of schematising, is directed against the fact that the followers of the cycle theory have never looked for or seen anything in the natural forms except the realisation of the special case which Davis had designated as such. Thus even opponents of the American doctrine have taken their stand not against the general principle of the cycle of erosion, but against its application; and they referred merely to the one special case that alone was used. Thus there seems throughout to have been a misunderstanding with regard to the cycle of erosion: its originator meant by it something different from what is generally understood. The way in which the theory is applied, the trend of the criticism it has received, hardly permit any doubt of this. Thus it is necessary to consider more closely the application of the *cycle of erosion* and the criticism directed against it.

As a method, the theory of the cycle of erosion introduces a completely new phase in morphology. Deduction, so far used only within the framework of inductive investigation, or as an excellent method of presentation, has become a means of research. Starting from an actual knowledge of exogenetic processes, the cycle theory attempts to deduce, by a mental process, the land-form stages which are being successively produced on a block that had been uplifted, is at rest, and is subject to denudation. Not only is the order of the morphological stages ascertained by deduction, but also the forms for each stage; and the ideal

[2][Endogenetic processes, such as diastrophism and vulcanism, originate within the earth; exogenetic processes, such as the work of running water, the wind, glaciers, and waves and currents, originate outside of the solid earth.]

forms arrived at in this way are compared with the forms found in nature. There are two points in this method which must be considered critically: (*a*) deduction as a means of investigation; and (*b*) the facts on which the assumptions are based.

To begin with, it is obvious that the ideal forms, which are supposed to develop on *a stationary block,* can be deduced successfully only if there are no gaps in our knowledge of the essential characteristics of the denudational processes. Should this prerequisite not be fulfilled, the deduction is nothing but an attempt to find out from the land forms alone both the endogenetic and the exogenetic conditions to which they owe their origin. It is like trying to solve an equation having three quantities, two of which are unknown; we can expect only doubtful results. The American school may be justifiably reproached with not considering it their next task to eliminate one of the unknown quantities by systematically investigating the processes of denudation all over the world. On the whole, their part in throwing light upon the exogenetic processes has been a very modest one. Yet this is not a decisive blow to the cycle concept. For amongst the 'exogenetic' assumptions made, there is no principle which has not been verified by experience, and criticism by opponents has been unable to show any mistakes in this field.

·　·　·　·　·

The second point was the use of deduction as a method of morphological research—though of course in addition to induction and essentially based upon it. . . . *In morphology, as in any other branch of knowledge concerned with physical problems, deduction as a means of research is not only permissible, but also imperative; unless we wish to renounce the greatest possible exactitude and completeness in the results, and to exclude our branch of learning from the rank of an exact science, a rank which it both can and should acquire in virtue of the character of the questions with which it deals.* It is merely a matter of finding out where, in the process of investigation, we should resort to the method of deduction; and above all making sure that correct and complete data are then provided for it. The provision of these is, as before, exclusively the domain of inductive observation; it only can accomplish this, the deductive process never. It is by no means the deductive character of the method itself which makes it impossible to follow the American way of applying the cycle of erosion, but the incompleteness and, as will presently be shown, the incorrectness of the assumptions made. Thus opposition to the deductive method as a tool for use in morphological investigation has been unable to do serious harm to the theory of the erosion cycle, and it is not to be expected that it will ever succeed in doing so.

.  .  .  .  .

Exogenetic and endogenetic forces begin to act against one another from the moment when uplift exposes a portion of the earth's crust to denudation. So long as uplift is at work, denudation cannot be idle. The resulting surface configuration depends solely upon whether the endogenetic or the exogenetic forces are working the more quickly. Were there no denudation, a block, however slowly it is rising, might in course of time reach any absolute height; and its increase in altitude would be limited solely by the physics of the act of formation, provided that it is inherent in this not to continue indefinitely. It is rather like the way in which an impassable limit has been set to the increase in height of volcanoes by the extinction of volcanic activity, which often comes to an end prematurely, as soon as a certain height has been reached, because lateral effusions replace the summit eruptions. However, it is from the outset that exogenetic breaking-down at the earth's surface works against endogenetic building-up, i.e. denudation works against uplift, in-filling by sediments against subsidence. It is easily understood that an actual elevation can come into existence only if uplift does more work in unit time, and so is working more rapidly, than denudation; a hollow appears only when subsidence takes place more quickly than sediment is supplied, than aggradation. *This state of affairs forms the substance of the fundamental law of morphology: the modelling of the earth's surface is determined by the ratio of the intensity of the endogenetic to that of the exogenetic displacement of material.*

.  .  .  .  .

The above short survey shows that it is essential, when investigating the origin and development of denudational forms as they appear at the earth's surface, to *ascertain the relationship between the intensity* of the endogenetic and of the exogenetic processes—in short, between uplift and denudation; and it is necessary to follow out how this changes as time goes on. None of the present methods used in morphology brings us nearer to achieving this end; none even attempts to do so. The assumption generally introduced, that uplift and denudation were successive processes, or could at any rate be treated as such, has stood in the way. In this respect the only difference between the cycle theory and its opponents is that Davis made the above assumption in order to provide a specially simple case, of particular use in illustrating the cycle concept; but, at the same time, he kept well in mind the importance of concurrent uplift and denudation. To be sure, this was a notion of which he scarcely ever made use, and his followers never. Those of the other school, no less schematically, start in every case from the same assumption; they, moreover, have occasionally tried to justify the general correctness and permissibility of such a course. It is as if they made use of a device familiar in school physics, which is merely a makeshift for presenting in a physically correct manner the resultant of processes acting concurrently. This is a grave mistake in method.

It is permissible to proceed in this way only in the case of *uniform forces* which, in successive units of time, produce effects that remain of equal magnitude. If, in a diagram such as Fig. 1, the co-ordinates $a\,b$ and $b\,c$ represent the effects of simultaneous, uniform forces, the straight line $a\,c$ represents the resultant effect *during* the whole process. In order to ascertain this, it is sufficient to follow the events first from $a$ to $b$, then to $c$.

It is quite different, however, when forces acting simultaneously are *not uniform*, i.e. are changing their intensities in successive units of time and are therefore doing different amounts of work. To find out the resultant during the whole process, it is here necessary *to follow* the course of Nature *continuously,* as was made possible in physics, where such problems are constantly cropping up, only by the invention of differential calculus. To make this clear, let us remind ourselves of the prob-

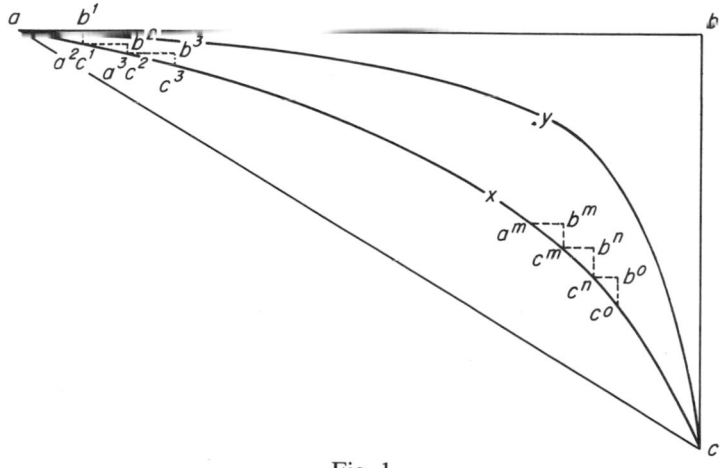

Fig. 1.

lem: to find the trajectory of a missile fired horizontally from a point $a$ (Fig. 1). As the effect of the firing, it would reach $b$; but at the same time, under the influence of the force of gravity, it would drop down by the amount $bc$. To find point $c$, which the projectile reaches, it would really be sufficient to follow events first from $a$ to $b$, then from $b$ to $c$, that is, to imagine the effects of the firing and of gravity as coming into play successively. The trajectory, however, has not been found in that way. It lies on a curve of some kind between the initial and final points, between $a$ and $c$. To determine it, we must find out how the magnitude of the operating forces alters in successive exceedingly small units of time. This can be done by plotting a diagram of forces for each moment, as in our figure, e.g. $ab^1c^1$, $a^2b^2c^2 \ldots a^mb^mc^m$, etc., so that the simultaneous effect of the forces is represented by the very minute distances $ac^1$, $a^2c^2 \ldots a^mc^m$, etc., as if they were uniform during these extremely short intervals of time and took place successively. The error thus made becomes infinitesimally small, if the values chosen for the diagram are made infinitesimally minute; and this method, consisting of an infinite number of infinitely small variables, comes infinitely near the *continuous* course of Nature. This becomes clear if in our figure the triangles $ab^1c^1$, $a^2b^2c^2$, etc., are, as is necessary, made infinitely small; they then disappear completely in the full line $axc$. Since the forces are now changing from moment to moment, the very small distances $ab^1$, $a^2b^2$, etc. and $b^1c^1$, $b^2c^2$, etc., are thus of different lengths, and so the infinitely small resultants $ac^1$, $a^2c^2$, etc., are also of different lengths and at different inclinations. Strung out after one another, they do not form a straight line, but bend in a curve: the trajectory $axc$ which was to be found. *This is the differential method. It is the only way that leads to our goal, which is the exact representation of the resultant of several simultaneous processes that are not acting uniformly during their course.*

*The forces which take part in modelling the land do not act uniformly.* It has already been shown that this is so for denudation, and it is a matter of course for crustal movements. They begin from the position of rest, so they must then be accelerated; and they end with the position of rest, having then suffered deceleration. Whether or not the starting point and the end coincide with a position of absolute rest is of no importance. If indeed we think of the alternation of uplift and subsidence, as has so often, if not as a general rule, taken place on the earth, then the position where subsidence changes to uplift (or vice versa) is the position of rest. *In any case, the movement of the crust is a non-uniform process, which becomes uniform only temporarily during its course, but can never begin uniformly with any definite velocity.* It is not superfluous to stress this obvious factor in view of the often inadequate conceptions which are widespread as to the physics of motion, and even of the fundamental concepts of physics.

To illustrate the position, let us draw a diagram (Fig. 1), in which the co-ordinates represent the effects of crustal movement ($a\,b$) and of denudational processes ($b\,c$). The result of their simultaneous action, the forms of denudation, then appears in the shape of curves between $a$ and $c$. Naturally they are all situated within the triangle $a\,b\,c$; since any curve drawn outside it, as for example, a curve deviating in convex fashion downwards from the straight line $a\,c$, would signify that denudation had begun before subsequent endogenetic action had exposed the crustal fragment to exogenetic destruction or, in other words, that denudation was the prerequisite for crustal movement. Within the triangle an infinite number of curves are possible, all of which begin at point $a$ and end at $c$. Each of these curves represents not a single form, but a *developing series of forms* through which a crustal fragment passes when it is being uplifted and denuded. It is obvious that all the series of land forms which can possibly develop on the earth have one common starting point and one common final form. The former is characterised by the beginning of uplift and denudation (point $a$), the latter by the extinction of endogenetic and exogenetic displacements of material (point $c$). In between lies the endless variety of forms that correspond to the varying ratio of intensity of exogenetic processes to that of endogenetic ones; and they are arranged on an infinite number of curves, each of which represents a series of forms peculiar to the surface development of a crustal fragment which has had a particular course of endogenetic development.

*Thus we see that land forms are not, as the erosion cycle postulates, a single developing series, but that they form an infinite number, and that they are arranged* [on the diagram], *not in a line, but on a surface.* This surface is enclosed by two limiting curves that, at least as regards total dimensions, represent developing series which, on the earth, are *just not possible:* the straight line $a\,c$, that is, the series of forms arising from the uniform development of uplift and denudation, and the axes $a\,b$–$b\,c$, which would be the series of forms that would arise if uplift and denudation succeeded one another. Whether *fragments of the limiting curves* can be observed as component parts in the development of forms on the earth, and which fragments might in that way be realised, will have to be decided by the following investigation.

The relationship of the cycle of erosion (and of methods based upon similar assumptions) to the complex of problems concerning development of land forms now becomes evident. Point $b$ in the diagram represents denudation which sets in only after the completion of uplift; and the series of forms that arise purely as the work of denudation on a motionless block is represented by one limb of the limiting curve: the line *b c*. Its starting point *b* by no means coincides with the point (*a*) from which all development of forms on the earth begins. The perfectly arbitrary choice of that starting point is clearly shown. But, on the other hand, there also emerges the fact that although the method adopted for the erosion cycle (in its applied form) is incorrect in principle, yet it must nevertheless lead to the discovery of the correct final form common to every one of the series of denudational forms that develop on the earth, provided that the method was logically correct and not based upon faulty exogenetic assumptions. The theory of the cycle of erosion does satisfy both these requisites, as cannot be doubted even by its opponents. Point *c* in the diagram represents the end-peneplane, or peneplain, the origin of which was made clear by W. M. Davis, and a littler later, independently, by A. Penck, both basing their conclusions upon detailed inductive observation. One could not, however, in this way deduce a single one among the infinite series of developing land forms which are not only possible but actually exist on the earth in the different parts which have had various endogenetic histories. Almost everything in this field still remains to be done by morphology. Not merely must the investigation start at the beginning of uplift and denudation (point *a*); it must take into account not only the simultaneous effects of endogenetic and exogenetic action, but above all their variable intensities. *For this one must turn to the methods of physics, and indeed to such as permit a continuous following of the variable quantities, that is, the differential method.* This method not only can, but *must* be used in investigating the interdependence between the *processes of movement* which take part in the modelling of the land. For mass-transport of eroded material depends upon a gradient, the factors producing which are crustal movements; and mass-movement of denuded material depends upon a gradient, the processes producing which arise from the results of erosion.[3]

# AHLMANN Hans Wilhelmsson Ahlmann (1889– ), Swedish glaciologist and climatologist, has contributed much to our knowledge and understanding of world-wide climatic fluctuations by studying their effects on glaciers. His clear-sighted initiative has led to extensive international cooperation in scientific research.

[3] Translators' note: The author's distinction between erosion along the line of a watercourse and denudation over a whole surface must constantly be borne in mind.

## ACTIVE AND PASSIVE GLACIAL ICE
## AND A CLASSIFICATION OF GLACIERS *

. . . The activity and passivity of a glacier depend upon its depth, speed of flow, and balance-sheet. The rate of movement of an active glacier is generally large in relation to its size and slope, while that of a passive glacier is small. The balance-sheet of an active glacier is also relatively large; the regime, however, may be positive or negative, for even when it is negative the material transported from the accumulation to the ablation area will be so large that the movement will be considerable. The south side of Vatnajökull, among the regions examined, is one with the most intensive glacial energy, for although its regime has probably long been negative, its total balance-sheet is exceptionally large.[1] Thus a glacier may be active although its tongue is in retreat. The degree of activity or passivity of glaciers in more continental districts and with relatively small regimes will as a rule depend on whether the regime has for any large number of years been positive or negative. Small glaciers, e.g. the Fröya Glacier, are especially sensitive to this. Conditions are more complicated on large areas of inland ice, where the accumulation is insignificant. Their large mass may give them a not inconsiderable movement long after the regime has ceased to be positive. This particularly applies to their outlet glaciers, especially if these slope strongly, as in Greenland.

The rate of movement of a glacier has a definite relation to its thickness: the thinner a glacier grows owing to a progressively negative regime, the slower will be its movements, and the more will the mass of ice carried from its upper to its lower parts be reduced. The consequence of a protracted negative regime will be a diminishing thickness of the glacier and a recession of its front. What happens at the margin is an expression of what takes place in the accumulation area.

Scandinavian Quaternary geologists have, up to the last two decades, mostly interested themselves in the linear forward or backward movement of the glacier margin. In his extensive work on northernmost Fennoscandia during the first decade of this century, V. Tanner[2] has, however, studied both the vertical and horizontal shrinkage of the last inland ice, and recently C. Mannerfelt[3] has treated this same subject in central Norway and the southern Swedish high mountains.

With regard to most areas of inland ice, a negative regime must be

* From *Glaciological Research on the North Atlantic Coasts,* Royal Geographical Society, London, Research Series no. 1, 1948.
[1] H. W. Ahlmann and S. Thorarinsson, "The Vatnajökull Glacier, preliminary report," *Geograph. Rev. 28* (New York, 1938).
[2] V. Tanner, "Studier öfver kvartärsystemet i Fennoskandias norra delar," *Fennia 36* (Helsingfors, 1914–15).
[3] C. M. Mannerfelt, "Några glacialmorfologiska formelement," *Geogr. Annlr. 17* (1945).

maintained for a long time to reduce the thickness sufficiently to affect appreciably the rate of movement and to indicate a passive stage. In the Pleistocene glaciation period, the strong polar climate had in all probability ceased long before the ice became so much thinner that the rate of movement was reduced and the recession set in.

When the negative regime has continued until the movement of the remaining ice is no longer caused by the transfer of material from an accumulation area, but is determined by the slope of the bed, the ice is said to be dead. Dead ice need not lack movement, but what there is will be mostly due to local topography.

This definition of dead ice is based on its movement, or dynamic property. From a climatological point of view an ice mass should be designated dead when it no longer receives any material from accumulation excess above a firn limit, but exists on its bulk alone. If a glacier is very large, e.g. inland ice, a long time—up to several thousand years—elapses between its climatic and dynamic deaths.

Dynamically dead parts may also occur in the margins of glaciers which are otherwise active. They are then often remnants from stages of larger extension and activity of the glaciers. On the northern, leeward side of Vatnajökull, large marginal portions of Brúarjökull are dead. Sudden advances of interior parts, produced by increased surplus accumulation and earthquakes, will push these momentarily active ice masses over the dead portions.

The shrinkage of the Fourteenth of July Glacier during the last decades has produced conditions which justify our assuming continued development in the following way. The firn limit rises gradually, and the yearly excess accumulation above it diminishes concurrently; the thickness, and therefore the rate of movement of the glacier, decreases. The contact between the tributary glaciers and the main glacier then diminishes, reducing the supply of ice to the latter. The continued ablation assists the increasingly rapid recession of the glacier margin. The firn limit gradually rises above the glacier, the whole of which then forms part of the ablation area. During this development the melt water and the precipitation drains off, partly in open lateral channels, partly subglacially in tunnels and cracks. As the thickness decreases, the lateral channels will be gradually situated at lower levels. Finally, isolated dead ice is all that remains in the main valley where the glacier was thickest. Temporary lakes will form both above this dead ice and in the tributary valleys. These ice-dammed lakes are drained suddenly by catastrophic incidents, either supra- or subglacially, as described by Sigurdur Thorarinsson from the Iceland glaciers.[4] The same

[4] S. Thorarinsson, "Vatnajökull; scientific results of the Swedish-Icelandic investigations, 1936–37–38," chap. IX, *Geogr. Annlr. 21* (Stockholm, 1939), 216–242.

course of development has proceeded on a gigantic scale in the Pleistocene glaciation districts of Scandinavia and North America.

It is also possible to differentiate between regions of active and passive glaciation in large glaciated districts.[5] In the area of north European glaciation, the Norwegian mountain regions were at first active, as the glaciation probably began there owing to their great altitude and heavy precipitation. The lower districts east of them were passive and were only gradually invaded by ice from the growing glaciers in the west. When the ice-shed moved eastward, these districts were progressively transformed from passive to active glaciation areas until the Baltic basin was filled with ice.[6] Recent research in Denmark[7] has also shown that the first ice-stream reached the country from Norway across the area now occupied by the Skagerrak Sea. The ice moving across Sweden, following the present Baltic Sea, arrived much later.

When the inland ice reached its extreme limits, its front was active mainly during its advances. Later, its margins soon became passive or dead, as the most northerly parts of Vatnajökull are now. It is also generally considered that the margins of the North German and Jutland inland ice were largely dead.[7]

To understand active and passive glaciation districts, due attention must also be given to the fact that a progressive glaciation of a region will necessarily change the climatological character of its parts. This in turn may change the direction and strength of one ice-stream in relation to another, as has happened, for instance, in various North American glaciation areas. In some regions progressive glaciation may shut off the precipitation-carrying winds to such an extent that there will be no further glaciation, or that earlier ones will decline or disappear. An example of this is the present northernmost parts of Greenland and Norwegian Finnmark at the maximum stage of the last Pleistocene glaciation. A steady concentric expansion of a glaciation area is, from a glaciological point of view, inconceivable.[8]

It is quite conceivable that the excess accumulation on the Scandinavian inland ice had begun to diminish or had quite ceased by the

[5] H. W. Ahlmann and S. Thorarinsson, "The Vatnajökull Glacier, general conclusions," *Geograph. Rev. 28* (1938); cf. R. Foster Flint, "Growth of the American ice sheet during the Wisconsin Age," *Bull. Geol. Soc. Am. 57* (1943).

[6] K. Milthers, "Ledeblokke og Landskabsformer i Danmark," *Danmarks Geol. Undersögelse 2*, no. 69 (Copenhagen, 1942).

[7] In his valuable work, "Les Actions écoliennes périglaciaires en Europe" (*Soc. géol. de France, Mém. 46*, Paris 1942), Cailleux points out that the most severe climate prevailed during the growth and advance of the north European inland ice, and that even after this optimal severity the ice continued to extend, whereas the alpine glaciers reached their maximal extension in connection with the severe optimum.

[8] Ahlmann and Thorarinnsson, "The Vatnajökull Glacier, general conclusions," *Geograph. Rev. 28* (1938).

time the ice margin was receding across the southernmost part of Sweden. Recent investigations[9] have shown that the inland ice was passive and in a dying condition when it melted from the southern Sweden highland. It was later active for some centuries; this caused the margins to stagnate and to form the large terminal moraines of central Sweden and southern Finland. Later, it rapidly became passive again, and became dead in the interior of Norrland. From the glaciological point of view it is important to note that this ice, the recession of which was geo-chronologically elucidated by G. de Geer[10] and his school, was passive, dying, or dead during the greater part of its existence. The well-known eskers or *oses* and other marginal formations in Sweden and Finland were not formed by any active glacier mass.

· · · · ·

The fact that a glacier is growing necessarily means that its accumulation excesses are thickening; but at the same time its rate of movement increases, and the ice moves down towards the ablation area at an increasing rate. When the thickness has increased sufficiently to upset the previous equilibrium, the rate of movement is suddenly still more accelerated. It is well known that the front of an advancing glacier moves forward rapidly, while the retreat of a shrinking glacier is slow. Even when the advance is protracted, e.g. during an actual glaciation, it is probably discontinuous and jerky. The influence of the thickness of the glacier on the rate of movement, and consequently also on the rate at which ice is transported from the accumulation area to the ablation area, is in the case of valley glaciers probably so great that the thickness of the accumulation area will have little chance of increasing greatly, always provided that the physical nature of the glacier does not change. A change of a glacier from the temperate to the polar type would, for instance, probably reduce the rate of movement. A. Penck has pointed out that even when the last Pleistocene glaciation was at its maximum in the Alps, accumulation was not appreciably larger in the firn areas of the glaciers than it is now. He therefore concluded that glaciations are due rather to a lowering of the temperature than to an increase of precipitation. His conclusion is correct, but hardly his premises. At the same time, it should be remembered that a moderate reduction of the temperature will increase the solid precipitation, particularly in districts of relatively heavy precipitation in the summer, a considerable portion of which would then fall as snow. . . .

· · · · ·

[9] E. Nilsson, "Gotiglaciala issjöar i södra Sverige," *Geol. Foren. Stockholm Forh. 64* (1942).

[10] G. de Geer, "Geochronologica Suecia: Principles," *Kungl. Svenska Vetenskapsakad. handl.* [3] *18* (Stockholm, 1940), 6.

From our experiences in North-East Land in 1931, and those of J. P. Koch and A. Wegener in Greenland in 1912–13,[11] had already[12] proposed that glaciers, from the geophysical point of view, should be divided into temperate and arctic glaciers, and the latter into high-arctic and subarctic.[13] These were defined as follows, using the more correct word "polar" instead of "arctic."

I. *Temperate glaciers* consist of crystalline ice formed by fairly rapid recrystallization of the annual surplus of solid precipitation due to great quantities of fluid water. Throughout these glaciers the temperatures correspond to the melting-point of the ice, except in winter time, when the top layer is frozen to a depth of not more than a couple of metres. The glaciers of Scandinavia and the Alps are included in this group.

II. *Polar glaciers* consist, at least in their higher and upper parts, of hard crystalline firn formed by slow recrystallization of the annual surplus of accumulated solid precipitation. The temperature of the glacier is negative even in summer down to a certain depth. These polar glaciers can be subdivided into:

(a) *High-polar glaciers,* which consist, at least in their accumulation areas, of crystalline firn with temperatures below freezing-point to a considerable depth. Even in summer the temperature in the accumulation area is so low that as a rule there is no melting accompanied by formation of water.

(b) *Sub-polar glaciers,* which in their accumulation areas consist of crystalline firn down to a depth of some 10 or 20 metres. In the summer the temperature allows surface melting accompanied by the formation of fluid water.

This classification is based on the consistency of the upper parts of the glaciers firn or compact ice and on the temperature in these. Both depend on the air temperature, particularly in the summer, and the melt-water formed by the ablation plays a very important part. Conditions on Isachsen's Plateau and the Fröya Glacier as well as in North-East Land in 1935–36 confirmed the latter observation, and so did the glaciological results of the Wegener Expedition in 1930–31, which were not published until after 1933. On the interior portions of the Greenland inland ice, and in practically the whole Antarctic, the

[11] "Wissenschaftliche Ergebnisse der dänischen Expedition nach Dronning Louises-Land und quer über das Inlandeis von Grönland, 1912–13," *Medd. om Grönland 75* (Copenhagen, 1930).

[12] Thorarinsson, "Scientific results of the Swedish-Icelandic investigations, 1931," pt. 8, *Geogr. Annlr.* (Stockholm, 1933).

[13] Quite independently of my classification, M. Lagally in "Zur Thermodynamik der Gletscher," *Z. Gletscherkunde* (1932), defined on theoretical grounds the three glacier types: the cold, the warm, and the transitional, which completely agree with my high-polar, temperate, and sub-polar types.

air temperature is so low both in winter and summer that very little or no melt-water will form. The firn is therefore recrystallized very slowly, and the glaciers consist of frozen firn to great depths. We do not know at what depth this frozen firn changes into ice at "Eismitte," the central station of the Wegener Expedition, but it must be well over 75 metres. This change is probably due to pressure. At lower levels, where both the winter and the summer temperatures are higher than at "Eismitte," the Greenland inland ice is of sub-polar nature, and its outlet glaciers are temperate, at least in the lower latitudes.

Conditions in a high-polar glacier will obviously differ in many respects from those in a temperate glacier. Its movements, for instance, are sure to be different. Its relations to, and effect on, its bed must also be different. I see proof of this in the sharp peaks and ridges of "Neu Schwabenland" in the Antarctic, which were probably bared relatively recently and seem to be quite unaffected by glacial erosion. In the central portions of formerly glaciated districts, it is also necessary to take into account the considerable physical changes of the inland ice during a period of glaciation.

# GUTENBERG Beno Gutenberg (1889–1960), German-American seismologist, received his doctorate in geophysics at Göttingen, Germany, in 1911, was for a time in charge of the seismological station at Frankfurt-am-Main, and from 1930 until his retirement in 1957 was Professor of Geophysics and Director of the Seismological Laboratory at the California Institute of Technology in Pasadena. He was an acknowledged leader among the world's seismologists in the analysis of earthquake vibrations and the information they provide concerning the physical properties of the earth's interior.

## MOBILITY OF THE EARTH'S INTERIOR *

The general results, in combination with other data, allow us to get a better idea of the facts which must be considered in interpreting tectonic processes. So far as is known, the visible mountains have not changed their height appreciably in historic times. More data bearing on the accuracy of this statement are very desirable since the experiments of Griggs[1] on "creep" of rocks suggest the possibility of changes during long periods. The greatest differences in elevation between nearby

---

*From "Changes in Sea Level, Postglacial Uplift, and Mobility of the Earth's Interior," *Geological Society of America Bulletin* 52 (1941), 721–772.

[1] D. Griggs, "Creep of Rocks," *J. Geol.* 47 (1939), 225–251. [See also page 407 of this volume.]

points of the earth's surface do not exceed about 10 km, producing stresses just below the strength as determined by laboratory experiments. Gravity determinations lead to the conclusion that in general the weight of the mountains or the deficiency of material in oceanic regions is compensated within the uppermost layers of the earth, not over 60 km thick, except for certain regions with gravity anomalies. However, in most of these exceptional regions earthquakes occur rather frequently, indicating that tectonic processes are going on in such regions, either with a tendency to restore equilibrium or as a consequence of processes which maintain or increase the anomalies. The strength of the material in the uppermost layers down to a depth of about 50 km prevents plastic flow as long as the stresses are less than about $10^{10}$ dynes per square cm, and must lead to earthquakes as soon as the breaking strength of the material is exceeded by the stresses. Tsuboi[2] has estimated the maximum energy which can be stored in the earth's crust without disturbing isostasy beyond the observed values and found an excellent agreement with the maximum energy liberated in earthquakes ($10^{25}$ ergs).

Whereas at present we have no observations proving plastic or "pseudo-plastic" flow in relatively large sections of the lithosphere, the postglacial uplift leaves no doubt that some kind of flow must occur in the deeper parts, say below 60 or 80 km. Seismic observations lead to the conclusions that at a depth of about 70 km there is a small but distinct decrease in the wave velocity, which has been interpreted as a consequence of the transition from the crystalline to the vitreous state. This would explain the fact that at about this depth the strength of the material decreases noticeably and in the asthenosphere below permits plastic flow even if the stresses are small. However, the speed of this flow is very slow. It takes thousands of years to reduce deviations from the equilibrium to one half. If the stresses accumulate at a rate much faster than they are reduced by plastic flow, the breaking strength of the material will be reached practically as quickly as in the lithosphere, and earthquakes must result in just the same way. Since in certain regions the time interval between earthquakes is measured by centuries or even years, as in the Hindu Kush region at a depth of over 200 km, the possibility of rapid accumulation of stresses due to unknown processes is proved. Thus far there is no contradiction among the observations, the conclusions from laboratory experiments, and the results of the theory based on the assumption of the properties at the various depths which we have just outlined. In particular it is not nec-

[2] Ch. Tsuboi, "Isostasy and maximum earthquake energy," *Proc. Acad. Tokyo 16* (1940), 449–454.

essary to look for an explanation for the "deep focus earthquakes" as a spurious phenomenon; all observations on these shocks fit the theoretical conclusions excellently, and there is practically no possibility of explaining the observations on the assumption of a focus at a depth of less than 50 km; on the other hand, contrary to the opinion held by a few, there is no reason why tectonic earthquakes should not occur at greater depths than 50 km. On the contrary, the question must be raised why observations do not indicate their occurrence at depths greater than about 700 km. Do the forces which produce the stresses act mainly in the upper few hundred kilometers? Or does the viscosity at a depth of about 700 km decrease to values below the order of $10^{20}$ or $10^{19}$ poises, allowing so rapid a plastic flow that stresses are reduced to one half within a few years or less? Or does the breaking strength increase at a depth of about 700 km so rapidly that below this depth earthquakes are practically prohibited? Findings by Goranson[3] indicate that beyond a certain confining pressure the breaking strength increases rapidly; the relatively great energy of many very deep shocks would also agree with this possibility.

Finally, it is not unreasonable to assume that inside the core of the earth the viscosity, as well as the rigidity, is much less than in the mantle and permits relatively rapid plastic flow.

More far-reaching conclusions may be drawn. The deficiency in mass in the regions of postglacial uplift corresponding to gravity anomalies of about 30 milligals produces plastic flow throughout the mantle of the earth with only slightly decreasing displacements in the upper half of the mantle. It is therefore safe to conclude that the larger anomalies in tectonically active regions, as, for example, off the East Indies, the Philippines, and Japan, are connected with still stronger subcrustal currents throughout the mantle of the earth. The active source of these processes need not be close to the surface of the earth but may be deep seated. The location of the deep-focus earthquakes around the Pacific Ocean has been interpreted as an indication that even at a depth of 700 km there is a difference in structure; such a hypothesis is not necessary, although it is possible. Forces acting at any given depth in the circum-Pacific region will set up stresses and plastic flow throughout the mantle. Wherever the stresses exceed the breaking strength of the material, earthquakes will accompany the processes.

As we have seen, defects of mass producing only relatively small gravity anomalies are able to produce noticeable plastic flow, if sufficient time is available. The lower limit, below which the processes stop or

[3] R. W. Goranson, "Fracture and flow in stressed solids," *Trans. Am. Geophys. Union*, pt. 2 (1940), 698–700.

are too small to have observable effects, is of importance for the answer to the question whether certain small forces may produce considerable changes during long periods. Especially, is the *Polfluchtkraft,* producing stresses with an order of magnitude of about one hundredth of the stresses in Scandinavia, large enough to maintain plastic flow? If it is, then we should not be surprised to see continents being shifted by subcrustal flow during the history of the earth under the action of such small but persistent forces.

READ Herbert Harold Read (1889–    ), British geologist, was a member of His Majesty's Geological Survey in 1914, and after serving in the First World War he continued his research as a member of the Geological Survey of Scotland until 1931, when he became Professor of Geology in the University of Liverpool. From there he transferred in 1939 to the Imperial College of Science and Technology in the University of London where he occupied a similar chair until his retirement as Professor Emeritus in 1955, having been also the Dean of the Royal School of Mines from 1943 to 1945. He was President of the International Geological Congress for its meeting in London in 1948, and his distinguished career was continued as Senior Research Fellow at the Imperial College from 1955 to 1964. The address from which the following excerpt was taken was delivered at the time of his retirement from the presidency of the Geological Society of London in 1949.

## THE TIME FACTOR IN PLUTONIC GEOLOGY *

### TIME AND TIME AGAIN

Among the many profound observations of that distinguished potomologist, Mark Twain, is one that states that very few things happen at the right time, and that the rest do not happen at all—it is added that the conscientious historian will correct these defects. Maybe, as today's proceedings advance, my conscience will come into action along these lines, but the attentive critic will surely recognize the event. Nevertheless, at any moment of exaltation, I should be humble to remember the sage of the Mississippi, for my purpose is to add time as a fourth dimension to the three-dimensional place of last year's inquiry into plutonic happenings.[1] We have to endeavour to see how far we can

*From "A Contemplation of Time in Plutonism," *Geological Society of London Quarterly Journal, 105* (1949), 101–156. The excerpt is from pp. 101–107.

[1]H. H. Read, "A commentary on place in plutonism," *Quart. J. Geol. Soc.* (London) *104* (1948), 155.

watch the wheels go round—this is always a pleasant occupation, but one made still more pleasant on this occasion by the variety of the wheels and the diversities of their speeds, for time in plutonism seems to have many qualities. We have to begin by surveying some of their general aspects.

A first concerns length of time. We often find a refuge in the immensity of geological time, but this refuge is not always secure. For example, uniformitarianism cannot be eternally true and, when we know a great deal more about plutonism, we shall have to discuss whether the time-dimension has changed with time and whether distinctions based on age are to come back into petrology. Again, we are given to quoting from the classics—Hesiod, Herodotus, and the rest—that if we had enough time we could do anything. This can be only a half-truth. An inadequate force cannot become adequate by virtue of time—it is unlikely that, however long I lean against the Bank of England, I shall unaided bring it down in ruins. We have therefore to distinguish between an eternally inadequate force and one that appears inadequate over our short period of observation. Though diffusion, for example, may be slow it may still be able to produce gigantic results given time. The speed of plutonic processes such as metamorphism and granitization is one of their fundamental qualities and has to be integrated with the speed of tectonic and other mechanical operations going on in the crust.

A second aspect concerns what start and what end shall be given to the time of development of a plutonic rock and how shall this be divided. All rocks, because their elemental materials are all of the same age, are complex documents, but they may record either countless episodes of a long history or only the very last chapter. An equilibrium-rock, for example, witnesses to the one final act in its production and two equilibrium-rocks that might have had profoundly different earlier histories may by metamorphic convergence come to be essentially alike in that they record a common concluding act. The abrupt temporal limitations of geological maps must be early realized in plutonic studies; space they record but rarely time, and they assume too readily that every rock is an equilibrium-rock capable of being related to one or other of a small number of episodes in the history of that part of the earth's crust. We shall begin to advance in the interpretation of such terranes as the Lewisian and Dalradian of Scotland, for example, when we represent time as well as place on the geological map, when we turn the map from a still into a film.

The choice of the limits of a plutonic history may be difficult to make. We must free ourselves, I feel, from the compartmentalism of the stratigraphical column and be prepared, if need be, to envisage a plutonic story requiring the half and even the whole of geological time for its telling. When we see displayed on a geological map a granite labelled Upper Carboniferous, for example, we must realize that we are being told only the date of the death of that particular plutonic rock. Death, I agree, is an important event to a man, but his life is much more important to posterity—and so it is with the plutonic rocks. Besides, just as all members of a family do not usually die all on the same day, so genetically related granites may complete their courses at widely different dates; we ought not to shy from discussing the possibility of a granite labelled Devonian by the field-geologist belonging to the same genetic series as one labelled Carboniferous or Tertiary and, indeed, of all granites belonging to one series. The notion of eruptivity has brought with it the notion of a sudden happening and many geologists have been influenced thereby; it is important to remember that eruptivity refers to place—the eruptive rocks appear suddenly to the geologist as the geological map is being made, but they themselves have been emplaced as the final act of a very long history.

As it is with the granitic portion of the plutonic rocks, so it is with the metamorphic portion. We cannot date a metamorphism, we can only date the end of what is usually a long and involved process, not capable of being unravelled by the study of equilibrium-rocks but of petrographic relics and geological records. On occasion we may be lucky enough to observe the birth-time of a metamorphic rock in a sedimentary series, but often we can make only an arbitrary choice and it is our custom to denote the state of the rock at that given time as original. The history of a plutonic rock is never finished; we have to inquire how far it can be broken up into chapters before the appearance of the rock at the surface of the earth. But we must remember that a major tectonic event recorded with violence in the stratigraphical column does not automatically terminate a plutonic history. Into these high themes I enter later on, but in this general survey there still remain a number of plutonic time aspects to be introduced.

The contrast is often made between the prolonged sequence of crystallization of the components of the igneous rocks and the simultaneous crystallization of the crystalline schists as these differences are revealed in their textures. But this simultaneity, if it is applicable at all, can apply only to the equilibrium-rocks which, fortunately, are relatively rare and imperfect in development. At the present time there is a danger in some schools of paying overmuch attention to the classificatory virtues of the metamorphic facies concept. We have to keep the equilibrium-rocks in their proper perspective and give the greater heed to the non-equilibrium portions of the plutonic rocks since these reveal earlier episodes in the metamorphic history. Metamorphic facies, by itself, will not get us far; it is only the study of relict minerals and textures that can make the rock live. One of the fundamental branches of plutonic geology, therefore, is concerned with textures as indicating the time-relations of the rock components. Certain textural relations are capable of clear and unambiguous interpretation, others are not. Slowly a body of experimental and geological evidence is being built up that may resolve some of the present ambiguities.

But whilst I may seem to have frowned upon the glorification of metamorphic facies *per se*, I must admit that this may yet prove to be of great time-significance in the study of plutonic history. If we could be sure that, possibly over a somewhat restricted field, a metamorphic facies was peculiar to a given time in the development of the metamorphic rocks of that field, then the plutonic geologist would have gained a principle as valuable to him as William Smith's Second Law is to the stratigrapher. There are certain limited advances already clear to me. Thus, it seems reasonable to propose that identical metamorphic facies in the same ground are isochronous as well as isophysical. This proposition is, of course, the core of metamorphic convergence and is one, I feel, that lies at the heart of the solution of many gigantic problems of the plutonic rocks, notably, for example, that of the origin of the granulites and granite-gneisses of the old massifs of central Europe. We must, clearly, be as cautious as we are able in this matter and, in view of the variety of factors controlling metamorphism, not be unduly astonished at metamorphic irregularities. In any event, the correlation of metamorphic facies must not be construed as indicating a stratigraphical correlation, an admonition particularly applicable in the study of the Scottish Highlands.

In the consideration of plutonic time, a number of dates have to be distinguished and kept distinct when possible. First is the age of the original material, sedimentary or otherwise, that has subsequently become metamorphosed, migmatized, or granitized; but debates on this topic, in that they are largely an affair of comparative stratigraphy, must be kept apart from the discussion of the more purely plutonic ages. There is general agreement—though, so far as I remember, no one has given any cogent reasons for the opinion—that granitization and metamorphism are very slow processes requiring great spans of time for their accomplishment. It is required, therefore, to determine the geological dates of the beginning and the ending of the metamorphism or other plutonic activity, and in certain cases this has been found possible. But plutonism does not appear to be a steady process advancing at a uniform rate, but rather one of energetic pulses interrupted by operations of diverse kinds, especially those of deformation. One of the greatest fields of inquiry in plutonism is concerned with the time-relations of crystallization and deformation or, as the learned say, of crystalloblastesis and clastesis. Here, again, certain cases are clear: deformation has followed crystallization or crystallization has concluded the metamorphic action, and so forth. But here also doubts arise, especially in the cases where movement and crystallization may be synchronous or where mimetic crystallization may have operated.

Though it be admitted that plutonic processes revealed in the rocks require great time, and maybe all time, for their accomplishment, there still arises an associated inquiry of major importance. This considers the question whether all the phases, pulses, or episodes seen to have operated in a plutonic rock constitute one cycle or many independent cycles. We are here really scrutinizing the validity and limits of polymetamorphism. The French maintain that metamorphism is the normal and permanent phenomenon under certain thermodynamic conditions probably related to crustal depth. The conditions of metamorphism can be changed, in particular, by dynamic action which places the elements undergoing metamorphism in another thermodynamic envelope. The evolution ends in the metamorphic state that the rocks now present to us. Plutonic rocks, therefore, might supply evidence of their sojourn in a succession of different thermodynamic envelopes; they would be styled polymetamorphic and we would interpret them as having undergone several metamorphisms. As I have already said, the appearance of the rock at the surface of the earth should terminate at least a chapter in its history, but yet this chapter may not be the last in that volume. This great problem as to whether plutonic history is one unit, several unrelated units or a series of episodes can only be attacked by a number of small assaults. We may, however, obtain a clue for final success by regarding the prime cycle: formation of migma, formation of magma, movement of magma, consolidation, upheaval and denudation.

In the foregoing, I have outlined some of the general aspects of time in plutonism. I have now to discuss in such detail as is permitted certain features of this survey, but before this is done, a decision has to be made on two matters. First, I repeat once again my opinion that the plutonic granitic rocks are not near blood-relations of the volcanic basaltic rocks. I propose to assume that this opinion is by now commonly accepted by all reasonable men. Secondly, I repeat once again my opinion that the constant use of progressive in the description of metamorphism and other plutonic processes is in many cases unwarranted and misleading. This second opinion may seem trivial beside the first, but it is, to my mind, of fundamental importance in the interpretation of plutonic history. Metamorphism, for example, is presented to us so often as a sequence of progressive changes that we tend to lose sight of the fact that the sequence may be only one of place and not of time. Graphic pictures of the metamorphic or migmatitic front passing through the crust, or of the depression of a geosynclinal filling into greater and greater depths with the successive production of zones of increasing metamorphism are often specious simplifications. The preservation of original sedimentary textures, for example, in the high-grade rocks of a so-called progressive series and their obliteration in the low-grade rocks—a fact about which there can be no question—indicate that the observed series is not one of time; the high-grade rocks did not pass through the low-grade stage. The demonstration of a time-sequence depends on detailed textural studies, as we shall see later. Moreover, whilst we admit progression in metamorphism, we must not thereby exclude regression; we must be prepared to consider the proposal that even the highest-grade rocks are regressive from a grade still higher but not exposed to us in the earth's present crust. With these two decisions made, we can pass to more specific considerations.

### TIME AND CRYSTALLIZATION

We have seen that the plutonic class of rocks encloses the genetic series of granitic, migmatitic and metamorphic portions which in some measure result from an accentuation of a steady process. Whilst this may be so, the records of the process may be very differently displayed in the three portions. In the granitic rocks, for example, crystallization may be the last dominant act and may blot out or at least blur the evidence of earlier history; on the other hand, metamorphic rocks often reveal a dozen stages in their development. The common massive character of the granites, contrasted with the schistose or foliated character of the metamorphites, expresses this same diversity. But this diversity is more apparent than real as it arises from the temporal and local balance between the two controlling processes of plutonism—the chemical and the mechanical. In the first process, the rock becomes chemically reconstructed into a mineral assemblage in accord with the operative temperature, pressure and concentration; in the second, it is subject to deformation depending in type again upon a physical and chemical environment. For convenience, we may call the first process crystallization and the second deformation.

Crystallization and deformation are rarely simultaneous—even when they are said to be so, they seldom begin and end at the same time but usually overlap. Crystallization can be entirely earlier or later than deformation, or the two processes can vary in dominance during the same plutonic event and so make a pattern of phases in the proceedings. Either process may be so overwhelming that a special character is given to the products, as is seen in dislocation-metamorphism and contact-metamorphism. It is clear, therefore, that even if the consideration of those detached and mobile portions of the plutonic rocks that are frequently called igneous is postponed, there still remains for unravelling a sufficiently complex set of time-relations in the autochthonous products such as granitization-granites, migmatites, and metamorphites. It will be convenient to begin this task with cases in which the crystallization factor is dominantly involved and then, later, to bring deformation into the time-picture. We are therefore now to be concerned largely with the sequence of crystallization in the classic Rosenbusch sense, or with the time-differences between minerals as revealed in the in-situ products of plutonism.

We have first of all to agree that there are time-differences in the constituents of the plutonic rocks, though this leads to rejection of the dictum of our master Becke,[2] who, with his over-emphasis on equilibrium, saw the metamorphic constituents as of simultaneous formation. If simultaneous means what I take it to mean, then the examination of the textures of almost any plutonic rock—and even of the equilibrium types of them—will show that crystallization has not been simultaneous for all components but is a diversified and lengthy sequence of events. In this study of textures we can derive great help from metallurgy and ore-microscopy, but, if we accept this help, we must remember several cautions. The chief are these: a given texture, as for example the graphic, may arise in several ways; the experimental conditions of metallurgy are different from the natural conditions of plutonism; the lattices of plutonic minerals are silicate and not metal or sulphide lattices, and plutonic rocks are multigrain and multicrystal aggregates.

In textural studies dealing with sequence of formation, we are concerned mainly with three inquiries—simultaneous crystallization, either absolute or approximate, replacement and veining. Simultaneous crystallization is exceedingly difficult to establish from an examination of textures. Even an apparent exsolution association may be misleading, since one of the components may be oriented relics in the later replacement.[3] Smooth and regular contacts between minerals—the mutual

[2] F. Becke, "Über Mineralbestand und Struktur der kristallinischen Schiefer," *Compt. Rend., IX Congr. geol. intern.* (Vienna, 1903), p. 563; "Über Mineralbestand und Struktur der kristalliminschen Schiefer," *Denkschr. K. Akad. Wiss. Wien, Math.-Nat. Kl. 75* (1913), 4–35.

[3] Yu-chi, Cheng, "A hornblende complex, including appinitic types, in the migmatite area of North Sutherland, Scotland," *Proc. Geol. Assn.* 53 (1942), p. 80, Fig. 5.

boundaries of the ore-microscopist—are often put forward as evidence of simultaneity, but such boundaries have been produced in artificial replacements and are shown by pairs that can be demonstrated by other criteria to be of different ages. Again, intimate and intricate intergrowths do not prove simultaneity, as can be illustrated in many partial pseudomorphs of limonite after pyrite and in the sericitization of felspars. Graphic intergrowths are often loosely taken to be the result of simultaneous crystallization. These intergrowths may look like eutectics but that does not make them eutectics, and essentially similar textures are produced by a variety of operations such as replacement, unmixing and recrystallizaton of an aggregate. There is no proved eutectic in the plutonic rocks nor, from the nature of the case, is any to be expected.

The erection of criteria of replacement has occupied ore-microscopists since their special study began. Unlike simultaneous crystallization, replacement can often be proved beyond reasonable doubt but several criteria may be required to establish the case. Surface relations of crystal units have perforce to be used and a three-dimensional check is generally lacking. The host controls replacement and some host-character must persist into the new guest; replacement may be guided by a cleavage or by some crystallographic direction in the host-mineral, or by a texture such as bedding or slaty cleavage in the host-rock. The form or the texture of the host may be partly or entirely pseudomorphed by the guest, the contacts between them being jagged and irregular—the caries contact—and islands of host with similar orientation to that of a mainland left in several dissimilarly oriented guest-grains. These criteria are excellent and may often be reinforced by those provided by veinlets, since veining is likely to be of replacing character. Veinlets of irregular width, with walls that do not match, and cutting across several diversely oriented host-grains are of the greatest significance, but veining must yet be used with care. Threads running between crystal grains or incipient tongues inserting themselves into a mineral are not to be trusted. Further, replacement may be selective, so that it is possible for a vein to be earlier than its present walls, its original walls having been replaced; veins can be pre-wall or post-wall.

Even with all these chances of error, it is possible to demonstrate a sequence, absolute or overlapping, in the crystallization of the constituents of the plutonic rocks—examples are provided immediately. For the most part, we are dealing with a sequence exhibited by different minerals, but on occasion it is necessary to determine the crystallization history of a monomineralic rock such as a quartzite or limestone. Here it is reasonable to use a variation in grain-size since, in any one event, the form-energy of the grains would be approximately equal over the limits of a thin section. Thus, in the siliceous Moine granulites of the Tongue area in Sutherland, the normal regional grain-size of quartz is much reduced along certain planes and greatly increased along certain paths—a circumstance I interpret as indicating two different kinds of event affecting the original granulite.

In time-studies of the kind we are considering, it can often be inferred that the sequence of mineral formation belongs to a unified episode—there is a reasonable progression in the crystallization and often it is apparent that a later mineral is the consequence of an earlier reaction; this is particularly well shown in many migmatites. But sometimes it is likely that the sequence is divisible into episodes separated by considerable stretches of time. In this case, the geological history of the region is of fundamental significance; it would be just as unwise to study the Alps or the Highlands by thin sections alone as it would be to study them without thin sections. In this broader time-differentiation, relics of earlier crystallizations, as of earlier fabrics, are of course of the greatest interest.

**BRAGG** Sir William Lawrence Bragg (1890–     ), British physicist, has been awarded a Nobel Prize in conjunction with his father, Sir W. H. Bragg, for research concerning X-rays and crystal structures. From 1919 to 1937 he was Langworthy Professor of Physics at Victoria University in Manchester and from 1938 to 1953 Cavendish Professor of Physics at Cambridge University; since 1954 he has been Scientific Director of the Royal Institution in London.

Soon after it was discovered in 1912 that X rays could be diffracted by crystals, the Braggs, father and son, commenced their pioneer research on the orderly arrangement of atoms and ions in crystalline solids. This led later to the concept of the crystal lattice and the gaining of knowledge that has prime importance in mineralogy, metallurgy, geochemistry, and other fields. The paper from which the following excerpt is taken summarizes the information concerning the fine structure of silicate minerals available at the relatively early date of 1930.

## THE STRUCTURE OF SILICATES *

During the last few years numerous silicate structures have been analysed in our laboratory by X-ray methods, and in the present paper an attempt is made to summarize the results of our investigations in a convenient form. Representatives of most types of silicates have been

*From *Zeitschrift für Kristallographie 74* (1930), 237–305.

completely or partially analysed and it is possible to review this class of compounds as a whole although so much investigation still remains to be done.

Views on the structure of silicates have been proposed recently by many writers and it is often difficult to assign the original authorship. These views have been put forward almost simultaneously, as inevitably suggested by the progressive experimental determination of the structures themselves, each successful analysis pointing the way to a plausible hypothesis about types as yet unanalysed. Particular mention must be made, however, of the importance attached by Machatschki[1] to the linking of tetrahedral groups in the silicates, and of the very fertile hypothesis of the balancing of electrostatic valence which Pauling[2] makes the basis of a wide treatment of ionic compounds in general. The present paper treats the question from the experimental point of view, and summarizes those structures for which the positions of all atoms have been discovered; the author has ventured to discuss the subject as a whole because a large number of silicate structures have been determined by investigations with which he has been associated.

The work was commenced with the object of developing a technique for the analysis of crystals in which the atomic positions are defined by a large number of parameters. The silicates provide excellent material for this purpose, owing to their complexity and the ease with which well-formed natural crystals can be obtained. Quite recently it was held to be only possible to get an accurate determination of parameters by X-ray analysis when these parameters did not exceed two or three in number. Quantitative measurements of diffraction make it possible to attack directly far more complex crystals, and it may now be claimed that precise determinations of crystals with fifteen or twenty parameters can be made, each parameter being fixed independently. The exactitude with which the coordinates can be determined is only limited by the amount of labour expended in making measurements.

In the course of the examination of the silicates, the general laws which govern the structures of these compounds begin to shape themselves. The existence of these general laws and experience with other structures make it possible to dispense with much of the direct analysis. Possible structures for any crystal can be built, and tested by more approximate estimates of diffraction such as those yielded by the various photographic methods. It was necessary at the start, however, to establish the general lines on which the structures are built by making as

[1] F. Machatschki, *C. Min.* [A] (1928), p. 97.
[2] L. Pauling, *Sommerfeld-Festschrift,* Leipzig, 1928, and *Am. Chem. J. 51* (1919), 1040.

few assumptions as possible and finding the parameters of each atom independently. . . .

The feature which distinguishes the silicates as a class from other inorganic compounds may be summed up as follows. In the typical inorganic salt, atoms such as phosphorus, sulphur, and chlorine build with oxygen the groups $(PO_4)'''$, $(SO_4)''$, $(ClO_4)'$, and these groups or acid radicles combine with metallic ions to form the salts. More complex groups such as $(S_2O_7)''$ exist, but such groups are always discrete units in the structure. The silicates are distinguished from such combinations of metal and acid radicle, however, by the way in which $(SiO_4)$ groups can be linked together to form silicon-oxygen complexes with indefinite extension in space. It is this feature which gives rise to the variety of silicate structures, and which has caused the role which silicon plays in the inorganic world to be compared to that which carbon plays in organic chemistry. As contrasted with the carbon-carbon linking, any linking between one silicon atom and another in the silicates is always effected through an intermediate oxygen atom. Silicon has the power of building these extended groups with oxygen, which may be compared to acid radicles stretching indefinitely in one, two, or three dimensions. It has an intermediate position between the atoms P, S, Cl which form with oxygen self-contained acid radicles, and the metals Mg, Al, which form continuous ionic lattices. Aluminium has a dual role, replacing silicon or magnesium in many minerals, so that there is a continuous gradation of properties in this row of the periodic table.

As well as forming extended acid radicles, silicon forms the simple group $(SiO_4)^{4-}$ in the orthosilicates, and more complex self-contained groups. In such cases we may think of the structure as built of discrete acid radicles and metallic ions, like other inorganic salts. It is the existence of the acid radicles with indefinite extension in space, however, which is so exceptional a feature. It explains the difficulty often encountered in the past in writing formulae for the silicates. Such structural formulae must take into account the spatial extension of the silicon-oxygen groups in order that their significance may be clear. This recalls the stereochemistry of organic compounds, though the fundamental features are very different.

In all the structures which have been analysed, silicon is found between a regular group of four oxygen atoms. The distance between silicon and oxygen is about 1.62 Å and that between oxygen centres about 2.6 Å. Quantitative X-ray measurements indicate that more electrons are associated with silicon, and fewer electrons with each oxygen atom, than would be the case if silicon had a charge $4e$ and oxygen a charge $-2e$. The inner constitution of the group is not, however, of primary importance when we consider the way in which it is incorporated into the silicate structures. The whole group behaves as if a charge $-4e$ were equally distributed amongst the four oxygen atoms. These atoms, like other oxygen atoms not attached to silicon, obey the general rule of an approximate distance of 2.7 Å between oxygen centres.

In the othosilicates the $SiO_4$ groups are independent. In other silicates, the linking between $SiO_4$ groups takes place through one oxygen atom being common to two groups (sharing of corners between tetrahedra). In this way more complex silicon-oxygen groups are built up. An oxygen atom which is thus shared has little residual attraction for other atoms. We may regard this as due to a balance of electrostatic valency, the double charge on the oxygen atom being neutralized by the lines of force coming from the two silicon atoms on either side. Alternatively we may regard the bonds as homopolar and similar to those in organic compounds. The result as far as external field is concerned is the same. Oxygen atoms attached to two silicon atoms have no residual valency, while those only attached to one silicon atom behave as if they had a charge $-e$. The single charges on these latter oxygen atoms, along with charges on other ions $O''$, $OH'$, $F'$, are neutralized by the metallic ions.

We may distinguish types of silicon-oxygen complex which differ in their spatial extension, and which are all formed by the linking together of the simple $SiO_4$ groups of the orthosilicates.

a) Self-contained groups, represented by the formulae $(Si_2O_7)^{6-}$, $(Si_3O_9)^{6-}$, $(Si_4O_{12})^{8-}$, $(Si_6O_{18})^{12-}$. The two linked tetrahedra of the diorthosilicates, and the six tetrahedra in a ring of beryl, are examples. Such groups may be regarded as complex acid radicles joined by metal atoms as in a salt.

b) Silicon-oxygen chains, as found in the pyroxenes and amphiboles. The pyroxene chain is the simplest possible form, and the row of linked tetrahedra, each sharing two of its oxygen atoms, has the composition $(SiO_3)^{2-}$. In the amphiboles a further condensation $(Si_4O_{11})^{6-}$ takes place by the linking of two such chains side by side, a process which if continued would result in the type of linking in the next group.

c) Silicon-oxygen sheets, which we suppose to be characteristic of the scaly mica-like minerals. If three oxygens of each tetrahedral group are linked to other groups, the fourth remaining free, the oxygen silicon ratio is represented by $(Si_2O_5)^{2-}$.

d) Three-dimensional silicon-oxygen networks, as in the forms of silica. As was first pointed out by Machatschki one has only to suppose a partial replacement of Si by Al to obtain a three-dimensional negatively charged network, like a vast extended acid radicle, in which metal atoms can be incorporated. The most striking examples are the zeolites, where the network remains unaltered when metallic ions are substituted for each other, and the water content varied.

These successive spatial extensions represent a successive decrease in the oxygen silicon ratio as illustrated by the following simple cases

$SiO_4$    Orthosilicate group.
$Si_2O_7$    Complex group.
$SiO_3$    Chain.
$Si_2O_5$    Sheet.
$SiO_2$ or $(Si, Al)O_2$    Three-dimensional network.

These silicon-oxygen groups are bound together by metal atoms, which are found inside more or less regular groups of the oxygen atoms. As a general rule the metals to which smaller ionic radii are assigned are surrounded by a lesser number of oxygen atoms, and the group is more regular in form. The type of grouping round metal atoms varies, however, from crystal to crystal since it must conform to the greater rigidity of the silicon-oxygen complex. In the case of certain metals common in the silicates, the groups are so regular that it is convenient to regard the structure as built of group units (expressed by Pauling as a linking of regular polyhedra by sharing corners, edges and faces). In the case of other cations as Na·, Ca··, K· the group is so irregular as to lose its individuality. The most general description of the structures is one of silicon-oxygen complexes, which come together so that their large oxygen atoms form with each other more or less regular groups. Into these groups the metal atoms are packed, and bind together the whole structure.

Aluminium can partially replace silicon in the complex groups. The classification of a silicate structure into one of the above types may depend on whether the aluminium within tetrahedral groups is ranked with silicon or not, and the boundary between the types is in consequence somewhat arbitrary.

In isomorphous replacement, the number of oxygen atoms (and of fluorine atoms or OH groups) in the unit cell remains constant. Changes in composition take place by the substitution of Si by Al, of Al, Mg, Fe by each other, of Na by Ca, and so forth. When a silicate is analysed, the atomic composition should be expressed on the basis of a constant number of oxygen atoms characteristic of the type of structure. If this is done the analyses become easy to understand. The great importance of oxygen in expressing the atomic composition was largely overlooked before X-ray analysis was applied. There is in general not sufficient room to add oxygen atoms to the unit of structure, and to remove them would break down the regular groups. This led the author in 1927 to propose that a silicate should be regarded as a structure having a constant number of oxygen atoms in the unit, with a constant number of places for metal and silicon which can be filled by these elements in varying proportions consistent with a balance between valencies. This view has been amply supported by subsequent work.

The silicates are an assemblage of silicon, oxygen, and metal atoms which as crystalline structures occupy a position intermediate between the metallic oxides and the inorganic salts. To single out silicon-oxygen complexes in them, and compare these to acid radicles, is somewhat arbitrary and is perhaps only justified by convenience of description. The arbitrary nature of this view is increased by the dual role which aluminium plays in replacing silicon or a divalent metal. We may alternatively group silicon with the metal atoms, and regard the whole structure as an assemblage of oxygen atoms, with a universal distance of about 2.7 Å between neighbouring oxygen centres, in which the silicon and metal atoms are interspersed. It seems preferable, however, to single out the silicon-oxygen link as essentially different to the electrostatic bond between metal and oxygen. We must then think of the silicon-oxygen complexes as units, packed together with metal atoms between. Additional atoms of oxygen not attached to silicon, and of fluorine or the group OH, may be incorporated in the structure. The electrostatic bonds which hold the silicon-oxygen complexes together stretch between metal on the one hand and oxygen attached to only one silicon atom on the other; the oxygen atoms attached to two silicon atoms have no residual field.

In the packing together, features appear which result from the natural consideration that the arrangement must be such as to represent the least potential energy and greatest stability of the structure. In the author's first attempts to analyse these complex inorganic structures in which they were regarded as assemblages of the large oxygen ions with small metal and silicon ions in the interstices, the lowest potential energy was considered as realized by the most uniform dispersal of the cations, especially those with large charge, in the oxygen assemblage. Those structures were regarded as the more probable which did not crowd the positive ions into certain regions. Pauling has evolved a more precise and neater way of expressing this principle in his rule of the balancing of electrostatic valency. This rule may be stated in the broadest way as signifying that the positive ions are so dispersed amongst the negative ions that a local neutralization of electric charge is effected throughout the structure. Lines of force can be drawn from cation to anion which represent numerically their electric charges and which stretch between nearest neighbours. The wide dispersal of the ions is further expressed by Pauling as a tendency for his polyhedra to share corners or edges rather than faces. He has shown how very fertile these two hypotheses can be in suggesting why certain silicates exist and others do not; they are powerful because they enable estimates of the relative stabilities of different structures to be made.

If a model of a silicate structure be made, with bonds linking the oxygen atoms (and F or OH) to the atoms of metal and silicon, it shows certain features which give a striking impression of mechanical stability and balance between opposing forces. The regular grouping of the oxygen atoms around the metal atoms has already been discussed; it is equally interesting to consider the grouping of the metal or silicon atoms around each oxygen atom. An oxygen atom in general lies between two, three or four "cations." If between two, which must be two silicon atoms, or one silicon atom and such an atom as aluminium or boron, the two bonds are approximately in line. If it lies between three, and their relative strengths are taken into account, it is seen that the three bonds represent an approximate "triangle of forces." The forces of repulsion between the oxygen atoms represented by their "packing," and the rigidity of the $SiO_4$ groups, modify somewhat this equilibrium but it remains a characteristic feature of the structure and is of assistance in analysis. It may be remarked that the fluorine atom or group OH is frequently found in a position where the bonds all lie in one hemisphere; this may be due to the weaker bonds being over-mastered by the necessities of packing, or possibly to a polarization of the group. The arrangement of the bonds around each anion is equally a result of the wide dispersal of the cations, of the sharing of a minimum number of anions between neighbouring cations, or of the electrostatic valency rule. These features are alternative ways of expressing the tendency of the stable configuration to have a form of the lowest potential energy. They correspond to the two ways of regarding the equilibrium of a mechanical system as being due either to the balancing of opposing forces or to the assumption of a configuration which has the least potential energy. . . .

# SHATSKIY Nikolay Sergeyevich Shatskiy (1895– ), Russian engineer-geologist, graduated from the Moscow Mining Academy in 1929, and since 1935 has been head of the Tectonic Section at the Institute of Geological Sciences in the Soviet Academy of Sciences, in which he attained the rank of

Academician in 1953. Since 1934 he has been a member of the faculty at the Moscow Institute of Geological Prospecting where he is currently the head of the Department of Historical Geology. The term "placanticline," which he apparently originated, might well be used in describing the structural features of many regions.

## SYNECLISES, ANTICLISES, PLACANTICLINES, AND ASSOCIATED STRUCTURES*

Neither in the general nor in the specialized geological literature is there an established terminology for most of the tectonic forms that are developed in the Volga-Urals region. Therefore, for the following exposition it seems necessary to give short definitions of at least the best-known types of disturbances.

Several groups of tectonic disturbances must be distinguished in the Volga-Urals region. The principal group are the largest forms—huge, flat uplifts and depressions; to this group belong such typical platform tectonic forms as *syneclises* and *anticlises,* and also *marginal troughs,* which are characteristic of regions transitional between platforms and folded geosynclinal belts. To the group of second-order dislocations belong disturbances that complicate the principal structures listed above; these are *placanticlines,* developed on the platforms and the adjoining outer parts of marginal troughs, and *ordinary anticlinal and synclinal folds,* which in many places complicate the inner flanks of marginal troughs (i.e. those nearer the geosynclinal belt) and the main structures (anticlinoria, synclinoria, etc.) of folded geosynclinal regions. To this group of forms belong also specific structures of the marginal troughs, *diapir salt domes and anticlines,* which owe their origin to deformations of mobile salt deposits. Finally, we should distinguish on the platforms small disturbances that complicate all of the above types of structures: *joints, diaclases,* and also normal and high-angle reverse faults, graben, and so on.

All the disturbances of the Volga-Urals region are thus divided into principal groups by size. Syneclises and other major platform structures encompass areas of tens and hundreds of thousands of square kilometers; second-order dislocations are considerably smaller, though they

*From "Ocherki tektoniki Volgo-Ural'skoi neftenosnoi oblasti i smezhnoi chasti zapadnogo sklona Iuzhnogo Urala" [Outlines of the tectonics of Volga-Urals petroleum region and adjacent parts of the west slope of the Southern Urals]; *Moskovskoe obshchestvo ispytatelei prirody, Materialy k poznaniiu geologicheskogo stroeniia SSSR, novaia seriia, vypusk* 2 (6) [Moscow Society of Natural Scientists, Contributions to Knowledge of the Geology of the USSR, new series, no. 2 (6)], pp. 10–27, 1945. Translated by John B. Southard.

often occupy hundreds and thousands of square kilometers; finally, third-order disturbances are spaced fractions of a meter, or in any case a few meters, apart. . . .

*Syneclises and Anticlises*

*Syneclises.* Syneclises (*sineklizy*) are major structures, usually with elongated form, that complicate platforms. Syneclises are "negative" structures, i.e. gentle warpings of the crust with synclinal form. In defining the nature of syneclises as synclinal we are speaking of the geological essence of these forms and not their geometrical shape. Their geometrical shape is not synclinal because of the great size of syneclises and the sphericity of the Earth. Thus, the line of contact between Pre-Cambrian and Paleozoic rocks in a cross section through the Moscow Syneclise has the form of an arc that is convex upward, but with a considerably greater radius of curvature than the mean radius of the Earth. The Paleozoic-Mesozoic contact surface in the small Ukrainian Cretaceous basin approximates a plane. Only for very small syneclises and very great downwarping are the senses of the geological and geometrical forms the same.

Of the characteristic features of syneclises we should first of all note the extremely gentle dip of the strata in the flanks, amounting to fractions of m/km to 5 m/km on the average; steeper dips are usually local, often connected with secondary disturbances of the over-all synclinal structure of the syneclise. The dip of beds in syneclises is so insignificant that it cannot be measured with a compass, but it is easily determined by the characteristic general synclinal arrangement of geological units, and also by the isohypses of structural maps. The second basic feature of syneclises is that they always involve platform formations.

By formation (*formatsiia*) we mean a naturally recognizable complex of rocks whose individual members (beds, sequences, facies, etc.) are closely, genetically, related to one another both in a vertical, temporal sense and in a horizontal, spatial sense. It was noted long ago (by Haug, Kober, Arkhangel'skii and Shatskii, and others) that formations are not situated randomly over the area of the crust but are connected in the closest way with the various crustal structures. The distinction between platform formations and formations of folded geosynclinal regions is commonly accepted. In this, it should be emphasized that structures thus are associated not only with sedimentary formations but also with igneous formations. Even though ideas and general statements connected with the question of formations are fifty years old, there has not yet been any systematic development of the study of formations. It seems to the writer that this is because these questions have been dealt with mainly by petrographers, lithologists, and stratigraphers, and least of all by structural geologists, who in this case should play the leading role. In recent years there has been a sharp change in this respect, and undoubtedly new major systems and generalizations on this subject should appear in the near future in connection with the accumulation of a great mass of observational data on formations. . . . Formations are very often and quite incorrectly confused with facies. Facies (*fatsies*) is primarily a paleogeographic and paleogeomorphic concept; formation is above all a tectonic concept, because formations are connected with definite structures.

The dimensions of synclises vary within wide limits, but are always considerable; thus, the Moscow Syneclise is about 800–900 km across and 1500 km long, i.e. its area is greater than 1,000,000 km². The area of the West Kazakhstan (Caspian) Syneclise is only a little less than that of the Moscow Syneclise. The dimensions of synclises on other platforms are of the same order: the Interior Basin of North America has an area of about 500,000 km², and the enormous size of such synclises as the Paris Basin, the Tunguska and Viliui Synclises in Siberia, and others is well known. No less diverse is the shape of synclises. They are usually elongated, but not infrequently their shape is irregular. To a considerable extent their shape depends upon the particular features of their development and also upon the structure of the folded basement. Out of the general irregularity of outline of synclises two very constant and general features can be noted in the shapes of these structures: (1) the perimeter of the over-all outline of synclises consists of very short segments with small radii of curvature and very long segments that are almost straight; (2) the straight segments have a regular spatial arrangement. The latter point must also be noted with respect to other elements of synclises. In this respect synclises do not differ from other tectonic forms, both platform and geosynclinal. The structure of synclises is often somewhat asymmetrical: along with a very gentle dip of the flanks we nonetheless note, by the succession of stratigraphic units, that one has a steeper dip than the other. It should be emphasized that along with the over-all constancy of lithology and facies of the rocks in a syneclise there are always quite clear facies changes of the rocks and changes in the thickness of formations, depending upon position relative to the axis and the flanks of the syneclise, for example, the occurrence of gypsum and salt in the downwarped axial parts and the increase in thickness of formations from the flanks toward the axis.

Syneclises, as platform tectonic forms, were established by Pavlov in 1903. For a more precise definition of this term we must give its synonymy, especially those terms that are most often used in describing the Volga-Urals region. Of these terms we should note the following: "basin" (*vpadina*) and "trough" (*rov*), terms used by Arkhangel'skii, and "subgeosyncline" (*subgeosinklinal'*), a term used by Tetiaev; of foreign terms corresponding to syneclise may be noted *geodepression,* basin, and others. It is desirable to avoid using all the terms indicated in the synonymy, not only because of the priority of Pavlov's term but also because most of them do not give a fully accurate picture of these platform structures and include also such concepts as "marginal trough" and forms of geosynclinal type. The word syneclise comes from the Greek words, *syn,* together, and *ekklinomai,* to deflect or change.

*Anticlises.* Pavlov did not propose a term for the positive platform structures corresponding to syneclises. Usually large positive platform structures are called "shields" (*shchity*), arches (*svody*), or even anticlines (*antiklinali*). . . . Foreign authors have in part used the terms *Grossfalten* and *plis du fond.* It should be noted that in the Soviet geological literature the syneclise concept has not infrequently been contraposed to the anticlise concept. Mazarovich, using the former term on the whole correctly, called gentle anticlines of the Russian Platform of Oka-Tsna and Don-Medveditsa "swell" (*val*) type anticlises. Arkhangel'skii in his summaries reserved the term syneclise only for the so-called Simbirsk-Saratov Depression, as a synonym of the term "trough" (*rov*), i.e. he connected this structure with the so-called "swells" of the platform in its origin. Careful study of platform structures shows the "swells" do not represent those platform structures whose negative analogues are syneclises. As early as 1894 Karpinskii showed that anticlinal upwarps of "swell" type differ sharply from syneclises in genesis. In size, shape, and position, "swells" represent second-order structures that complicate the large disturbances of syneclise type. . . . Neither in origin nor in structure and position can "swells" be related in any way to syneclises and be called anticlises, especially because the latter term should be used for structures of shield type, if we accept the formulation of the term syneclise indicated in the present paper.

Thus, anticlises, from the Greek words *anti,* against, and *ekklinomai,* to deflect, should be applied to the positive counterparts of syneclises. These structures are related to each other in the closest way, and in essence syneclises and the related anticlises are, so to speak, one complete wave: the flanks of syneclises are at the same time flanks of adjacent anticlises. In pointing out the constant "wave-like" alternation of syneclises and anticlises we in no way ascribe such a relationship

261

to tangential deformations of the platform. On the contrary, all the data indicate that tangential stresses were unimportant in the formation of these principal platform structures. However, although in shape, size, position, and platform type of constituent formations, syneclises and anticlises are analogous structures of the same order, there are certain very important differences between them. During the long development of syneclises the thickest sequences are deposited in their axial parts; here the most complete sections are developed, sometimes with only a small number of breaks. On the other hand, as a result of prolonged uplift the thickness of formations is often decreased in the crestal parts of anticlises; here breaks are especially numerous, with entire series and formations present in adjacent syneclises often missing. In the most clearly expressed anticlises of Karelo-Finnish Arch type, all of the sedimentary platform cover is absent and the gneissic basement of the platform is exposed. . . .

### Marginal (Fore) Troughs

Marginal troughs (*kraevye progiby*), or as they are often called, fore troughs (*peredovye progiby*), are . . . very large and often complex downwarps of the same type as large synclines and synclinoria, situated on the boundary between typical platform and folded regions. They are thus the present transitional zones between platforms and geosynclines. Such an intermediate, transitional position is expressed in the fact that often in these synclinal downwarps the flank adjoining the platform is composed of platform formations and the flank adjoining the geosyncline is composed of thick geosynclinal formations. In exactly the same way the tectonic forms that disturb the synclinal downwarps in the outer flanks, adjacent to the platforms, have platform character, and those on the inner flanks, adjacent to the geosynclines, are often expressed as typical linear folded structures.

In studying a vertical section of deposits in a marginal trough it is easily noted that the regularities in distribution of types of formations and structures mentioned above are often broken in the deeper, older parts of these structures; this is explained by the migration of marginal troughs toward the platforms. More detailed study of marginal trough deposits shows that although these formations have a general similarity with platform and geosynclinal formations they have their own specific features, characteristic solely or principally of marginal troughs. Such formations distinguished by their great thickness as molasse, flysch, coal-bearing formations of Donets type, salt-bearing formations, and so forth, are widely developed here. Such formations are not found in typical platform regions, but formations similar to them, if not the same, appear also in the inner parts of geosynclinal regions, but always during the closing of the geosynclines, i.e. in the stage of transformation into platform regions.

As numerous observations show, the complexity of marginal troughs depends upon the age and type of the folded basement. Those marginal troughs which by migration are located over an ancient folded basement of the same type as the Russian Platform basement show the simplest structure. The inner boundaries of marginal troughs are marked by a replacement of downwarping by the first series of anticlinal uplifts (anticlinoria) of the folded zone. The outer boundary, toward the platform, is often not so clearly expressed. In the simplest cases this boundary is a typical platform anticlise.

Marginal troughs are very often termed fore troughs; this latter designation is especially suitable for those marginal troughs in which there has been a sharp migration of the trough toward the platform. Of the synonyms for this type of structure we should point out such terms as "pre-montane basin" (*predgornaia vpadina*), "pre-montane depression" (*predgornaia depressiia*), *Vortief* of German geologists, and fore-deep of English-speaking geologists. . . .

Marginal troughs are not uniform along their entire length. As in other negative structures, in marginal troughs we always observe transverse uplifts that divide these synclinal structures into separate cells or basins. The question naturally arises whether marginal troughs actually exist at the margins of all geosynclinal belts. Theoretically we can hypothesize that in some cases these marginal troughs may be replaced along the strike by large uplifts. Up to now such structures have not been described and their structural and formational features have not been recognized. If such structures do exist, then they apparently are rare and difficult to distinguish. It seems to the writer that study of the marginal structures of our eastern Trans-Baikal region and the Mongolia-Okhotsk belt as a whole, the northern part of the Norwegian Caledonides, and perhaps the Adirondack Dome in North America will be especially important in solving this problem.

## SECOND-ORDER FORMS

### *Placanticlines*

Anticlinal and anticline-like tectonic forms developed on the Russian Platform, and especially widespread in the Volga-Urals petroleum region, are so distinctive that they have always been distinguished as an independent group of dislocations. Morphologically these disturbances differ quite sharply from the ordinary anticlines of geosynclinal folded belts; therefore their recognition and terminology do not depend upon conceptions of their genesis. In the Soviet geological literature these forms have most often been called "swells" (*valy*), less often anticlises. . . . There is no clearly worked-out terminology for these forms in the foreign literature. German geologists also call them "swells" (*Wälle* of Bubnoff), or domes (*Beulen* of H. Cloos); American geologists call the corresponding forms on the North American Platform domes or plain-type folds. The latter term emphasizes better than the others the most important feature of these forms, namely, that they are restricted to tectonic "plains"—in this case, platforms. In one of Milanovskii's manuscripts, in the description of several similar dislocations from the Volga region, he uses this term in a Latinized form—planianticline (*planiantiklinal'*), from *planum*, plain; according to the rules of scientific terminology, to the Greek-derived word anticline should be attached a word of the same language, and therefore instead of planianticline it is better to use the term placanticline (*plakantiklinal'*), from *plax, placos*, plain. The writer proposes to use this term in the following as the shortest and the most appropriate to the nature of the dislocations being discussed.

Characteristic features of placanticlines are the following: (1) Placanticlines are very gentle anticline-like uplifts, usually with asymmetrical form. Dips on the gentle flanks are often measured in minutes. Dips, particularly of the lower, older beds, in the steep flanks reach $45°-75°$ in some structures; such flanks have the form of steep flexures. (2) In plan the form of placanticlines is highly varied. Some are elongated asymmetrical uplifts with smooth periclinal ends, while others are wide shield-like asymmetrical bulges; still other placanticlines have the form of box-like structures (blocks of Offman) or very irregular uplifts with a number of branches from the main placanticline. (3) One of the principal features of these disturbances is that they are situated over the area of the Volga-Urals petroleum region and over other parts of the platform in some places sporadically, as isolated uplifts . . . and in other places as elongated series . . . but they do not form such parallel series as are characteristic of linear folds in geosynclinal regions. In contrast to the linear folding of geosynclinal regions, in a single region the individual placanticlines are often situated at angles to one another, and are sometimes perpendicular. This circumstance, which to some extent indicates that mainly vertical movements acted to form these structures, is very sharply expressed in the special form of the placanticlines of the Rocky Mountains. It should be noted, however, that this is not connected only with platform formations, because many large structures of geosynclinal regions (anticlinoria and synclinoria) have the same properties. (4) Perhaps still more typical is that series of placanticlines are not accompanied by series of synclinal structures; we nowhere observe the wavelike structure in the attitude of beds that is so characteristic of folded zones. This feature, noted also by American geologists for corresponding structures of the North American Platform, is very important for clarifying the genesis of these tectonic forms. Often the synclinal zones indicated in the Soviet literature, parallel and situated in series with "swells" . . . are not independent synclinal belts but arise passively as a result of uplifts of placanticlines on the flanks of syneclises. . . . (5) In studying placanticlines we observe in the section a progressive downward increase, from younger to older strata, in the dips in the flanks. This is connected with the increase of thickness in the flanks compared to the sequence of equivalent deposits in the crestal parts of the uplift and is accompanied by the dropping-out of individual horizons in the crest and the appearance of breaks and sometimes facies changes. . . .

Such are the main features of the dislocations that are here being called placanticlines. The diversity of form of these disturbances forces us to divide them into groups and classify them. Unfortunately this cannot be done with the necessary completeness, because only very few placanticlines have been exposed in a sufficient number of boreholes. On the basis of the available material we can, however, at the present time recognize the following main types of placanticlines.

a) *Placanticlines of Zhigulev type.* Here belong the large forms which in plan, from structural maps, have the form of drops. Their thickened end represents a more or less regular periclinal termination. With increasing elevation the width of such placanticlines first increases somewhat and then begins to decrease gradually. The structure narrows, sometimes coming down to nothing. As yet the terminations have not been studied in a single one of these structures. These forms are usually asymmetrical, sometimes very strongly so. . . .

b) *Placanticlines of Tuimaza type.* These are asymmetrical placanticlines having on the whole a doubly plunging anticlinal outline, sometimes somewhat angular, but with well expressed although often nonuniformly developed periclinal terminations. These forms are usually large. They often are arranged in a chain one after another, forming a series of placanticlines that merge into an elongated "swell". . . .

c) *Placanticlines of Saratov type.* As shown by the studies of Sobolevskaia and Offman, placanticlines of this type are distinguished in plan from the previous types by their angular, boxlike outline, usually very irregular. The flanks of these forms are steep, often flexure-like, and the crests are very wide and broad, according to Offman sometimes depressed. . . .

d) *Placanticlines of Buguruslan type.* Forms of this type are closest on the one hand to flexures and on the other hand to placanticlines of Tuimaza type, but their more gently dipping flanks are very weakly expressed and are often absent. Dislocations of this type are usually traced over great distances, i.e. elongated along the strike, which makes them even more similar to flexures; however, the angle of dip of the steep flank is usually very low. Such disturbances are apparently present in the Volga-Urals region also, and are very widespread on the Russian Platform, but they are usually recognized only by detailed mapping and comparison of structural maps. . . .

e) Besides the easily recognizable types of second-order disturbances described above that complicate the large-scale warpings of the Russian Platform, the wide distribution in the Volga-Urals region of symmetrical or slightly asymmetrical placanticlines, and also poorly expressed disturbances of this type having a shield-like, often very irregular form, should be pointed out. The small amplitude of the uplifts of the latter type and the diffuse, unclearly bounded form do not always sufficiently determine the tectonic nature of these disturbances. It is possible that some of these, most probably some of the gentlest and most irregularly outlined ones, were formed not by tectonic movements but by non-uniform deposition of sediments on the floors of Paleozoic and Mesozoic marine basins and by "cloak-like" deposition of sediments on irregularities of the sea floor. . . .

The types of placanticlines distinguished above are certainly not the only ones; to all appearances, with careful study of a large number of these structures, other types will be recognized and the types proposed above will be defined more clearly. . . .

*Some Disturbances Complicating Placanticlines*

The crestal parts of placanticlines are not regular, simple flexures. As is easily noted on detailed structural maps of such tectonic forms developed in the Volga-Urals petroleum region, the regularity of the curvature of the isohypses of strata are usually disturbed by the appearance on the crests, and in a number of cases also on the flanks, especially the gentle flanks, or secondary disturbances; these disturbances, outlined on maps by the closed contours of the isohypses, have the form sometimes of flat, gentle domes, sometimes structural noses, and sometimes transverse upwarps.

Despite the fact that these small disturbances are in a number of cases . . . of particular interest, because oil fields of industrial importance are connected with them, their form, location, and origin are less well known than that of the principal structures they complicate. This is because the amplitude of the uplifts of such dislocations is so insignificant that they are revealed only by detailed structural mapping and careful reconnaissance drilling. If we accept the view that placanticlines are the reflection, in the sedimentary cover, of faults that cut the folded basement composed of intensely metamorphosed schists and gneisses and large plutons, then the origin of the small disturbances on the crests of the placanticlines must be explained by the same reasons. In the exposed part of the Pre-Cambrian basement it is seen that the crystalline basement is a complex mosaic of different blocks separated from one another by joints, without apparent displacement or with very insignificant displacement. However, individual blocks with significant relative vertical, and sometimes also horizontal, displacement are always distinguished.

There is no doubt that in the buried part of the platform of interest to us the deformation in the basement is approximately the same as in regions where the basement is exposed. Therefore, it is extremely difficult to suppose that the gneissic basements of placanticlines are simple, uniform, uplifted massifs. It is most likely that these massifs are in turn divided into series of smaller ones; some of them nevertheless underwent such appreciable vertical displacement that their movements at depth were reflected at the surface as the dislocations complicating the crests of placanticlines. . . .

Another type of secondary disturbance is possible. Study of the joints in the crystalline basement of the platform in Sweden and Finland shows that along with a large number of steeply dipping joints (75°–90°) the dip of some of the joints is considerably less (45°–75°). With great vertical displacements of blocks bounded by the gently dipping joints, weakly consolidated rocks of the sedimentary platform cover can form flexures under the influence of local tangential stresses arising during decrease in area of the crystalline basement. . . .

The problem of the genesis of the disturbances being described, as for placanticlines as a whole, is still far from being solved conclusively. This problem is one of the vital questions of theoretical and practical platform geology, because its solution will allow more rational planning of exploration and reconnaissance for oil-bearing structures.

# BAGNOLD Ralph Alger Bagnold (1896–    ), British physicist and civil engineer, is a leading authority on eolian processes and the mechanics of sediment-transport. His wind-tunnel observations were made in the laboratories of the Imperial College of Science and Technology, London, and his

267

field investigations, largely in the Sahara and the Middle East, were supported in part by the Royal Geographical Society. His studies, two small segments of which are reprinted here, provided the guidelines for much subsequent work in deserts and with eolian sediments.

## AN EXPERIMENTAL STUDY OF THE PHYSICS OF BLOWN SAND*

### SALTATION OVER A LOOSE SAND SURFACE, INITIATED BY GRANULAR IMPACT

To make the conditions as simple as possible, experiments were initially carried out with sand of nearly uniform grain size. All grains other than those between 0.3 and 0.18 mm were removed by sifting. This particular grade was chosen because it forms a large proportion of the more mobile parts of desert sand dunes.

The sand was spread loosely but evenly over the tunnel floor to a depth of 1.5 cm, and a very gentle wind was turned on, whose speed was well below the threshold at which it was able to disturb the surface grains. An electric switch then started a small but steady stream of sand falling from the roof of the tunnel near its mouth. The grains fell diagonally through the wind like rain drops. On striking the ground they made little craters in the surface, and either ejected other grains or themselves rose a centimeter or so into the air. The wind carried these secondary grains forward a few centimeters before they in turn struck the ground. In doing so they might cause a few more grains to jump feebly, but the disturbance died away to nothing a short distance down-wind of the point where the primary stream hit the ground. It ceased altogether the moment the incoming stream was cut off.

At a rather greater wind speed, but still less than that required to start grain movement without the disturbance of the incoming sand stream, a sudden change took place. On switching on the sand supply, the jumping movement along the tunnel, instead of rapidly dying away down-wind from the mouth, continued on indefinitely; and further down the tunnel it appeared as a steady cloud. The movement ceased, as before, directly the stimulation at the tunnel mouth was stopped.

Two important ideas are suggested by this experiment:

(*a*) It is evident that below the critical wind speed the energy of the grains as they move feebly along the surface comes partly from their initial fall from the roof, and partly from the pressure of the wind upon

*From *The Physics of Blown Sand and Desert Dunes* (London: Methuen, 1941; New York: Morrow, 1942; New York: Dover, 1964). Reprinted with the permission of Methuen & Co. Ltd., London. These excerpts are from pp. 31–37 of the 1942 edition.

them. But after the initial energy of the fall has been expended in disturbing the surface at each subsequent impact, the energy received from the wind is not sufficient to make up for the impact losses. Hence the movement dwindles to nothing. At the critical wind speed, however, the energy received from the wind by the average saltating grains becomes equal to that lost, so that the motion is sustained.

(*b*) The occurrence of a steady sand movement at wind speeds so small that the wind alone is incapable of disturbing the surface grains indicates that these, once the saltation is started, are jerked up into the air, not by the direct action of the wind but by the impact of descending grains.

The critical threshold wind at which an initial disturbance of the sand becomes a continuous movement along the down-wind surface, plays an important part in the mechanism of sand movement in general. In papers already published I have called it the 'dynamic threshold,' but I now think a more suitable name for it is the *impact threshold*. . . .

The speed at which the initial disturbance travels along the surface could be easily measured. The vertical illuminated beam was placed some distance—25 feet—down the tunnel, and by watching, control switch in hand, it was possible to time the first appearance of the saltation after the disturbance at the tunnel mouth had been started. It travels slowly; from a half to a third of the speed of the wind, depending on the height at which the latter is measured. The first signs of it could be seen in two ways; either by the appearance of the silver thread-like grain streaks in the light beam; or, if the surface was first pressed smooth with a sheet of glass, by the eruption in it of tiny impact craters.

## SALTATION INITIATED BY DIRECT WIND PRESSURE

When the wind speed was increased above the impact threshold—the stimulating sand inflow being cut off—another critical wind speed was reached when the surface grains, previously at rest, began to be rolled along the surface by the direct pressure of the wind. The particular wind speed at which this happened was not so definite as in the case of the impact threshold, for the rolling started at different points in the tunnel according to the strength of the wind. For instance, even at the highest wind speeds no movement took place at the extreme up-wind end of the sand floor. It began at the down-wind end, and, as the wind was increased, the point of initial movement shifted further and further up the tunnel. This is to be accounted for by the fact that fully developed turbulence does not set in till the wind has travelled some distance from the tunnel mouth. The grains first start to roll when acted upon by the faster-moving air of the turbulent eddies.

I have previously called this the 'static' threshold wind speed, to distinguish it from the 'dynamic,' but I shall take this opportunity to rename it the *Fluid Threshold* (that at which sand movement starts owing to the direct pressure of the fluid only). A foot or so down-wind of the point at which the rolling began, the grains could be seen to have gathered sufficient speed to start bouncing off the ground; and over the remainder of the floor the 'sand cloud' effect of true saltation was maintained.

### SALTATION AT HIGHER WIND SPEEDS

Both photographs and direct visual observation at greater wind speeds indicate that the grain movement is always of the same type, a saltation, or movement by bounds. The height of rise depends on the initial upward velocity with which the grain leaves the surface. The higher the grain rises, the longer it is exposed to the force of the wind, and the greater is the velocity with which it hits the ground; hence, in turn, the more violently is another grain ejected into the air. . . .

### THE SURFACE CREEP

. . . The grains in saltation strike the surface at a comparatively flat angle. A portion of the energy they have acquired from the wind is passed on to the grains that are ejected upwards to continue the saltation. The bulk of the energy is, however, dissipated in disturbing a large number of surface grains. This energy is ultimately all lost in friction between the surface grains, but the net result of the continued bombardment of the surface is that a slow forward creep takes place on the part of the grains composing it.

Individual grains are knocked onward by the blow they receive from behind. At low speeds they can be seen to move in jerks, a few millimeters at a time; but as the wind is raised, the distance moved lengthens and more grains are set in motion, till in high winds the whole surface appears to be creeping slowly forward.

Although there can be no exact distinction between the motion of the surface grains and of those grains in saltation whose paths through the air are very low, yet there exists a clear difference between the causes of these two kinds of sand motion. The grains in saltation receive their momentum directly from the pressure of the wind on them after they have risen into it. The grains in *surface creep*, on the other hand, remain unaffected by the wind. They receive their momentum by impact from the saltation.

The amount of the surface creep, that is, the weight of surface sand which moves past a fixed mark in a given time, can be measured very

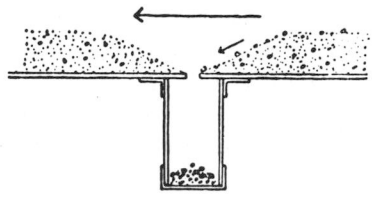

simply by means of a 'sand trap.' A narrow transverse slot, 1 to 3 mm wide, was cut in the tunnel floor, and a closed container attached underneath. The grains in saltation passed over the little gap in the ground, but the surface grains, as they were knocked forward, tumbled over the crest of the sand slope and fell into the trap.

Of the total weight of sand which flows past a fixed mark per second, the surface creep accounts for between a quarter and a fifth. Though the saltation thus greatly preponderates, the surface creep plays a very important part in sand movement in air.

(*a*) It is the means of transport whereby those grains can be moved about whose weight is far too great to be shifted by the unaided pressure of the wind. A high-speed grain in saltation can by impact move a surface grain six times its diameter, or more than 200 times its own weight.

(*b*) In a normal sand of mixed size the grains in surface creep are on the average larger than those in saltation. Thus, owing to the different speeds of travel—a fraction of an inch a second in the case of the surface creep, as opposed to many feet per second in the case of the saltation—the surface creep is responsible for changes in the size-grading of sand deposits.

(*c*) The rippling of wind-blown sand is due to an unevenness of flow on the part of the surface creep, which causes alternate piling-up of the grains and denudation, like traffic blocks and intervening spaces on a road. . . .

### SURFACE RIPPLES

After the sand movement has gone on for a short time, the surface becomes uniformly rippled, the crests and troughs running nearly at right angles to the wind direction; but since the ripples advance downwind at a slightly greater rate in the centre of the tunnel floor, where the wind is strongest, than at the sides, the crests are generally curved backwards on each side. With sand of nearly uniform grain size the ripples are very flat and can only be detected by the shadows thrown in the troughs by a horizontal beam of light. In section they are nearly symmetrical.

As the sizes of the grains depart from uniformity the symmetry is reduced, the lee slopes becoming steeper. The height of the crest above the trough greatly increases and the ripples are much more noticeable.

The ripple length, or the distance from crest to crest, increases with the strength of the wind. For sand of nearly uniform grain size, between 0.3 and 0.18 mm the ripple length was found to be 2.4 cm at the lowest wind speed at which movement was possible (the impact threshold), and to attain a maximum of 12 cm. When the wind exceeded a certain speed the ripples flattened out and disappeared, leaving a smooth flat surface. . . .

### SALTATION OVER HARD GROUND

In the preceding sections we have noticed what happens when sand is driven over a bed consisting of grains of the same size as those in the sand cloud passing overhead. If the surface grains are larger, the impacts of the grains descending from the saltation assume in an increasing degree the character of bouncing rather than splashing. Less energy is dissipated in disturbing the surface and more is retained by the grains, which now tend to rebound after impact. As a result, (a) the sand cloud formed by the saltation rises to a much greater height, so that the average range of the grains down-wind, from impact to impact, is far longer; and (b) the surface creep ceases altogether when the grains on the ground are too big to be moved at all.

The difference in the behaviour of the saltation could be seen very clearly in the tunnel. For when the surface was of uniform fine sand the top of the cloud was but a few inches high, but when small pebbles were scattered over the surface the whole tunnel height became evenly filled with flying grains from floor to roof. The descending grains bounced violently off the pebbles, so that they rose to the roof and even rebounded off it. In fact, when a small hole was cut in the roof, grains could be seen to fly out of it (against the inrush of air caused by the suction in the tunnel) and rose a meter or more above the floor level whence they started.

The difference is shown diagrammatically in Fig. 10.

### THREE POSSIBLE TYPES OF GRAIN MOTION: SUSPENSION, SALTATION, AND SURFACE CREEP

As we have already seen, sand grains are in general too large to be carried in true suspension. But the motion of the smallest sand grains may in a high wind approach to suspension, in that the upward wind eddies may check the descent of a grain and so cause it to remain in the air longer and to travel further before it again strikes the ground. A

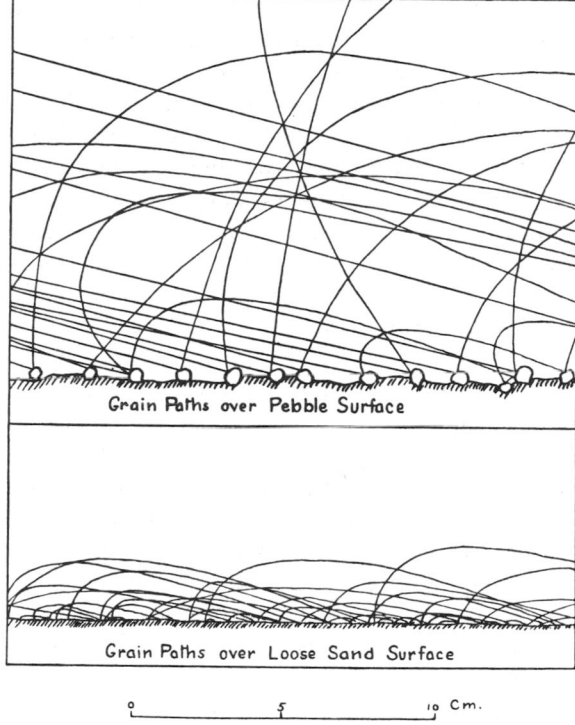

Grain Paths over Pebble Surface

Grain Paths over Loose Sand Surface

0        5        10 Cm.

Fig. 10. Difference between the saltation over sand and over pebbles.

grain in true suspension, since it never comes in contact with the ground, must travel at the average forward speed of the wind and so cannot offer any appreciable obstruction to it.

Similarly the grains in surface creep, since they remain always on the ground and receive their forward momentum from the impact of other grains, also offer no extra resistance to the wind by virtue of their motion.

It is only the third type of grain motion, the saltation, which by alternate contact with the air and the ground removes momentum from the air and so opposes a special kind of resistance to the wind. . . .

## IMMOBILITY OF SETTLED DUST AND LOESS*

It is evident from the results of the preceding section that once fine solid particles smaller than about 0.03 mm have settled on the ground

*From *The Physics of Blown Sand and Desert Dunes* (London: Methuen, 1941; New York: Morrow, 1942; New York: Dover, 1964). Reprinted with the permission of Methuen & Co. Ltd., London. These excerpts are from pp. 90–92 of the 1942 edition.

after carriage in suspension by a wind, they cannot be swept up again individually, because they sink into a viscid surface layer of air and are out of reach of the disturbing influence of the eddies of turbulence. The surface of the ground acts as a sort of dust trap. But the wind can still exert its local pressure on small aggregations of particles—little projecting heaps, the sharp edges around the impresses of feet or wheels—which the wind can treat as though they are sand grains. So that when a wind begins to blow, its first action is to tear off such projections and re-disintegrate them into dust. Once these projections have gone, however, the wind has no further effect on the surface until it is disturbed again by some third party.

This explains a common soil phenomenon. In arid pastoral plains of alluvial or wind-deposited material, dust lies thick and loose over the many converging cattle tracks which surround villages. Though a strong wind may be blowing it is often noticed that the air is only slightly hazy and no dust is picked up. It is not until a flock of sheep or a caravan passes that the familiar dense local cloud of dust appears. This moves along with the disturbance, leaving the ground dust immobile again immediately in rear of the last animal.

The disturbing influence is not confined to animals. Driving sand grains can also break up a powdery surface which would otherwise be too smooth to be affected by the wind alone. This can be demonstrated in the wind tunnel by covering the up-wind half of the floor with sand and the rest with powder such as cement. When the sand surface is fixed by wetting, no movement of the powder occurs, but if the sand is allowed to drive over the powder, a cloud of dust immediately appears. But only for a time. For the softness of the powder surface allows the sand grains to sink into it. The sand surface eventually creeps over the powder and covers the up-wind portion of it. The extent of the covering depends of course on the depth of the powder, for the layer may be eroded away down to the floor before the advancing sand covering can reach the down-wind portion. On the other hand the supply of sand from up-wind may run short, in which case the sand covering is itself removed and the powder may again be uncovered.

In this connexion should be noticed (a) the almost entire absence of recent deposits of fine material in erosion deserts, even though the production of loose fine material must here far exceed that of sand; (b) the absence of sand grains in the vast deposits of loess often found sufficiently far down-wind of such deserts to be out of range of the slowly advancing sand, e.g. in China; (c) the mean diameter of loess grains is about 0.05 mm, which is just smaller than the critical diameter in the curve of Fig. 28 [reproduced here, accompanied by Fig. 29

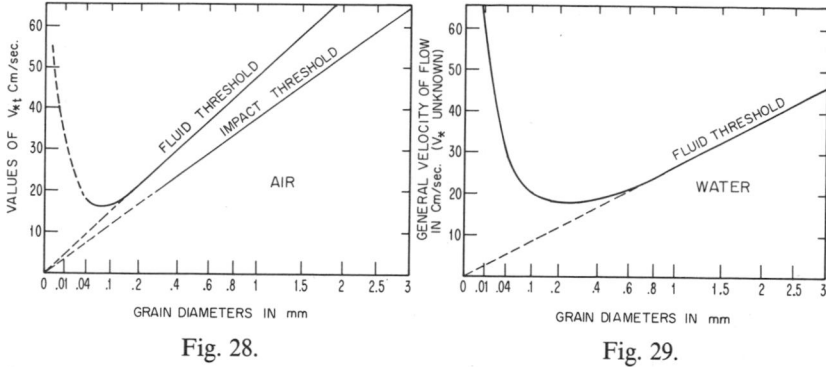

Fig. 28.                    Fig. 29.

Variation of the threshold velocity with grain size for air and water. (Grain size is drawn on a square-root scale to exhibit the relation $v \propto \sqrt{d}$ for the larger grains.)

for comparison with the corresponding curve for water]; (*d*) the great depth attained by sunken roads and tracks in the loess country in China exemplifies the differential erosion of disturbed and undisturbed surfaces of fine material.

In the case of air the change of type of fluid flow is not the only cause of the relative immobility of small particles, though, as is shown by the parallel phenomenon in water, its effect is very real and probably predominates, at any rate for particles as large as those of loess. The adsorption of moisture also plays an important part, by holding the grains together. Evidence for this can be obtained from the changes in the angle of repose which take place when the humidity of the air is varied. Carefully dried clean quartz sand of average diameter 0.08 mm begins to slip when the surface is tipped at an angle very little different from that for large grains. But when exposed to air of normal humidity it tends to stand in vertical walls like a powder.

By a curious coincidence there is also a change in the feel of the grain between the fingers when its size falls below about 0.07 mm. The material suddenly begins to feel smooth instead of gritty. Thus, as the size is reduced through the narrow range from 0.15 to 0.07 mm four distinct changes occur in the properties of grains of the same material and the same shape. (*a*) When raised into the air they become so susceptible to the wind that they begin to be maintained aloft as dust by the wind's internal eddies. (*b*) They pass the critical diameter for which the threshold wind is a minimum and so are picked up from the ground with greater difficulty. (*c*) They begin to collect moisture to such an extent that they are noticeably bound together and become sticky. And (*d*) they cease even to feel like sand.

275

COX Benjamin Burton Cox (1898–    ), American petroleum geologist, has been associated throughout most of his adult life with corporations concerned with the discovery and exploitation of petroleum resources, especially in North America and the Middle East. From 1945 to 1956 he was staff geologist of the Gulf Research and Development Company, Pittsburgh, Pa., and since 1957 he has been director of the Technical Information Service of that company. The article excerpted here is a perceptive survey of the state of knowledge of the subject at the time it was written.

## TRANSFORMATION OF ORGANIC MATERIAL INTO PETROLEUM UNDER GEOLOGICAL CONDITIONS: "THE GEOLOGICAL FENCE"*

The recognition of source beds of petroleum is essential to the evaluation and successful prospecting of many great areas throughout the world where some of the conditions common to oil-yielding areas are known to be present but where thus far little or no oil has been discovered. This includes areas where there are important oil fields in restricted parts of a great sedimentary basin but where prospects for petroleum in much larger parts of this same basin are undetermined. Laboratory studies might be directed toward explaining whether there is a fundamental reason for this connected with the original nature of the organic material, the environment of deposition, and the history of accumulation or alteration which took place during and after burial. If no reason can be found, then the industry must continue to explore these apparently unpromising areas. If criteria for the recognition of source beds are to be established, then a coordinated attack within the limits of geologic history must be made by all the fields of science involved—chemistry, physics, biology, and geology.

A few observations bearing on the problem are briefly noted. Although some of these observations may be proved irrelevant, five because of multiple occurrence are considered irrefutable and are dubbed "posts" in the "geological fence." It may be desirable to do some browsing in the range outside the fence as the grass may look greener there, but safety lies within the "corral." The herd of facts and data must be brought within the corral. Additional observations and others which might be added are considered as "stakes" in the fence. They may be broken and discarded and new stakes supplied, provided they fit conditions of observed geologic history.

The "posts" are: organic origin, marine environment, temperature, pressure, time.

*From *American Association of Petroleum Geologists Bulletin 30* (1946), 645–659.

## Organic Origin

Most geologists believe that petroleum is of organic origin because it is closely associated with sediments containing relatively high content of organic matter. Nitrogenous compounds, optical activity, and chlorophyll derivatives have also been advanced as evidence of organic origin but these conceivably could have been picked up by petroleum migrating through rocks containing such substances. Petroleum-like products can be formed in the laboratory from inorganic substances, but the natural occurrence and distribution of such substances do not fit geological history. Products so formed are inert optically, and do not contain chlorophyll derivatives or nitrogenous compounds.

Equally important is the absence of oil fields where all essentials, except source, are present. The requirements for oil fields are: (a) source, (b) porous reservoir, and (c) trap that will stop upward movement of oil. The second and third requirements can be found in association with rocks of all types—granites, lavas, sediments that accumulated under desert conditions, on the flood plains of rivers and in the sea. No oil pools have been found in such traps and reservoirs in sections devoid of or lean in organic matter, and this has not been due to lack of search.

## Marine Environment

Ninety-nine per cent of the world's oil fields are associated with marine sediments. Known producing formations are limited to certain associations with certain types of marine sedimentary rocks. Rocks deposited in fresh water, non-marine basins, not different in lithologic character from marine rocks which yield petroleum, contain no petroleum. Multiple occurrence of reservoirs and their associated fine-grained marine sediments containing organic matter appear to be significant. In about one per cent of known petroleum occurrence non-marine sections yield petroleum but the sediments were deposited in brackish water. No crude oil has been found in a sedimentary basin containing only fresh water, terrestrial sediments. Many geologists believe that sediments deposited in enclosed, or partly enclosed, shallow, marine basins yield more petroleum than sediments deposited in more open parts of epi-continental seas.

Trask compared the organic content of many recent marine sediments with that of ancient marine sediments, the latter likewise based on thousands of samples. The average organic content of recent marine sediments near shore is approximately 2.5 per cent, of ancient marine sediments 1.5 per cent. Ninety per cent of the samples analyzed had less than 4 per cent. These averages, however, are greatly exceeded in local geographic areas and in limited parts of the stratigraphic section. Organic content of more than 8 to 10 per cent has been reported from ancient rocks in some cases. Many geologists believe that the high organic content in marine rocks may be important in oil origin, but Trask did not find any statistical relationship between quantity of organic matter and the occurrence of petroleum. There is ample residual solid organic material, if it could be converted into petroleum, to account for far more petroleum than is known in the world.

Analyses of solvent extracts of four recent marine sediments were made by Trask and his associates. These studies indicate that liquid petroleum probably does not occur in sediments at the time of their deposition although small quantities of solid paraffins are found. Trask concluded that if any liquid petroleum is present in recent marine sediments, it is less than one per cent of the organic content. ZoBell reports finding 10 to 20 milligrams of liquid hydrocarbons in 100-gram samples of fresh recent marine sediments; if we assume an average organic content in these sediments of 2.5 per cent, the liquid hydrocarbons detected would amount to only 0.4 to 0.8 per cent of the organic content of the sediment. Much of the oil detected in ZoBell's studies disappeared after a few days' storage at room temperature, ostensibly due to bacterial activity.

Fatty and oily substances constitute less than one per cent of the organic content of the four organic-rich marine sediments which Trask studied. He considered that this was not enough to account for all of the known petroleum. Fatty acids ranging from cerotic ($C_{26}H_{52}O_2$) to melissic ($C_{30}H_{60}O_2$) constitute 0.002 to 0.006 per cent of the sediment. Organic sulphur compounds form about 0.03 per cent of the deposits. Free sulphur is a common minor constituent of all sediments and ranges from 0.02 to 0.1 per cent. Trask's studies did not completely exhaust the possibilities of water-soluble organic matter.

Organic material present in recent marine sediments also includes carbon-hydrogen-oxygen compounds such as cellulose, as well as haemoglobin and chlorophyll and their derivatives. Lignin occurs but geologists do not believe that oil was derived from lignin for the same reason they do not believe it was derived from torbanite and the like. Most simple carbohydrates and proteins are readily decomposed by bacteria soon after reaching the sea bottom.

Geologists do not believe that non-marine, pyrobituminous substances such as oil shale, tasmanite, torbanite, and boghead coal are a source of crude petroleum. Many sedimentary basins which yield petroleum are devoid of such rocks. Oil fields have not been found in non-marine basins where high concentrations of such pyrobituminous substances occur.

Torbanitic deposits have a matrix of partly decayed plant debris, probably ulmic or humic in nature, with variable amounts of unaltered algal cups, cuticles, cuticular secretions, resins, and oily spores, and pollen exines.

The oil fractions which can be retorted from such rocks are derived chiefly from oily or resinous materials which were formed during the life cycle of the plant. Lesser amounts of hydrocarbon products result from the pyrolysis of the matrix. Pond algae for instance, which convert starch to terpenes in their life processes, are preserved in torbanites unaltered throughout geologic time under overburden pressures as great as those which have prevailed in petroliferous areas. These algae and spores are exceedingly resistant to bacterial alteration. Laboratory pilot-plant attempts to liberate the oil from torbanitic deposits by pressures far greater than pressures commonly occurring in petroliferous basins have failed.

A single living alga before cell division and before the oil formed is absorbed by its cup will release a small drop under moderate pressure.

Most oil-field reservoir rocks are hydrophilic. The interstitial water which coats the pore walls commonly has high chloride content which in some cases is much higher than in sea water. This is also true of the bottom and edge waters of most oil fields. Occurrences of relatively fresh interstitial and edge water are believed by the geologists to be exceptions caused by either: migration of meteoric water into the reservoir at the outcrop, resulting in dilution as in the case of the Kern River oil field, California; or migration of oil into sands already saturated with meteoric water.

## Temperature

In rare cases, temperatures slightly higher than the boiling point of water occur in petroliferous basins. Temperature of at least 113°C. (235°F.) has been recorded. This is a salt-dome temperature where the salt mass may be acting as a conduit for higher, deeper-seated temperatures. Geologic history, however, indicates that most oil-basin temperatures have been low throughout geologic time. The maximum temperatures have probably been approximately 100°C. for most oil basins. The presence of chlorophyll derivatives in petroleum indicates that a maximum temperature has been less than 200°C. Geologic history does not permit the temperatures required under hypotheses of Engler and his followers.

Geologic observation suggests that the critical original thickness of sediment in which petroleum has been formed is a vertical section of about 5,000 feet. If the average temperature gradient was 1°C. per 100 feet and the average surface temperature 15°C., the minimum temperature under which petroleum could have been formed would have been 65°C. (149°F.). This could have been increased by heat due to exothermic chemical or biochemical reaction or possibly to shear pressures generating heat in fine-grained sediments. Shear-pressure experiments of Hawley and Rand did not raise temperatures. Their samples, however, were air-dried so that they did not completely simulate geologic history.

Temperatures in oil fields are commonly but not always higher than temperatures in adjacent synclinal areas after correction for depth, possibly suggesting some type of exothermic reaction.

## PRESSURE

Since some petroleum occurs in basins which have had a stratigraphic thickness of about 5,000 feet but not much more than 5,000 feet, minimum pressures are limited. The hydrostatic head in such a thickness of rock at the deepest part of the basin would not greatly exceed 2,000 pounds per square inch but this pressure probably was exceeded in fine-grained or colloidal sediments at point contacts by the weight of overburden sediment or by shear pressures. Overburden pressure of 5,000 feet would be approximately 5,000 p.s.i. However, shear pressure would exceed this by an unknown amount.

## TIME

Petroleum occurs in rocks of all ages from the Cambrian to the Pliocene inclusive, but no evidence has been found to prove that any petroleum has been formed since the Pliocene, although sedimentation patterns and thicknesses in Pleistocene and Recent sediments are similar to those in the Pliocene where petroleum has formed. Residual carbon and gas which may have been derived from petroleum occur in metasedimentary pre-Cambrian rocks. The scale factor for time since the Pliocene cannot be reckoned accurately in calendar years but may be taken for scale purposes as about a million years for the formation of the youngest known petroleum in geologic history. Time since the Cambrian can be taken as one billion years. The apparent absence of formation of petroleum subsequent to the Pliocene must be explained in any study of the transformation of organic material into petroleum.

# WANLESS AND WELLER

Harold Rollin Wanless (1898–    ), American geologist, received his baccalaureate degree in 1920 and his doctorate in 1923 from Princeton University. He immediately joined the faculty of the University of Illinois, where he has been Professor of Geology since 1946. He has been a member of the Illinois State Geological Survey since 1925 and of the U. S. Geological Survey since 1954. In 1958–59 he was a Fulbright Fellow at the University of Sydney, Australia.

James Marvin Weller (1899–    ), American geologist, received his baccalaureate degree in 1923 and his doctorate in 1927 from the University of Chicago. From 1916 to 1919, with time out for Army service in the First World War, and again from 1925 to 1945 he was associated with the Illinois State Geological Survey. From 1920 to 1922 he was engaged in explorations in India for a British petroleum company; in 1923 he was in the employ of a zinc-producing company in Missouri; and in 1924 and 1925 he was a member of the Kentucky State Geological Survey. He was an assistant professor of geology at the University of Illinois in 1936–37 and he conducted exploratory surveys in China and Tibet for an American oil company in 1937–38. Since 1945 he has been Professor of Invertebrate Paleontology at the University of Chicago.

## CORRELATION AND EXTENT OF PENNSYLVANIAN CYCLOTHEMS*[1]

The heterogeneous strata of the Pennsylvanian system in the central and eastern states constitute a complex succession so different from the older Paleozoic systems that the interpretation of the Pennsylvanian is difficult and few geologists have attempted more than a generalization of its geological history. Because of variable lithology and the generally long or unknown range of invertebrate fossils, these standard means of correlation have proved, up to this time, to be of negligible service,

---

*From *Geological Society of America Bulletin 43* (1932), 1003–1016.

[1] *Cyclothem* is derived from two Greek words: *cyclos,* cycle, and *thema,* a deposit. It has been proposed that each of the cyclical series of beds in the Pennsylvanian system be considered a formation (Weller, *J. Geol. 38* (1930), 101). Inasmuch as the word "formation" is very loosely employed in stratigraphy to designate a single bed, a group of beds having some character in common such as age, composition, or origin, a group of more or less unrelated beds combined for convenience into a cartographical unit, etc., this term seems inappropriate for the very definite subdivisions of the Pennsylvanian system that are coming to be widely recognized, unless it be always prefixed by the adjective "cyclical." The word "cyclothem" is therefore proposed to designate a series of beds deposited during a single sedimentary cycle of the type that prevailed during the Pennsylvanian period. A cyclothem ranks as a formation in the scale of stratigraphic nomenclature (J. M. Weller).

and the fossil plants, which are probably no more accurate stratigraphic indices than are the invertebrates, have furnished the basis for practically all previous correlations between the Pennsylvanian strata of the different basins or between remote portions of the same basin.

## THE CYCLICAL HYPOTHESIS

In 1926 a broad stratigraphic study of the Pennsylvanian system in Illinois was begun by the Illinois State Geological Survey under the direction of J. M. Weller. As this study proceeded he was impressed by the remarkable similarity of the stratigraphic section associated with almost every coal bed. His observations at hundreds of localities in all parts of Illinois and Indiana during the course of three field seasons furnished the basis for certain generalizations regarding the succession of the various types of strata which were supported by Wanless' detailed studies in the Alexis and Havana quadrangles[2] of western Illinois, where a standard stratigraphic section of the lower Pennsylvanian beds was compiled.[3] Their studies showed that the Pennsylvanian system in the Eastern Interior basin consists of repeated series of beds, or cyclothems, each of which is composed of a similar succession of members:

*Marine sediments:*
8. Shale with "ironstone" nodules and bands
7. Limestone with marine fossils
6. Black sheety shale with large concretions

*Continental sediments:*
5. Coal
4. Underclay
3. Limestone without marine fossils
2. Sandy shale
1. Sandstone unconformable on lower beds

An interpretation of the physiographic conditions both in the sedimentary basin and in the land area from which the sediments were derived has been presented as a hypothesis of cyclical Pennsylvanian sedimentation,[4] which explains the successive deposition of these re-

[2] H. R. Wanless, "Geology and mineral resources of the Alexis Quadrangle," *Illinois State Geol. Survey Bull. 57* (1929); "Geology and mineral resources of the Havana Quadrangle," Illinois State Geol. Survey unpublished manuscript.

[3] H. R. Wanless, "Pennsylvanian cycles in western Illinois," *Illinois State Geol. Survey Bull. 60* (1931), 179–193; "Pennslyvanian section in western Illinois," *Bull. Geol. Soc. Am. 42* (1931), 801–812.

[4] J. M. Weller, "Cyclical sedimentation in the Pennsylvanian period and its significance," *J. Geol. 38* (1930), 97–135; "The conception of cyclical sedimentation during the Pennsylvanian period," *Illinois State Geol. Survey Bull. 60* (1931), 163–177.

curring cyclothems and their subsequent preservation. One of the most important points of this hypothesis was the postulation that each of the cyclothems should be widely extensive in the sedimentary basin. Should this postulation be established, a new method of correlation would be available, dependent not on a few key horizons nor on faunas or floras, but on a succession of cyclothems.

## RECENT INVESTIGATIONS

The general section established by Wanless in the Alexis and Havana quadrangles of western Illinois has been traced, supplemented, and extended by him from Rock Island to Murphysboro, Illinois, in three seasons of regional studies. Dr. H. B. Willman has studied in detail the Pennsylvanian strata exposed along Illinois River in north-central Illinois, and S. E. Ekblaw has worked out the upper Pennsylvanian section west of the center of the Illinois basin. Weller has studied and correlated the strata between Danville, Illinois, and Wabash River, and Weller and Wanless have traced these strata southward into Edgar County, Illinois, and southern Vermillion and Park counties, Indiana. Weller has also made rapid reconnaissance studies of the Pennsylvanian system in other States from Oklahoma to West Virginia,[5] and the best exposures of the lower Pennsylvanian beds in the northern part of the Western Interior basin were later restudied by Weller and Wanless.

All of these studies have shown (1) that the entire Pennsylvanian system in the Eastern Interior and northern Appalachian basins and the lower Pennsylvanian strata in the northern part of the Western Interior basin consist of a similar succession of cyclothems, (2) that individual cyclothems are persistent, and (3) that correlation of cyclothems at widely separated localities is possible.

## CORRELATION OF PENNSYLVANIAN STRATA

Many of the cyclothems are nearly as varied within a single county as within the entire State of Illinois. For this reason a detailed study of only a small area may leave the impression that the beds vary greatly, whereas a more general survey of almost the entire Eastern Interior basin has revealed that the Pennsylvanian system throughout this region is remarkably uniform. Although all of the cyclothems consist of the same general members and reflect the repetition of the same general sedimentary cycle, physical, chemical, and biotic conditions were never exactly duplicated in the different cycles, and practically every cyclothem possesses unique characteristics by which it may be recognized.

[5] These studies were made possible by a grant-in-aid from the National Research Council.

Although all of the members of each cyclothem vary in thickness and lithology from place to place, the character of some beds is remarkably similar at localities a hundred miles or more apart.

Correlation of Pennsylvanian strata is accomplished by careful study of the exposures with special regard to the cyclothems. After a cyclothem has been carefully studied and its relations to other cyclothems noted in a local area, it may be easily traced by studies of exposures at about 10-mile intervals, for many members persist with but little change over such a distance.

It is also possible but somewhat more difficult to correlate strata in widely separated exposures. Certain cyclothems can be identified with more or less certainty, and the section above and below commonly furnishes much substantiating evidence when it is carefully worked out. Although invertebrate fossils have generally proved to be of little value in precisely correlating Pennsylvanian cyclothems, they are of great service in making approximate correlations or in verifying correlations based upon stratigraphic evidence.

$$\cdot \quad \cdot \quad \cdot \quad \cdot \quad \cdot$$

## Conclusions

Field studies have demonstrated that most of the Pennsylvanian cyclothems extend throughout the Eastern Interior basin and can be traced from outcrop to outcrop for long distances or recognized in isolated localities by peculiarities of lithology, fauna, and stratigraphic succession. Cyclothems in addition to those first recognized in western Illinois appear to the south and east, where they are for the most part incompletely developed. They are represented only locally in the northwestern part of the basin by seemingly erratic beds which could not be interpreted according to the cyclical hypothesis so long as only their local occurrence was known.

That part of the section which occurs below the Liverpool cyclothem offers some difficulties in interpretation and correlation because of the general thinness of the cyclothems, their more or less incomplete development, and their variable lithology. The correlation of the Liverpool and younger cyclothems is easier, but difficulties are also introduced by certain features such as (1) the incomplete cyclothem in the lower part of the Liverpool, (2) the erratic development of the St. David cyclothem in the St. Louis region, (3) the provisional Jamestown cyclothem, and (4) the possible composite character of the Gimlet cyclothem.

Observations in the northern part of the Western Interior basin have demonstrated that the Lower Pennsylvanian strata may be divided into cyclothems which can be correlated with those in Illinois on the basis of faunas, stratigraphy, and lithology. Data sufficient for definite correlation of higher strata have not been obtained.

The remarkable similarity of the Lower Pennsylvanian strata on both sides of Mississippi River substantiates the postulation (1) that the Pennsylvanian strata in the various coal basins are but remnants of an originally continuous sedimentary blanket, (2) that the marine invasions which occurred periodically throughout the Pennyslvanian period were very extensive and connected the various basins in nearly every case, and (3) that the cyclical repetition of strata in the different basins was controlled by the same series of diastrophic movements which must have affected the entire eastern half of North America. Strictly, the evidence so far warrants these conclusions only for the Eastern and Western Interior basins, but inasmuch as the Pennsylvanian strata in the northern part of the Appalachian basin occur in a similar cyclical succession it may soon be possible to make precise correlations between that region and the Eastern Interior basin.

The rudimentary cyclothems present an interesting problem unrecognized when the cyclical hypothesis was formulated. Their interpretation awaits further studies.

# BRADLEY, BRAMLETTE, CUSHMAN, and HENBEST Wilmot Hugh Bradley (1899– ), American geologist, received his baccalaureate degree in 1920 and his doctorate in 1927 from Yale University. Joining the U. S. Geological Survey in 1920, he progressed through the various grades from field assistant to principal geologist, becoming Chief Geologist in 1944 and continuing after 1959 as research geologist.

Milton Nunn Bramlette (1896– ), American geologist, graduated from the University of Wisconsin in 1921 and received his Ph.D. degree from Yale in 1936. Associated at various times with the U. S. Geological Survey, the Gulf Oil Company, and the University of California at Los Angeles, he was Professor of Geology in the Scripps Institute of Oceanography at La Jolla, California, from 1951 until his retirement in 1962.

Joseph Augustine Cushman (1881–1949), American micropaleontologist, graduated from Harvard College in 1903 and received his Ph.D. degree from Harvard University in 1909. From 1912 to 1921, he was a member of the U. S. Geological Survey and then for a few years a consultant for various oil companies. In 1923, he established the Cushman Laboratory for Foraminiferal

Research in Sharon, Massachusetts, and after 1925 devoted the rest of his life to research. He was largely responsible for the recognition of the stratigraphic and ecological implications of fossil Foraminifera and thus laid the foundations for the burgeoning of micropaleontology during the middle third of the twentieth century.

Lloyd George Henbest (1900–    ), American paleontologist, graduated from the University of Arkansas in 1924, received an A.M. degree from the University of Kansas in 1927, and continued his studies in geology and paleontology at Yale University until he began his long career with the U. S. Geological Survey in 1930.

The report of their studies, excerpted here, opened new vistas for research concerning deep-sea sediments and provided guidelines for much of the subsequent interpretation of the voluminous data made available by the widely ranging oceanographic surveys of the mid-century years.

## NORTH ATLANTIC DEEP-SEA CORES *

### Significance of the Investigation (by Bradley)

The long cores of deep-sea sediment considered in this report represent a longer span of the earth's late geologic history, as recorded in abyssal sediments, than has been heretofore accessible. In a measure, therefore, this study has been exploratory. Because of that exploratory aspect we have not only presented the observations but also have deliberately speculated upon various possible interpretations of the features observed in the cores and upon their relations with one another. Because the cores are few in number and widely spaced, we offer many of the interpretations not as definite conclusions but rather as suggestions to be tested by whatever coring may be done in the future in that part of the North Atlantic.

From this investigation it appears that glacial marine deposits may prove to be sensitive indicators of the climatic changes that caused the growth and decay of continental ice sheets during the Pleistocene. In particular, it seems that the glacial marine record may throw light on the climatic fluctuations that determined substages of the Pleistocene. The marine record was the result of a continuously operating series of causes such that the deposits of each glacial substage were separated from one another by the deposits of the intervening warmer substage. The record of each substage has remained intact and was not obliterated by readvances of the ice. As the equatorward extent of the glacial marine deposits implies a corresponding expansion of continental ice sheets,

---

* From "Geology and Biology of North Atlantic Deep-sea Cores between Newfoundland and Ireland," *U. S. Geological Survey Professional Paper 196-A* (1940).

the extent of the deposits may be used as a measure of the intensity of the climatic changes, and their thickness may be used as a rough indicator of the duration of glacial substages. Similarly, the thickness and poleward extent of tongues of nonglacial sediment—the foraminiferal marl—are measures of deglaciation. The areal extent of these tongues of sediment can be determined by additional cores taken at properly located stations.

When the glacial marine record is more fully known it should provide a basis for correlating the Pleistocene history of Europe and North America. . . .

As the pelagic Foraminifera in these abyssal sediments are reliable indicators of surface-water temperatures in the Recent and Pleistocene epochs, it should be possible to trace southward into the tropics layers or beds of foraminiferal ooze that are the time equivalents of glacial marine zones. Such layers of foraminiferal ooze could then be correlated with the layer of globigerina ooze in the tropics that Schott[1] identified as a relatively cold-water deposit that probably represents the last glacial epoch of the Pleistocene.

The study of climatology as well as geology may be advanced by the information to be derived from long sea-bottom cores. Significant evidence bearing on postglacial climatic changes may be obtained from minutely detailed study of the Foraminifera in cores taken in parts of the ocean where postglacial sedimentation has been comparatively rapid, as, for example, near the seaward edge of the blue-mud zone. On the assumption that such sediment accumulates at an essentially uniform rate, climatic fluctuations may be located approximately in time within the postglacial interval and may be correlated from place to place along the ocean margins from the Arctic to temperate or even tropical latitudes and perhaps also from continent to continent.

Archeology, also, might profit from the knowledge of a relatively timed and correlated sequence of climatic changes, for such changes may well have made a significant impress on the habits and migrations of peoples, particularly those that dwelt in regions where small changes in either temperature or rainfall were critical. . . .

### LITHOLOGY AND GEOLOGIC INTERPRETATIONS
#### (BY BRAMLETTE AND BRADLEY)

More than ordinary interest attaches to the interpretation of the zones of glacial marine sediments revealed by these cores because they may ultimately be correlated with events on land during the Pleistocene

[1] Wolfgang Schott. See pp. 367–371 of this volume.

287

epoch and because cores of ocean-bottom sediments open a new approach to the study of glacial epochs.

. . . . .

An epoch when all the oceans were colder than they are today seems to be implied by the fact that three types of cool-water or cold-water deposits formerly had a greater areal extent than they do today and are, therefore, locally buried beneath a comparable thickness of foraminiferal ooze or limy blue mud such as that now forming in various parts of the ocean. The old glacial marine deposits extended much farther from the poles, in both northern and southern hemispheres, than the glacial marine deposits now forming; the areas of red-clay deposition were much larger; and the sediments characterized by a colder-water foraminiferal fauna extended even into the equatorial regions. Some very general cause seems necessary to explain these three types of colder-water deposits, all buried beneath a comparable thickness of warmer-water deposits. The conclusion seems logical that they are all essentially contemporaneous and represent the last glacial maximum of the Pleistocene. How much of the Pleistocene may be represented by these and other deeper-lying cold-water deposits penetrated by the cores is quite another question, which leads us back to further consideration of cores . . . from the western part of the North Atlantic. Each of which shows four more or less distinct zones of glacial marine deposits.

Three possible interpretations have been considered: first, that each glacial marine zone represents a separate glacial stage of the Pleistocene epoch; second, that the two upper glacial marine zones, which are less distinctly separated, represent a bipartite last-glacial (Wisconsin) stage, whereas each of the two lower glacial marine zones represents a pre-Wisconsin glacial stage; and third, that all four glacial marine zones represent only substages of advance and retreat within the Wisconsin stage.

. . . . .

Although the evidence available is insufficient to determine which of these interpretations of the glacial marine succession is the more nearly correct, we are inclined to favor the third interpretation—that all four glacial marine zones are substages of the Wisconsin stage. Only more and longer cores can provide adequate data for a completely satisfactory answer.

. . . . .

The texture and structural features of the sediments in several parts of these cores seem to indicate rather plainly that, locally, currents move over the sea bottom with sufficient velocity to sweep the finer particles from the higher ridges and scatter them about over the bottom of the adjacent deeper parts of the ocean. . . .

. . . The thinness of the postglacial deposits . . . and the conspicuous amount of sand and pebbles that is mixed with the postglacial types of Foraminifera support Peach's interpretation[2] that currents of appreciable velocity sweep the bottom close to the edge of the continental shelf.

Currents of sufficient velocity to move silt and sand-sized particles may not be restricted to these more exposed parts of the sea floor but may also operate to an appreciable extent even at depths exceeding 4,820 meters. The distribution of the shards of volcanic glass in both ash zones of these cores presents evidence that may be interpreted as the result of such currents. The shards that are scattered through a considerable thickness of sediment above the base of each ash zone may be so distributed because, for a long time, gentle currents continued to remove them from the tops of low mounds or ridges on the ocean floor and scatter them about over the adjacent flatter areas while the foraminiferal ooze continued to be deposited. This implies that, by reason of the currents, parts of an ash zone remain exposed for a long time on the mounds and ridges to supply shards to the adjacent areas. Such a hypothesis to account for the distribution of the shards in the ash zones might be tested conclusively in some particular locality by a group of cores that sampled the sediment on the top of a low ridge and on the adjacent flatter parts of the ocean floor.

. . . . .

Several layers of sediment in these cores that are rather sharply set off from the adjacent material by distinctive textural changes suggest submarine slumps. . . .

. . . The regular gradation in size of this material, the sharp boundary at the base, the irregular occurrence of clay pellets, and the gradation into material of yet finer grain above suggest that this sample consists of material thrown into suspension by a submarine slump, carried beyond the slide itself and deposited rapidly. Material thus thrown into suspension would be expected to settle according to the respective settling velocities of the various constituents.

. . . . .

[2] B. N. Peach, *Proc. Roy. Soc. Edinburgh 32* (1913), 267–275.

289

## Foraminifera (by Cushman and Henbest)

The Foraminifera in the cores are species or varieties that have been recorded in existing oceans or in Recent and Pleistocene sediments. No Foraminifera known to be exclusively characteristic of Pliocene or earlier epochs were found. These circumstances set a limit to the time span with which we have to deal, but a number of difficulties, that are for the present insurmountable, stand in the way of determining precisely the age and correlation of the faunas by strictly paleontologic methods. One of the principal obstacles is that the historical range of the pelagic species remains as indefinite, within certain limits, as their taxonomy is generalized. Another is that good stratigraphic sequences of beds bearing late Cenozoic to Recent Foraminifera are rare, and few of these have been completely described. This is true not only for the Foraminifera enclosed in sediments of epeiric seas, from which most marine faunas heretofore available to paleontologists are derived, but it is particularly true for deep-sea faunas. All the bottom faunas in the cores are of a deep-sea facies and therefore belong to the group whose history is least known.

The evolutionary and faunal changes in the Foraminifera as a whole during and since the Miocene have been so gradual that the historical aspect of faunal differences cannot be clearly distinguished from the complex of existing geographic differences. . . .

. . . Because of these obstacles, our method of determining the age of the faunas and the associated sediments was the indirect one of comparing the temperatures indicated by the Foraminifera with the physical history of the Recent and Pleistocene epochs. The faunal differences related to ecology and geographic distribution were also obstacles to the direct use of the Foraminifera as agents for the detailed correlation of horizons from core to core; however, by indicating warm and cold periods that were presumably of broad geographic extent, the Foraminifera did furnish criteria that could be used along with zones of volcanic ash and peculiarities of lithology for suggested correlations, which have been worked out by Bramlette and Bradley.

# KORSHINSKIY Dimitriy Sergeyevich Korshinskiy (1899– ), Russian petrographer, graduated from the Leningrad Mining Institute in 1926 and for the next eleven years was attached to the Central Geological Survey in Leningrad. From 1937 to 1956 he was a member of the faculty of the Institute of Geological Sciences in the Soviet Academy of Sciences, in which he at-

tained the rank of Academician in 1953. He is currently a Bureau Member of the Department of Geological and Geographical Sciences in that Academy. His principal contributions to science have dealt with the physicochemical analysis of mineralization processes.

## MOBILITY AND INERTNESS OF COMPONENTS IN METASOMATISM *

### INTRODUCTION

Metasomatic phenomena are distinguished by considerable complexity, and since they play an important role in crustal processes, they require special and careful study both from the standpoint of physicochemical regularities and from the standpoint of geology, mineralogy, and geochemistry.

During petrologic study of the Precambrian rocks of Eastern Siberia and the associated ore deposits, the writer repeatedly met with phenomena whose understanding required special theoretical analysis of metasomatic processes and development of special methods of investigation. In the present paper the writer has decided to deal only with certain partial regularities of metasomatic processes by introducing the concept of ideal mobility of components. The writer quite deliberately restricted the scope of the paper in this way, not wishing to touch upon other important regularities of metasomatism, such as Lindgren's "law of volumes," the effect of a drop in temperature, and so on. Aiming at brevity, the writer ruled out a number of phenomena and considered only a certain idealized metasomatic process—a method sufficiently justified by the successes of physical chemistry. Of course, concrete cases of metasomatism cannot be fitted completely into any such abstract scheme, but their study would be impossible without the aid of such abstractions.

The main importance of the simple regularities obtained here is that they can be taken as a basis for a geometric interpretation of various processes. . . .

### PRELIMINARY CONDITIONS

Metasomatism occurs as a result of interaction between a rock (a mineral aggregate) and a liquid or gaseous solution. In general the temperature of the solution and its composition vary during this process, and often different stages of the process are superposed upon one another, giving complex metasomatic rocks with minerals of different

*From *Akademiia nauk SSSR, Izvestiia, Otdelenie matematicheskikh i estestvennykh nauk* (Academy of Sciences of the USSR, Bulletin, section on mathematical and natural sciences), no. 1 (1936), pp. 35–65. Translated by John B. Southard.

generations. However, as petrologic experience shows, simpler cases in which the minerals of the rock were formed mainly or even entirely at constant conditions and the subsequent stages of the process had little or no effect upon the rock, are not uncommon.

### The Concept of Mobility and Inertness of Components

Microscopic study of metasomatic rocks shows that replacement of minerals takes place primarily along grain boundaries and along small cleavage cracks, which are often so small that they are indistinguishable even at great magnification. Flow of the solution is hardly possible along these very fine cracks; most likely the material here moves by diffusion in a motionless or almost motionless solution. On the other hand, large cracks, such as, for example, ore fissures, joints, and parting planes, must be present for metasomatism to be possible. Solutions flow along these larger cracks; however, the solutions and the rock interact via a system of very fine, almost submicroscopic cracks that permeate the entire rock. The circulating solutions thus interact with the rocks not directly but by diffusion through motionless solutions in a system of submicroscopic cracks.

The concentrations of the various components of the circulating liquid or gaseous solution will in general be arbitrary and will differ from the concentrations in the solution that is saturated by the rock. There should thus be an interaction between rock and solution, in which part of the components of the rock will go into the solution and part of the components of the solution will be deposited in the rock. In this, different components of the solution may behave differently.

(1) For some components the quantity of material transported by diffusion will be so small compared to the quantity of material reacting with the rock that the concentrations of these components in the solution rapidly equilibrate with the concentrations in the local solutions that are saturated by the rock. Consequently, the reactions will proceed at some singular concentration of the solution. Only after completion of the reaction can a slow change of the concentration of the solution begin. Components that behave in this way in the given process we shall call "inert."

(2) For other components the quantity of material entering into reaction with the rock may be insignificant compared to the diffusibility of these components. The concentrations of such components in the solution will thus be always maintained at a particular level, as if the entire rock were reacting directly with the solution flowing in the larger cracks, with constant concentration. We shall call such components "fully mobile" in the given process.

The extreme case of inertness is that for which there is no appreciable inflow or outflow of the component from the solution after the rock is formed; we shall call such a component "fully inert." Thus, the system made up of the solution plus the rock is closed relative to fully inert components and open relative to fully mobile components, with the former fixed by their quantity in the system and the latter by their concentration in the solution. We can also say that the concentration of the solution that saturates the rock is fixed externally for mobile components and fixed by the saturation of the solution by the rock for inert components.

However, not every inert component is "fully inert," with constant content in the given region of rock. During the period of formation of the rock a more or less considerable amount of the inert components have time to go into the rock or leave it by diffusion, in accordance with the directions of the relations between solution and rock. If we consider only the final chemical equilibrium state, for such reactions with inert components this final state is determined by the quantity of material supplied or given out, but for mobile components it is determined only by their concentrations in the solution, and for these components exchange of material is considered to be ensured.

As indicated above, the degree of mobility of the components is determined by the relationship between the quantity of material that can be transported by diffusion and the quantity of material entering into reaction. From this it is evident that in the general case the most easily soluble and the most easily diffusible components will be the most mobile, and the difficultly soluble components, with heavy, slowly diffusing particles, will be inert. On the other hand, with large quantities of components separating from the rock or entering the rock, even a very mobile component can show inertness, and conversely a usually inert component can in a particular case behave as a mobile component, if only neglible quantities of it take part in the reaction. It is clear also that the mobility of components depends upon the intensity of the process (see below) and upon the over-all composition of the solution (the presence of "mineralizers" can increase the mobility of certain components).

Thus, we shall use the following definition:

If for all reactions between rock and solution the concentration of a given component in the solution is maintained at a constant, arbitrary level, by influx of material from outside or by outflow of material, then we shall call such components fully mobile. Those components whose concentrations in the solution are determined by the saturation of the solution by the rock we shall call inert components.

### Derivation of Theorems of Fully Mobile Components

We shall consider first a system of two independent components $a$ and $b$. At arbitrary temperature and pressure in this system, let the minerals M, N, O, P, Q, and R, arranged in order of increasing content of component $b$, be stable, depending on the composition. We illustrate in Fig. 1 the compositions and potentials of these minerals, laying off the content of component $b$ along the abscissa axis and the value of the thermodynamic potential corresponding to each mineral along the ordinate axis. Points M, N, O, and so forth, in Fig. 1 are points corresponding to the minerals, giving their compositions and potentials. By joining these points by straight line segments we obtain the broken line MNOPQR, which must necessarily be convex downward. If for some part of this line the convexity were disrupted, for example for some segment OSP, then from this it would follow that the existence of mineral S under the given conditions of pressure and temperature is impossible, because the mineral S can break down into minerals O and P with lower potential, i.e. spontaneously.

Thus, with arbitrary chemical composition of the rock relative to components $a$ and $b$, the rock will consist of two minerals, M + N, N + O, or O + P, etc., depending upon this composition. This case, corresponding to Goldschmidt's mineralogical phase rule, will occur if both components $a$ and $b$ are "inert," i.e. are fixed by their content in the rock. The stable existence of any two such minerals together with the solution, for example, N and O, is possible only if the chemical potentials of their components in the rock and in the solution are equal; by drawing a straight line through the points of minerals N and O we obtain points O' and O at the intersections of this line with the

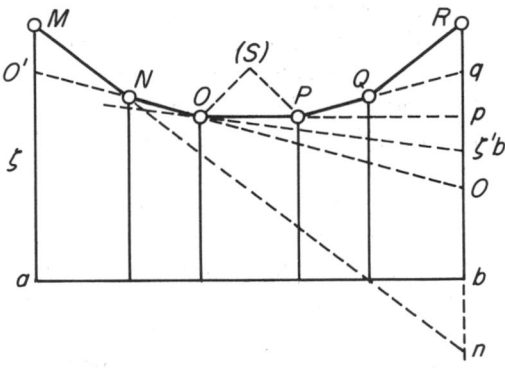

Fig. 1.

ordinates of the pure components. These points will express the values of the chemical potential that the components $a$ and $b$ must have in the solution for equilibrium to be possible. This will be some special value, indicating special values of the concentrations of the components in the saturated solution.

We shall now suppose that component $a$ is "inert" and that component $b$ is "fully mobile," i.e. fixed by its arbitrary concentration in the solution.

As is well known, the chemical potential of a component of the solution is uniquely related to its concentration and always increases with increasing concentration of the component. . . .

Depending upon the value of the concentration, the point for component $b$ in Fig. 1 will occupy different positions on the ordinate that passes through point $b$: the higher the concentration of the solution, the higher the point. For a solution saturated with component $b$ the chemical potential of component $b$ becomes equal to the thermodynamic potential of the mineral R, and precipitation of the pure component $b$ from the solution as mineral R becomes possible. At certain singular (special, isolated) values of the concentration, the point for component $b$ may coincide with the points $q$, $p$, $o$, or $n$ (Fig. 1). In these cases the simultaneous existence of two minerals in equilibrium with the solution becomes possible. Thus, if the point for component $b$ (i.e. the point expressing its composition and potential) coincides with point $q$, coexistence of the two minerals P and Q with the solution is possible. Each of the other minerals, M, N, or O, will react with the solution, being replaced by the minerals P or Q, and mineral R will simply dissolve. This is easily seen from Fig. 1 if we take into account that for each composition the state with the smallest value of the potential will be stable.

It is equally evident that for an arbitrary concentration of the solution, only one mineral can be in equilibrium with the solution. Thus, if the point for component $b$ of the solution lies between points $o$ and $p$, this single stable mineral will be mineral O. Minerals M and N will absorb component $b$ from the solution, transforming into mineral O with a decrease in potential, i.e. spontaneously, minerals P and Q will decompose into mineral O and the excess of component $b$ will be removed by the solution; this is also accompanied by a decrease in the potential.

Because the line of potentials MNOPQR is concave upward, when its segments are extended to intersect the ordinate at $b$ the points of intersection have a definite regularity: the richer in component $b$ of the two minerals through which the line is drawn, the higher the point, as is obvious from Fig. 1. From this it follows that with gradual increase in the concentration and thus in the potential of component *b* in the solution, minerals richer and richer in component *b* will be in equilibrium with the solution. As long as the point for component *b* in the solution lies below point *n*, mineral M will be stable; with increasing potential of component *b*, mineral N will be stable between points *n* and *o*; when the point for component *b* passes through point *o*, mineral N is transformed into mineral O, which will be stable until the point for *b* reaches the point *p*, and so on.

Of course, in all the transformations the concentration of the inert component *a* in the solution will also change, because the points for the stable minerals and their components in the solution on our "composition-potential" diagram (Fig. 1) must always lie on a straight line. Because of the insignificant quantity of impregnating solution, this change of concentration comes about, with inertness of component *a*, by an insignificant solution or crystallization of the minerals of the rock.

We shall now consider a three-component system with components *a*, *b*, and *c*. We shall let the possible minerals in this system at arbitrary pressure and temperature be M, N, O, P, Q, R, and S; according to the phase rule (pressure and temperature arbitrary, i.e. two degrees of freedom), three minerals can coexist at the same time, as shown, for example, in Fig. 2a, divided into triangles.

From each point of this composition triangle we now lay off, in the direction normal to the figure, the value of the thermodynamic potential corresponding to the mineral or assemblage of minerals; the ends of these normals then form the surface of potentials. Because the potential of a mixture of more than one phase follows the well-known "rule of mixing" as a linear function of their quantities, for a mixture of three minerals this surface of potentials will be represented by a surface that passes through three points that express the compositions and potentials of the three minerals. Thus, this surface of potentials will be similar to a mosaic-like, upwardly concave, searchlight mirror consisting of triangular planar mirrors. The principal feature of this surface of potentials is that it is convex in the direction of decreasing potential; every disturbance of this convexity would correspond to an unstable condition, as follows from the tendency of the system to approach a state with least potential.

We shall now assume that components *a* and *c* are inert and that component *b* is mobile. To investigate this case we shall draw on Fig. 2a a line through the apex *b* of the triangle of compositions and a point *d* that expresses an arbitrary composition of the two components *b* and *c*. By drawing the perpendicular surface we obtain a section of the surface of potentials in the form of a convex broken line giving the potentials

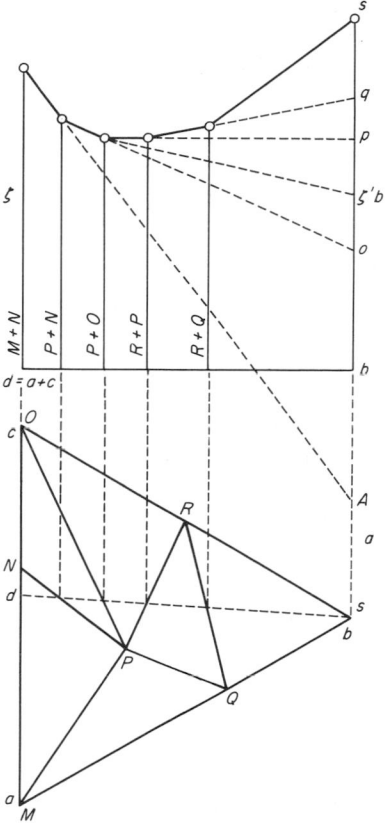

Fig. 2.

for the compositions of the line *bd* we chose (Fig. 2b). The picture for this section will be completely analogous to the case we chose for the two-component system (Fig. 1), with the following differences: (i) instead of component *a* (Fig. 1) we have the sum of components *a* + *c*; (ii) an arbitrary point on the line of potentials will correspond to a mixture of not two but three minerals; and (iii) the breaks in this line correspond not to individual minerals but to assemblages of two minerals. Reasoning in exactly the same way as for Fig. 1, we obtain similar results: (i) for arbitrary concentrations of the mobile component in equilibrium with the solution, not more than two minerals can exist, and at singular concentrations by threes; (ii) with gradual increase in the concentration of the mobile component there will be a discontinuous replacement of assemblages by others, each time richer in the mobile component. Each assemblage of two minerals will be in equilibrium

297

with the solution until the concentration exceeds some singular (critical) value. For example, if the concentration of the solutions is such that the chemical potential of component $b$ lies between points $o$ and $p$, only mineral assemblage P + O will be stable. When with increasing concentration the point for component $b$ in the solution coincides with the point $p$, an assemblage of the three minerals P + O + R becomes possible. If the point for the mobile component goes farther than $p$, the assemblage P + R becomes stable, and mineral O must disappear, being replaced by mineral R.

If we have a four-, five-, or higher-component system with one mobile component, we can investigate it in an entirely similar way with the aid of a diagram of the same type as Fig. 1 or Fig. 2b, if we take an arbitrary, constant ratio of all the inert components and construct lines of potentials for the mineral assemblages with different content of the mobile component. This line must be a broken line similar to the line MNOPQR (Fig. 1). By repeating the previous considerations we obtain similar conclusions: each time, the number of minerals in equilibrium with a solution of arbitrary concentration with respect to the mobile component will be equal to the number of inert components.

As for the number of phases, this follows directly from the phase rule:

$$phases = components + 2 - degrees\ of\ freedom,$$

because the addition of each mobile component increases both the number of components and the number of degrees of freedom by one (arbitrary concentration of the mobile component), i.e. it is not reflected in the number of phases.

At arbitrary temperature, pressure, and concentrations of the mobile components, only one mineral assemblage will be stable, with the number of minerals equal to the number of inert components. To each ratio of inert components will correspond one and only one mineral assemblage—i.e. the mineral assemblage will be uniquely determined by the ratio of inert components (in other words, the set of ratios of inert components is uniquely reflected in the set of all possible mineral assemblages, and these two sets are equivalent). Because of this, with three inert components present, for example, all the mineral assemblages can be represented by points on a plane such that each point (within the composition triangle) corresponds to a definite ratio of minerals and at the same time a definite ratio of inert components. Of course, for certain special (singular) values of temperature and pressure or concentrations of the mobile components, more than one mineral assemblage becomes stable, according to the phase rule; when these values occur there is a reaction, with one assemblage replacing another.

The only complication introduced by the presence of minerals of variable composition is that the composition of the mineral must be different in different assemblages and must vary continuously with changing concentration of the solution; nonetheless, our conclusions about the number of minerals and the successive character of the reactions remains completely valid. All the partial cases can be considered by the method of potentials used here, but there is no particular necessity for this. In essence all minerals are of variable composition, though the limits of concentrations of admixture components in them may be very narrow. The theorems below provide for the possibility of minerals of variable composition, and the presence of such minerals does not vitiate the applicability of the theorems.

All that has been set forth above is demonstration of the following propositions, which, being derived deductively, can be called theorems:

Theorem I. *At arbitrary temperature and pressure, let a mineral assemblage be in chemical equilibrium with a solution.*

*Then:*

1. *The maximum number of minerals is equal to the number of inert components (and does not depend upon the number of fully mobile components).*

2. *The mineral composition is uniquely determined by the ratio of the inert components.*

Theorem II. *At arbitrary temperature and pressure, let a mineral assemblage be continuously in equilibrium with a solution.*

*Then:*

1. *If for a given ratio of inert components the existence of several mineral associations with different content of a mobile component is possible, then if the concentration of this mobile component increases (decreases) without limit in the solution all of these mineral associations, without exception, will form successively, and they will replace one another in a strict sequence of increasing (decreasing) content of the mobile component.*

2. *These reactions of the assemblage with the solution take place only at singular values of the concentration of the solution. At intermediate values there can only be increases or decreases of the content of the mobile component in minerals of variable composition.*

Analysis of more complex concrete cases of metasomatism is very difficult if we do not use the methods of geometrical interpretation. Taking as a basis the simple regularities derived above, we can use geometrical methods of analysis that are extremely graphic and simple. They allow us to derive more complicated relationships, of which we note, for example, the following:

*If by interaction between a mineral assemblage and a solution there is a succession of chemical reactions, then for each of these reactions the ratio of the components entering (or leaving) the assemblage can be different, but the ratio of the concentrations of these components in the solution remains the same.*

Consequently, comparison of chemical analyses of metasomatic rocks does not make it possible to characterize the composition of the solutions, if we do not take into account the mineral composition. . . .

## The Mineralogical Phase Rule

In application to mineralogy and petrology, Goldschmidt has proposed the following simplified formulation of the phase rule, calling it the mineralogical phase rule: "of $n$ components, not more than $n$ minerals can (at arbitrary temperature and pressure) coexist stably."

The simplification compared to the Gibbs phase rule is obtained in this by referring the "degrees of freedom" exclusively to temperature and pressure, whereas the concentrations of the components can with the same basis possess degrees of freedom. Not enough attention has been given to this in the mineralogical literature. Because of Goldschmidt's formulation, for mineralogists the concept of "number of components" has taken on a special interpretation, different from the interpretation of physical chemists; this can hardly be welcomed. In the geological and mineralogical literature the number of components has come to be considered a more or less arbitrary and imprecise concept, requiring various conventional restrictions, whereas in physical chemistry, if the ratio of known phases is chosen, the number of components is a wholly precise and definite concept. Therefore, we should always keep in mind the precise phase rule of Gibbs. At the same time, the simplified formulation is of value, because concrete cases of formation of rocks are taken into account in it.

We shall now see how components are classified from the standpoint of the mineralogical phase rule. Above all, the division, considered above, into inert and mobile components is important: as we saw, the concentration of the mobile components always has one degree of freedom, and their presence does not affect the number of stable minerals. Of the inert components, it is convenient to further distinguish "admixture components," which we shall define in the following way: "admixture components are those whose content in all minerals is lower than the limiting content." Obviously the concentration of each such component, being arbitrary, has one degree of freedom, i.e. also does not affect the number of minerals. The remaining inert components can be called "virtual," because we must take them into account in studying mineral equilibria. Among the virtual components we can further distinguish: "surplus" components, which independently or in combination with mobile components produce a mineral that is present in all the assemblages studied; "saturating" components, an increase in the content of which can initiate their precipitation as an independent mineral, but cannot change other minerals in the rocks; and "non-saturating" components, comprising all the other virtual components. . . .

We obtain the following scheme of subdivision of components:

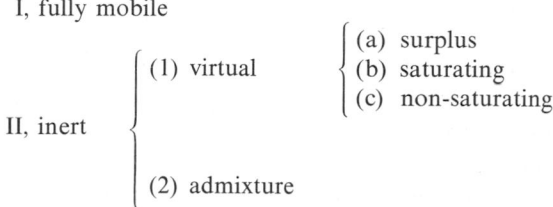

In using the mineralogical phase rule we should subtract from the total number of components the number of fully mobile components and admixture components, i.e. we should consider only the virtual components. Thus, we can supplement Goldschmidt's "mineralogical phase rule" in the following way: "in the general case the greatest number of stable minerals coexisting in the rocks is equal to the number of components of the rock after subtracting the fully mobile components and those whose content in all the minerals is below a limiting value," or ". . . after subtracting the fully mobile components and the admixture components."

To elucidate, every phase of the system must contain every component of the system, though perhaps in negligible quantities. With increasing potential (or vapor pressure, fugacity) of any component its content in each phase must increase, reaching a limit with the precipitation of the component in pure form, or with transformation of the phase into another that is richer in the component under consideration. Hence we see that the tautology, so to speak, that is inherent in the phase rule in general and which cannot be eliminated from it because it deals with two-sided relationships, is eliminated in the above formulation of the mineralogical phase rule.

## TYPES OF METASOMATISM

In analyzing metasomatic phenomena we must distinguish cases by the character of the physicochemical processes that took place and by the behavior of the components.

We must above all distinguish cases of change of composition relative to the inert components from cases of change of composition relative to the mobile components, because both cases have their own particular regularities. These regularities were considered above very briefly for inert components and in detail for mobile components. Study of the case of inert components is not part of the aim of this paper, and we shall consider only briefly the possible cases of interchange of inert components.

The formation of new minerals in metasomatism can take place either by chemical interaction between rock and solution or by simple precipitation from solution. . . .

Precipitation without chemical interaction is called impregnation; this takes place when the solution is saturated by a mineral that is in chemical equilibrium with the rock. Owing to constancy of volume in metasomatism, impregnation of the rocks by new minerals can only take place parallel with slow solution and outflux of other components, and this solution and precipitation, as observations show, often takes place uniformly within certain parts of the rock (for example, *fahlbands*). During the lengthy impregnation process the entire rock–solution system is in chemical equilibrium, and the concentration of the solution is singular, corresponding to saturation of the solution by all the minerals present; consequently, according to the definition, we are dealing with the case of influx of inert components.

Influx of inert components with chemical interaction takes place, for example, in the case of replacement of limestone by a calcite-wollastonite rock. The silica of the solutions or emanations enters into reaction with the calcite, giving wollastonite. Here, because the silica is bound up in the wollastonite, the concentration of the silica in the solution decreases so much that chemical equilibrium is established in the calcite–wollastonite–solution system at a singular concentration of silica in the solution. As more and more silica comes in, there is a gradual increase in the amount of wollastonite at the expense of silica and calcite. If there are not one but two inert components in the solution—for example $SiO_2$ and $Al_2O_3$—then at the expense of calcite (one inert component, one mobile component), in accordance with the total number of inert components, three minerals are formed, for example, calcite + wollastonite + grossularite.

Very often metasomatism takes place by inert components and mobile components at the same time. Thus, solutions with the mobile alkalies $H_2O$ and $CO_2$ can cause mutual metasomatism at the contact between two rocks that are not in equilibrium (pegmatites or other feldspathic rocks with serpentine or dolomite). Because of the presence of active solvents between the two nonequilibrium rocks, reaction zones are formed, and the composition relative to the inert components will change quite gradually from one rock to the other, increasing or decreasing. Such a regularity does not necessarily hold for mobile components: in the transition from one rock to the other we can find certain maxima and minima in the contents of these mobile components. . . .

We obtain the following scheme of types of metasomatism:

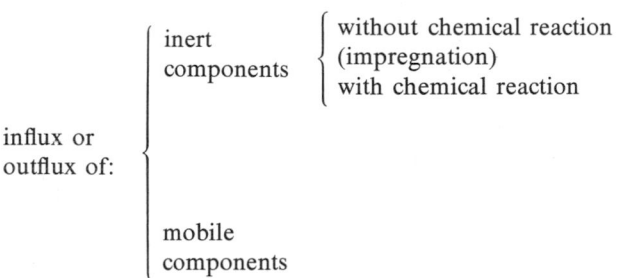

influx or outflux of:
- inert components
  - without chemical reaction (impregnation)
  - with chemical reaction
- mobile components

Furthermore, the different metamorphic processes can be divided into groups with different intensity of metasomatic phenomena. This intensity of metasomatism can be characterized by the mobility of the various components. Taking into account only the principal rock-forming components, we obtain the following grouping of metamorphic processes by intensity of metasomatism:

(1) Fully mobile $H_2O$ and $CO_2$ ("normal metamorphism").
(2) Fully mobile $H_2O$, $CO_2$, $K_2O$, and $Na_2O$.
(3) Fully mobile, in addition, CaO.
(4) Fully mobile, in addition, MgO.
(5) Only silica inert.
(6) Dissolving of all components, with possible formation of voids.

# GORANSON

Roy Waldemar Goranson (1900–1957), American geophysicist, graduated from the University of British Columbia in his native land in 1922 and received his Ph.D. degree in 1931 from Harvard University, where he had been a teaching fellow in optical mineralogy from 1924 to 1926. After various assignments in the Geophysical Laboratory of the Carnegie Institution, the U. S. Navy, and the Los Alamos Scientific Laboratory, he joined the staff of the Radiation Laboratory in the University of California (Berkeley) in 1953. The results of his laboratory experimentation, excerpted here, illustrate the important contribution that work in the laboratory may make to the refinement of geological theory.

## THE SOLUBILITY OF WATER IN GRANITE MAGMAS *

Data are presented on the solubility of water in granite glass as a function of pressure from 500 to 4,000 bars at 900° C. and as a function of temperature from 600 to 1,200° C. at 980 bars.

In this investigation water and granite glass were sealed up in platinum capsules in order to keep the water in contact with the glass and eliminate carbon dioxide, which was used as the pressure medium, from the system. These charges were brought to the required pressure and temperature in a bomb. The temperature was obtained by means of a platinum resistance furnace enclosed in the bomb, and pressure, by expansion of carbon dioxide. The runs were from 2 to 4 hours' duration, which was found to be sufficient time for attaining equilibrium between the gas-liquid phases. Temperature was then quickly dropped in order to retain the water dissolved in the glass, and since equilibrium in this latter direction was a much slower process, any errors introduced at this point were negligible. The amount of water dissolved in the glass was obtained from the loss in weight on ignition, due care being taken to correct for any losses which might occur while evaporating off the surplus water at 105° C. This granite glass was obtained by melting Stone Mountain granite, which is a medium-grained normal biotite-bearing muscovite granite.

The solubility of water in this glass at 900° C. is 3.75, 5.75, 8.15, 8.90, and 9.35 weight per cent at 0.5, 1, 2, 3, and 4 kilobars respectively. The solubility of water in this glass at 980 bars decreases by 0.3% per 100° C. rise in temperature in the 600–1,200° C. temperature range, i.e., at 800° C. the solubility of water is 6.0%, at 1,200° C. it has decreased to 5.4%.

The measured solubility on a natural rock glass (obsidian) from Mt. Kiamis, Java, of approximately the same composition as Stone Mountain granite gave the same result as was obtained from the Stone Mountain granite glass. A synthetic glass of composition corresponding to the proportions 75 orthoclase: 25 silica gave a value lower by one per cent than the granite glass.

It is concluded that natural rhyolite glasses could not very well have more than 10% of $H_2O+$, and that glasses with from 8 to 10% of $H_2O+$ should be extremely rare. This is borne out by published analyses made on fresh obsidians.

Reasons are presented for considering the possibility that granite magmas may have had a relatively high water content. If this were true, water would have an important effect in lowering the crystalliza-

*From *American Journal of Science* [5] 22 (1931), 481–502. The excerpt consists of the "Summary," pp. 501–502, followed by the "Concluding Remarks," pp. 499–501.

tion temperatures of such magmas. It would also largely influence surface igneous phenomena such as volcanism.

．　．　　．　　．　　．

The application to volcanology is immediately apparent, for if we know the water content of the magma and its temperature we can now calculate its vapor pressure. By vapor pressure is meant the minimum hydrostatic pressure necessary to exert on the magma in order to retain the specified amount of water in solution. The temperature effect is, however, not great at moderate pressures, and hence an uncertainty of a hundred degrees would not be fatal in calculating these pressures. For example, a magma at 900° C. and containing 6% water will have a vapor pressure of 1,160 bars. A lowering of 100° C. in the temperature would decrease the vapor pressure about 175 bars.

If we presuppose that crystallization took place from the centre outward in the early cooling stages of the Earth, the outer portions of the magma would be continually enriched in water except at and near the surface where water would evaporate and the magma freeze over. If we assume that the granite layer, about 15 km deep, will be the last stage in this process of crystallization, there could very easily be enough water available to be present to the extent of several per cent in the magma solution. For a conservative estimate of the amount of water in the oceans, seas, on the land surfaces, and bound up in surface rocks is $1.64 \times 10^{18}$ metric tons. A 15 km rock layer will amount to about $20.6 \times 10^{18}$ metric tons, a 60 km rock layer to about $81.8 \times 10^{18}$ metric tons. Hence the actual amount of water dissolved in the granitic magma might well have been limited only by the temperature and depth below the surface, if the temperature be assumed as 900° C., the amount of water in solution would then correspond with the depth-water concentration curve given in Fig. 3.[1] During this last stage, crystallization would take place also from the surface down, owing to the progressive lowering of the melting temperatures with increase in concentration of water and insufficient convection to keep the temperature uniform. It would thus be feasible to have a zone at about 20 km depth, in which magma pockets occur that have never been crystalline. Such an hypothesis would not be inconsistent with thermal gradient data since granite has been melted completely in the presence of water at 1,000 bars pressure and 720° C., the resulting melt containing $6\frac{1}{4}\%$ water in solution. If this were the case such a magma could be relatively rich in water.

[1][Not reproduced here.]

Let us assume that we have a magma ascending toward the surface. If the rock mantle surrounding the magma was not impervious to water vapor, the amount of water held in solution would be dependent on the hydrostatic head; at 10 km depth and 1,000° C. this would amount to about 6% of water. If from this chamber magma could ascend along a conduit, pressure would fall as the magma rose and consequently lower the solubility of water. Assuming the walls of this conduit to be impervious to water vapor the excess water would collect as globules in the magma until an equilibrium between the gas and liquid phase was attained. This process would continue until the magma reached a level at which the overlying rock strata became incompetent to withstand the pressure accumulated in the magma, when rupture would take place with explosive force and lead to the usual volcanic phenomena. If the conduit walls were not impervious, water vapor would escape until the vapor pressure of the magma had fallen to that of the hydrostatic head. However, chilling along the outer surface of the magma, owing to loss of water and heat conduction by the walls, might tend to seal up such open spaces.

The change in volume of the water in solution is not known, and hence the heat of solution of water in a granite melt cannot be calculated accurately. By extrapolation from the known pressure–volume–temperature relations of water the volume of a gram is estimated to lie between 3 and 4 cm$^3$ at 900° C. and 980 bars' pressure. The volume change of the water is then roughly 3 cm$^3$ per gram of water at 900° C. and 980 bars. $(\partial p/\partial t)_{m_1}$, obtained from the two solubility curves at 1,173° absolute (900° C.) and 980 bars, is approximately one where $p$ denotes pressure in bars, $t$ temperature in degrees Centigrade, and $m_1$ mass fraction of water. On inserting these values in the Clausius-Clapeyron equation, we obtain $-90$ gram calories as the heat absorbed when one gram of water dissolves in the granite magma at 900° C. and 980 bars' pressure. This value, if correct, would mean that the evaporation of 1% of water from a 5.7% water solution of granite would be accompanied by an absorption of one gram calory per gram of granite magma. If the heat capacity of the granite melt at this temperature and pressure be taken as 0.287 calories per gram, this heat absorption would lower the magma temperature 3 degrees. This heat of evaporation is about one fifth of the heat absorbed by water on evaporating at 100° C., but it is known to decrease considerably with increase of temperature. Conversely, solution of water in granite magma would be an exothermal reaction, assuming both to be at the same temperature—i.e., the temperature of the magma would be raised by an equivalent amount.

# RICHTER
Charles Francis Richter (1900–　), American seismologist, received his A.B. degree from Stanford University in 1920 and his Ph.D. degree from the California Institute of Technology in 1928. He was an assistant in the Carnegie Institution's Seismological Laboratory in Pasadena, California, from 1927 to 1936 and in 1937 he became a member of the faculty of the California Institute of Technology, where he has been Professor of Seismology since 1952. The scale of earthquake magnitudes, described in the paper excerpted here, has become widely used in seismology and is often referred to as the Richter scale.

## AN INSTRUMENTAL EARTHQUAKE MAGNITUDE SCALE*

In the course of historical or statistical study of earthquakes in any given region it is frequently desirable to have a scale for rating these shocks in terms of their original energy, independently of the effects which may be produced at any particular point of observation. On the suggestion of Mr. H. O. Wood, it is here proposed to refer to such a scale as a "magnitude" scale. This terminology is offered in distinction from the name "intensity" scale, now in general use for such scales as the Rossi-Forel and Mercalli-Cancani scales, which refer primarily to the local intensity of shock manifestation.

The writer is not aware of any previous approach to this problem along the course taken in this paper, except for the work of Wadati cited below. Total original energies have been calculated for a number of shocks, using seismometric and other data; but such a procedure is practicable only for a limited number of cases, whereas it is desired to apply a magnitude scale to all or nearly all of the shocks occurring.

Mr. Maxwell W. Allen states that he has for some time employed an arbitrary scale for rating large earthquakes, based on the amplitudes of earth motion calculated from the reports of distant stations. This laborious procedure is not far removed in principle from that adopted in the following discussion. Doubtless it has also occurred to others, but has failed of general application because of its paucity of dependable results.

In the absence of any accepted magnitude scale, earthquakes have occasionally been compared in terms of the intensity on the Rossi-Forel or some similar scale, as manifested near the epicenter. Even when reliable information is obtainable, this method is obviously exposed to uncertainties arising from variations in the character of the ground, the depth of the focus, and other circumstances not easily allowed for. In a region such as Southern California, where a large

*From *Seismological Society of America Bulletin 25* (1935), 1–32.

proportion of the shocks occur in almost unpopulated districts, while still others are submarine in origin, any general procedure of this kind is out of the question.

Despite the evident difficulties, the requirements of research, as well as the public interest, call for some estimate of the magnitude, in the sense here used, of each important shock in the California region. This led to an attempt at constructing a magnitude scale based on instrumentally recorded amplitudes at the seven stations of the Southern California group.

Precision in this matter was neither expected nor required. What was looked for was a method of segregating large, moderate, and small shocks, which should be based directly on instrumental indications, and thus might be freed from the uncertainties of personal estimates or the accidental circumstances of reported effects. The method used proved to be much more selective than had been anticipated, assigning observed earthquakes to as many as fifteen well-defined scale numbers, with possibilities of further extension and finer subdivision.

The procedure used was suggested by a device of Wadati,[1] who plotted the calculated earth amplitudes in microns for various Japanese stations against their epicentral distances. He employed the resulting curves to distinguish between shallow and deep earthquakes, to calculate the coefficient of absorption for surface waves, and to make a rough comparison between the magnitudes of several strong shocks. . . .

In practice we have to compare shocks from different foci, and probably different also in the mechanism of occurrence. Comparison is thus rendered very inexact. However, useful results can be obtained by comparison of the records at several stations. It is necessary to establish empirically a relation between the maximum seismographic amplitudes of a given shock at various distances; this is done by assuming that the ratio of the maximum amplitudes of two given shocks, as registered by similar instruments at equal epicentral distances, is a constant. That is, if shock $A$ is registered with maximum amplitude 5 millimeters at 75 kilometers and 2 millimeters at 200 kilometers, while shock $B$ registers with maximum amplitude 15 millimeters at 75 kilometers, then shock $B$ should register 6 millimeters at 200 kilometers.

The precision of magnitudes based on such an assumption is evidently impaired by a variety of conditions. The most obvious of these are the effects of inhomogeneity in the propagation of elastic waves, of varying depth of focus, of difference in mechanism of shock production, of the ground at the several stations, and of the instrumental constants.

[1] K. Wadati, *Geophys. Mag.* (Tokyo) *4* (1931), 231.

The most serious of these difficulties is the first. In most cases energy appears to be radiated unequally in different azimuths from the point of origin. This may arise from the circumstances of origination of the shock (strike of the fault, nature of displacement on the fault) or from differences in geological structure along the various wave paths. When the records of a number of stations surrounding the epicenter are available, this effect can be allowed for to some extent; but it remains an obstacle in the way of any precise determination of earthquake magnitudes, which can only be overcome with the advent of a more detailed understanding of the dynamics of shock production, and more complete information as to the various local structures.

Variation in depth of focus is less important. The majority of shocks in this region appear to originate at depths not far different from 15 kilometers. The effect of even considerable departures from this level can be reduced, for all but the smallest shocks, by using the records at stations distant 100 kilometers or over.

It is nearly certain that in most, though not all, of the stronger shocks the distribution of energy among various frequencies is not the same as for weaker shocks. Especially when there is evidence of extended movement along a fault, a high proportion of energy appears to go into waves of long period. As the maximum phase on the seismograms usually exhibits longer periods than the beginning of the record, the effect is to exaggerate the maxima. Comparison with the recorded maxima of a smaller shock then leads to an overestimate of the difference in magnitude. Fortunately, this effect does not appear to be larger than the other sources of error; and with long experience, or with more precise theories of shock production, it should be possible to take it into account quantitatively.

In comparing records from different stations, conclusions are affected by differences in ground and in the instrumental constants. If the latter are known with precision, the periods of the seismographic maxima may be measured, and the actual amplitudes of earth displacement calculated and used for estimating magnitudes. The procedure is somewhat laborious; and, as will appear presently, it can be dispensed with if the constants of the various instruments are approximately the same. The short period torsion seismometers installed at the Southern California stations are designed to have identical constants; but, owing to unavoidable irregularities in manufacture, some differences exist. It is not convenient to determine the constants from time to time; however, it is known that the constants of any one instrument remain relatively fixed over periods of years.

Determination of constants would make it possible to separate the purely instrumental effects from those due to ground; but, because of the uncertain elements in the latter, no great access of precision in estimating magnitudes would follow. In practice it is considered that the effect of ground and that of the instrument combine in each case into a fairly uniform deviation from the mean registered amplitudes for all stations and instruments; so that statistical study of a group of shocks will lead to average corrections applicable to the amplitudes registered by each individual instrument. These corrections turn out to be small, and of the same order as fluctuations due to other causes.

For precise purposes, it would be desirable to identify the phases of each seismogram, and to compare amplitudes of the same wave or set of waves at the various distances. Such identification is difficult and questionable for many of the smaller shocks, and is too time-consuming for use in routine work where hundreds or thousands of shocks must be dealt with. Thus the scale has been set up on the basis of measurements of the maximum recorded amplitude. This maximum will of course not always correspond to the same wave-group or phase. It will change especially with distance, coinciding with $\bar{S}$ or $Q$ for very near shocks, at intermediate distances with some member of the complicated $S$ series of phases, and at the larger distances with a slow surface wave. However, if the magnitude scale is set up empirically for the measured maximum amplitudes, these considerations do not directly affect its precision. If it were strictly true that all seismograms written by identical instruments at any one distance were simply enlarged or reduced copies of one another, such an empirical scale would apply perfectly, and magnitudes derived from it would be exact.

The foregoing considerations are preliminary to the actual setting up of a workable empirical scale of magnitudes. To derive such a scale, a representative group of shocks (those of January 1932) was carefully studied, and the logarithm of the recorded amplitude in each case plotted against the epicentral distance. Curves were drawn through the several points referring to each shock and were seen to be roughly parallel, as the hypothesis of proportional amplitudes requires. These were then combined into a single curve, parallel to the individual shock curves, and passing through an arbitrarily selected point. . . .

·   ·   ·   ·   ·

The procedure may be interpreted to give a definition of the magnitude scale number being used, as follows: *The magnitude of any shock is taken as the logarithm of the maximum trace amplitude, expressed in microns, with which the standard short-period torsion seismometer ($T_0 =$*

*0.8 sec., $V = 2800$, $h = 0.8$) would register that shock at an epicentral distance of 100 kilometers.*

This definition is in part arbitrary; an absolute scale, in which the numbers referred directly to shock energy or intensity measured in physical units, would be preferable. At present the data for correlating the arbitrary scale with an absolute scale are so inadequate that it appears better to preserve the arbitrary scale for its practical convenience. Since the scale is logarithmic, any future reduction to an absolute scale can be accomplished by adding a constant to the scale numbers. . . .

Until more instrumental data on larger shocks are available, it does not seem prudent to attempt an application of the magnitude scale to shocks which occurred in years when no instrumental data of the type here used were available. In the course of time it may become possible to assign magnitudes to the larger shocks on the basis of the extent of the area of perceptibility; but at present such estimates must necessarily be so tentative that it seems inadvisable to give figures which might readily lend themselves to misinterpretation. Something can be done in the way of comparing shocks occurring in the same general region; thus all the phenomena indicate that the major earthquake in Nevada on October 2, 1915, was of somewhat higher magnitude than the Nevada shock of December 20, 1932, studied above, which has been assigned a magnitude of 7.5 with some uncertainty. It would be unwise to go on to estimate by how much the magnitude of the two shocks differs. Opinion based partly on comparison of seismograms has classified the 1915 shock as of about the magnitude of the San Francisco earthquake of 1906; it appears safe to conclude that both of those shocks exceeded magnitude 7.0, and may have been of magnitude 8 or perhaps larger. In the case of the 1906 shock, the extended motion on the fault must have required a relatively long time for its completion; the seismograms in such a case would presumably not be representative of the total energy liberated.

Another case is that of the Imperial Valley earthquake of June 22, 1915, which very obviously exceeded the shock of February 25, 1930, in the same region, and therefore is known to have been of magnitude greater than 5.0. As shocks continue to occur, and our knowledge of the seismographic and other effects in the marginal areas of perceptibility increases, we may eventually be able to decide upon magnitudes for all the important earthquakes which have occurred in this region. . . .

Returning now to the discussion of the effects of various magnitudes, it appears that shocks of magnitude 1.5 ($10^9$ ergs) are the smallest definitely reported as perceptible. Such reports usually refer to aftershocks of larger earthquakes, when persons are in a specially sensitive frame of mind, or they come from observers in possession of instruments or mechanical indicators which they can use to test their impressions. The smallest shocks which are likely to be noticed in the immediate vicinity of the epicenter are of about magnitude 2.5 ($10^{11}$ ergs). A few reports are usually received when such shocks occur in settled areas. Magnitude 3 is almost always reported; while magnitude 3.5 ($10^{13}$ ergs) attracts general attention, is reported felt to distances of the order of 30 kilometers, and reaches intensity IV on average ground near the epicenter.

The lower limit of damaging shocks is about magnitude 4.5 ($10^{15}$ ergs). The most serious results at this stage are broken chimneys and injured brick walls, when constructed poorly and situated on bad ground. Examples are: the Brawley earthquake (4.5) of March 1, 1930 (in this case damage was probably increased by the weakening of inferior structures in the shock of magnitude 5.0 four days earlier), and the Whittier-Norwalk shock of July 8, 1929 (4.7).

The discussion has supplied several instances of shocks of magnitude near 5.0. Their effects are closely similar, and conform to the following description: On good ground, apparent intensity VII is manifested only within a few kilometers of the epicenter; but on soft ground it may occur at considerably larger distances, and some instances of apparent intensity VIII may be observed. The mean radius of the outer limit of IV is about 90 kilometers, and perceptibility extends to about 130 kilometers.

Two shocks of magnitude slightly exceeding 6 have been studied. In both cases, VII is manifested on good ground to about 25 kilometers from the epicenter. It is probable that the maximum intensity on good ground would be nearly VIII; in one case no data are available, and in the other the epicentral area lay in an alluvial basin, where VIII was manifested in many places, and possibly IX in a very few instances. The outer limit of IV is near 250 kilometers, and perceptibility extends to about 300 kilometers.

One shock has been assigned magnitude 6.5. Its effects definitely exceed those of the two shocks just mentioned. The Utah earthquake of magnitude 7.0 is the largest shock to which a magnitude can be assigned with the same precision as for smaller shocks. This and the Nevada shock of 1932 clearly manifested higher intensities at all epicentral distances than any of the other shocks here studied; and it is equally evident that the Nevada shock was much the larger of the two, which supports the magnitude 7.5 assigned to it.

In view of the foregoing facts, it seems assured that earthquakes destructive over even a moderately extended area are of magnitude 6

($10^{18}$ ergs) and over, except in cases where very bad ground and construction are involved. The lower margin of major earthquakes, in which phenomena of faulting, etc., are to be expected to a significant extent, appears to be about magnitude 7.5 ($10^{21}$ ergs). How far above this the magnitudes of actual earthquakes may extend is a difficult, and in one sense an unanswerable, question. Judging by the relative amplitudes of distant recorded shocks, there must be cases of at least magnitude 9, and very probably 10.

# BULLARD Fred Mason Bullard (1901–   ), American geologist, has been associated throughout most of his adult life with the University of Texas where he was Chairman of the Department of Geology from 1929 to 1939. His contributions to geological knowledge range widely from shore processes and sedimentation through Paleozoic and Cretaceous stratigraphy to vulcanology. From the birth of Paricutin in February 1943 until it became extinct in March 1952 that Mexican volcano provided an extraordinary opportunity for geologists to observe the construction, from start to finish, of a volcanic cone girdled with lava flows. Bullard spent many working days at that site; the following excerpt from his reports is in keeping with the time-honored principle that accurate knowledge about processes operating in the present provides the key with which to unlock the secrets of the past.

## THE CYCLE OF ACTIVITY OF A LAVA FLOW*

It is perhaps hazardous to outline a cycle of activity of a lava flow from the data now available. However, the following outline summarizes the observations of the writer, and it may be of value to future workers in this field.

The initial stage in the outbreak of a lava flow is the accumulation of pressure below the point of outbreak and a slow uplift of the surface. In the lava flow of September 27, tension cracks resulting from this upward pressure were noted as early as September 2. The amount of uplift before the outbreak of the flow is not known, but with adequate instruments this should be easily measured. The initial outbreak of lava occurs along one of the prominent fractures, or tension cracks. The lava usually erupts at a number of places, building up a series of spatter cones, or hornitos, until a definite outlet channel is established. The lava then follows this channel, and the spatter cones become gas vents. The lava is forced upward in many of the fractures and in some

*From "Studies on Paricutin Volcano, Michoacan, Mexico," *Geological Society of America Bulletin 58* (1947), 433–450.

places, where it does not reach the surface, it forms dikelike intrusions. As soon as the outbreak of lava relieves the pressure, probably in a matter of a few hours, the area settles, developing a graben. The floor of the graben in the September 27 flow dropped about 30 feet, although this does not necessarily represent the uplift, since the draining out of the lava may permit additional settling.

A typical boca has a width of about 50 feet, although variations in both directions from this figure have been observed. The lava front advances rapidly in the initial stage. Velocities up to 30 feet per minute, a quarter of a mile from the boca, have been observed. The velocity depends, of course, on the viscosity, temperature, gradient and nature of the channel, and probably other factors. The initial lava front is usually between 10 and 15 feet thick and it advances on the entire front, although the front is usually lobate because of the uneven topography. After the initial stage of rapid movement (feet per minute) the rate of flow becomes much less, usually a few feet per hour, and the thickness is the result of the uplift of the crust by pressure from beneath, that is, by sill-like intrusions. The final stage in the history of the flow is marked by the development of small marginal tongues or lateral flows. When the forward movement stops, or becomes quite slow, lava tongues break out at favorable points along the margin. These small flows develop a boca and have most of the characteristics of a primary boca. They range from 3 to 5 feet in width, and as the lava drains out from beneath the flow the crust subsides, and a graben develops over the lava channel. The marginal tongues are usually active for about 24 hours, and when they stop, the activity of the flow at that margin is completed. The lava coming from these small bocas, like the lava from the primary bocas, is squeezed out under pressure, and the upper surface has a characteristic extrusive pattern, locally called "toothpaste" lava, since it resembles the pattern formed when tooth paste is squeezed from a tube. It is interesting to note that renewal of activity of a dormant flow begins in (1) elevation of the surface, (2) development of marginal tongues, and (3) general movement along the entire front. . . .

# KRYNINE
Paul Dimitri Krynine (1901–    ), American geologist, was born in Russia but emigrated to the United States in his early youth. He received the A. B. degree from the University of California in 1927 and the Ph.D. degree from Yale University in 1936. In the meantime he had served as field geologist for the Standard Oil Company of California from 1928 to 1931. In 1937 he joined the faculty of Pennsylvania State University, where he has

been Professor of Petrology and head of the Department of Mineralogy since 1947. He has also been a member of the U. S. Geological Survey since 1946.

## THE MEGASCOPIC AND FIELD CLASSIFICATION OF SEDIMENTARY ROCKS *

At present the basis of sedimentary classification is somewhat arbitrary, with four main systems in general use. These classification systems, which may be combined in several ways, are as follows:

1. By mode of origin (very common)
   Clastic or fragmental rocks
   Chemical precipitates
   Biogenic products (plant and animal)
2. By medium in which rocks originate
   Aqueous (water-laid)
   Eolian (wind-laid)
   Glacial (ice-laid)
3. By bulk composition
   Arenaceous (sandy)
   Argillaceous (clayey)
   Calcareous (limy)—although many other chemical precipitates are frequently added to this scheme
4. By texture and grain size, with many variations, permutations, and the addition of much involved terminology
   Psephites (coarse clastic rocks)
   Psammites (medium clastic rocks)
   Pelites (fine clastic rocks)
   Crystalline (chemical rocks)
      Phanerocrystalline (coarse and medium)
      Aphanitic (fine and very fine)

None of these schemes can compare in completeness, simplicity, or objectivity with the mineral composition–texture scheme in use for the classification of igneous rocks. . . .

### THE MAKEUP OF SEDIMENTS

A rock, or any other solid for that matter, has only two basic, fundamental properties—composition and texture—meaning that a rock is made up of certain constituents (generally minerals) put together in a certain way. All other properties, such as color, density, and similar mass properties are only derived properties. Even structure is not entirely a

*From *Journal of Geology 56* (1948), 130–165.

primary property but is rather the reflection of changes—abrupt or gradual, horizontal or vertical—in texture and composition within one formation or between different formations. However, for practical purposes, structure can be considered as the third major property of sediments when describing entire sedimentary bodies.

A tenable (that is, objective and reproducible) classification of sediments must be based for hand specimens on composition and texture and for entire sedimentary bodies on composition, texture, and structure, with possible qualifications introduced by the addition of some of the subelements of texture (size, homogeneity) and possibly some of the principal derived properties, such as color.

There are altogether ninety-three important derived properties or parameters of sedimentary rocks, but most of these are quite unnecessary for purposes of megascopic identification. . . .

*Petrographic End-Members*

The composition of *all* sedimentary rocks can be reduced to two basic groups of end-members, which may be mixed in all proportions in a purely mechanical way.

1. A detrital fraction consisting of solid material brought in as *solid detritus* from outside the basin of deposition and precipitated through settling within this basin. In 99 per cent of the cases this detrital fraction is made up of silicates. The composition of this detrital fraction depends on the petrology of the source areas and the intensity (and effectiveness) of chemical weathering and erosion within the source area, plus some modification during transport.

2. A chemical fraction existing as a *solution* within the basin of deposition and precipitated chemically. This chemical precipitation may proceed through inorganic or biogenic agencies. The chemically precipitated material may not move on the sea floor after its precipitation, and then it develops a crystalline texture. Or it may be shifted about by bottom currents (particularly true of organically precipitated rocks composed of shell fragments), and then, although its origin is chemical, its texture will be clastic. More than three quarters of this chemical fraction is made up of carbonates, and most of the balance of silica. Other constituents (glauconite, phosphates, iron oxides) may be very abundant locally but are relatively rare on a volumetric grand-total basis.

•   •   •   •   •

PRINCIPLES OF IDENTIFICATION

The adequate description of any rock requires the naming of its mineral constituents and the definition of its texture. The degree of precision attained depends upon the character of the tools employed: megascopic or microscopic examination.

Proper identification of any rock is *impossible* without the *correct* identification of the principal mineral constituents. In such an incomplete case the classification at best can be based upon texture, bulk chemical or mineral composition, suspected mode of origin, or genetically active medium. As stated before, none of these methods is capable of yielding reproducible objective results or of conveying exactly in unambiguous petrographic terms what is meant by the name employed. Furthermore, the description and definition of texture must also be based on the use of objective and quantitative terms. . . .

## The Petrographic Classification of Sediments: The Main Name and its Qualifiers

Just as in igneous rocks, it is possible to apply the following typical basic standardized descriptive sequence to sedimentary rocks: color, subtexture, varietal minerals and cement, and, finally, main name.

However, sediments, as contrasted with igneous rocks, are usually characterized by a strong development of structures and in some cases may also be characteristically connected with a certain transporting medium. Hence, *if necessary,* these two additional properties may be introduced into the descriptive sequence in the following way: color—structure—subtexture—varietal minerals and cement-genetic affinity—main name. Some main names may have a definite genetic significance, such as tillite.

Examples of the classification are as follows:

1. Dark-gray, pebbly, micaceous graywacke.
2. Light-gray, thinly laminated, poorly consolidated, calcareous graywacke.
3. Red, cross-bedded, silty, siderite-bearing graywacke.
4. Red massive conglomeratic arkose.
5. White, fine-grained, rounded, dolomitic quartzitic sandstone.
6. Orange micaceous marl.
7. Pink massive feldspathic silt (or loess).
8. Gray, cross-bedded, coarse-grained, feldspar-bearing sandy dolomite.

## The Main Name

The main name of a sediment should reflect both the dominant texture and the typical mineral composition. Unfortunately, since the descriptive petrographic terminology of sediments is still in its infancy, there are not enough specific terms (not even in the medium-grained detrital class) to indicate even the principal possible combinations of texture and composition.

# MEGASCOPIC CLASSIFICATION OF <u>NORMAL</u> SEDIMENTARY ROCKS

(Most of the concentrates and placers are omitted or left undifferentiated in this table)

| | TEXTURES | | BONDING | |
|---|---|---|---|---|
| | MAIN TEXTURE | SUB TEXTURE | CHEMICAL CEMENT OR MATRIX | |
| **DETRITAL ROCKS** (>50% clastic silicates) | COARSE CLASTIC (average >2.0mm.) Conglomerate and Breccia class | Boulder Conglomerate (>64 mm.) CONGLOMERATE or BRECCIA (4-64mm.) Fine Conglomerate (<4mm.) | — cement (<10%) | Loose |
| | | | | Consoli-dated A, M-C |
| | | Sandy, Silty or Clayey Conglomerate (>20% sand, silt or clay) | + cement (>10%) | SiO₂ |
| | | | | CO₃ |
| | | | | Fe,G,P |
| | MEDIUM CLASTIC (0.0625-2.0mm.) Sandstone class | Conglomeratic Sandstone (>20% pebbles) Pebbly Sandstone (>10% pebbles) SANDSTONE | — cement (<10%) | Loose |
| | | | | Consoli-dated A, M-C |
| | | Silty Sandstone (>20% silt) | + cement (>10%) | SiO₂ |
| | | | | CO₃ |
| | | Clayey Sandstone (>20% clay) | | Fe,G, P |
| | FINE CLASTIC (average <0.0625mm.) Siltstone–Shale class | Sandy Siltstone (>20% sand) SILTSTONE (gritty) a. siltstone proper b. micro-conglomerate or micro-breccia | — cement (<10%) | Loose |
| | | | | Consoli-dated |
| | | Silty Shale (semi-gritty) SHALE (smooth) | + cement (>10%) | SiO₂ |
| | | | | CO₃ |
| | | | | Fe,G,P |
| **CHEMICAL ROCKS** (<50% clastic silicates) | SANDY (5-50% clastic silicates) | CLASTIC coarse : >2.0mm. medium: 0.0625-2.0mm. fine : < 0.0625 mm. | | SiO₂ |
| | | | | CO₃ |
| | | | | Miscel-laneous |
| | PURE (not sandy) (<5% clastic silicates) | I. Clastic or arenitic if more than 10% of fragmental particles of any kind (sizes as above) II. CRYSTALLINE coarse : >4.0mm. medium: 1.0-4.0mm. fine : <1.0 mm. | | SiO₂ |
| | | | | CO₃ |
| | | | | Miscel-laneous |

**1. CHEMICAL CEMENTS**

Fe –Ferruginous    SiO₂ – Siliceous
G  – Glauconitic    CO₃ – Calcareous
P  –Phosphatic        or Dolomitic

**2. MATRIX**

A - Argillaceous
M-C - Micaceous or chloritic

| COMPOSITION OF RECOGNIZABLE CLASTIC SILICATE FRACTION | | |
|---|---|---|
| QUARTZ ± CHERT | QUARTZ + ROCK FRAGMENTS + CHERT + MICACEOUS OR CHLORITIC CLAY<br>− feldspar (<10%) \| + feldspar (>10%) | QUARTZ + FELDSPAR (>20%) ∓ KAOLINITIC CLAY ∓ impurities (<20%) |
| QUARTZITE SERIES | GRAYWACKE SERIES | ARKOSE SERIES |
| Quartz or Chert Gravel | Graywacke Gravel (Till − Boulder Clay) | Feldspathic Gravel (Feldspathic Till) |
| − + <br> QUARTZ<br>+ OR<br>+ CHERT<br>∓ CONGLOMERATE | + Common \| Feldspathic + <br>− Graywacke ∓<br>± Conglomerate or Breccia −<br>− Fanglomerate or Tillite − | ARKOSIC CONGLOMERATE or BRECCIA + <br>+ <br>∓ <br>Fanglomerate or Tillite − |
| Quartz Sand | Quartz − Chert and Mica Sand ("Pepper and salt sand") | Feldspathic or Arkosic Sand |
| − ∓ "Sandstone" rare, usually passes into<br>QUARTZITE (Gannister)<br>+ IMPURE (CO₃, Fe) QUARTZITE (50-75% SiO₂ in cements)<br>QUARTZITIC SANDSTONE (25-50% SiO₂ in cements)<br>− + QUARTZOSE SANDSTONE (<25% SiO₂ in cements) | gray or red \| black or dark gray + <br>− Common Feldspathic + ±<br>± (low rank) (high rank) −<br>− ∓ + GRAYWACKE − | gray or red +<br>ARKOSE (<20% impurities) −<br>± ∓<br>Sub Arkose (20-40% impurities) ∓ |
| (Laterite) ◄───── Silt and Clay ─────► (Loess) <br>(Quartzose, micaceous-chloritic or feldspathic-kaolinitic) | | |
| − SILTSTONE OR SHALE (Quartzose, micaceous-chloritic or feldspathic-kaolinitic) [+ +] [∓] | | ± |
| ± Siliceous, Opaline or Chalcedonic Shale or Siltstone [− =] [∓] | | ± |
| + ◄─────── MARL ───────► [∓] [−] | | − ± |
| ∓ Ferruginous, Glauconitic or Phosphatic Siltstone or Shale [∓] | | − + |
| Sandy and Oolitic Cherts (rare) | Sandy Bedded Volcanic Cherts | Sandy Diatomites |
| + + SANDY LIMESTONE AND DOLOMITE [∓] ± ◄─ oolitic ─► ∓ [−] | | − + |
| SANDY: Gypsum, Anhydrite, Glauconite, Phosphates, Chemical Iron Ores, Salt (rare) | | |
| CHERT (nodular + bedded) | (rare) \| CHERT (bedded) | Diatomite |
| + + LIMESTONE AND DOLOMITE [− +] (clastic or crystalline) [= −] | | − + |
| SALT, GYPSUM, ANHYDRITE, PHOSPHATES, CHEMICAL IRON ORES, COAL | | |

SYMBOLS

+ and − signs indicate frequency of occurrence
and are quantitatively defined in the text

It has been thought best to refrain, for the time being, from coining new and fancy rock names, although a tenable terminology can easily be evolved from the present classification table [see Table on preceding pages]. This agreeable (from an author's point of view) occupation has been left to future students of the problem.

Hence some of the commoner names are used (some slightly redefined), in combination with qualifying terms based on additional information showing in greater detail the rock's composition (like the term "quartz-diorite" among igneous rock names). This is somewhat awkward but precise.

The main name, therefore, conveys both composition and texture; for example, an arkose is a medium-grained detrital rock made of quartz and feldspar. Similarly, a sandy arkosic limestone is a chemical rock of clastic texture containing more than 50 per cent of calcite (much of it in rolled grains), with a sizable amount of actual quartz and feldspar grains; or a quartzose marl is a fine-grained detrital rock made of very fine-grained, megascopically unrecognizable, aluminum silicates, with a large amount of calcareous cement and carrying recognizable quartz grains. Finally, a quartz conglomerate is a coarse-grained detrital rock consisting of rounded quartz pebbles, whereas an arkosic breccia is a coarse-grained rock, consisting of angular quartz and feldspar pebbles. If this breccia is demonstrably of alluvial-fan origin, the term "arkosic fanglomerate" is applicable; if it is certainly glacial in origin, the term, "arkosic tillite" may be used.

The main name is modified by color, subtexture, character of bonding material, presence of important varietal minerals, and, if necessary, structure and genetic agent.

### QUALIFICATION BY COLOR

The best and safest procedure in describing the color of a sediment is to use a recognized color chart. Since in practice this is generally very difficult, it is best to limit one's self to fairly objective and commonly understood names, such as those found in the basic colors of the spectrum (violet, blue, green, yellow, red), reinforced by the following additional terms: brown, olive, orange, pink, purple, white, gray, and black. Furthermore, it is permissible to combine any two colors (such as bluish-green or greenish-blue) with the second term being the dominant one. Finally, it is also possible to preface each term by the words "light" or "dark" to indicate the intensity of the neutral background (frequently kaolin in the one case, organic matter in the other). Subjective terms, such as "chocolate brown," should be avoided.

*In Detrital Rocks*

The following scheme is proposed for detrital sediments:

1. In the coarse-grained rocks the main name is the *XYZ* conglomerate, breccia, tillite, or fanglomerate. The *XYZ* refers to composition. This main name should be prefaced by the term "boulder," "fine," "sandy," "silty," or "clayey" if necessary. When normal and uncomplicated (i.e., 4–64 mm in diam. with no finer admixtures), the rock is just a normal unqualified conglomerate breccia, tillite, etc., of a definite composition.

2. In the medium-grained classes the main names, such as quartzite (or quartzitic or quartzose sandstone), gray-wacke, or arkose should be prefaced by the qualifiers "conglomeratic," "pebbly," "silty," or "clayey" if necessary. Additional terms implying a definite grain size, from very coarse to very fine (if correctly determined) should be added here.

3. In the finer-grained detrital rocks the main names "siltstone" (properly determined as to mineral composition) or "loess" are to be prefaced when necessary by the qualifier "sandy," whereas the main names—shale, clay, or marl—may be prefaced again, when necessary by the term "silty."

The angularity or, conversely, the rounding of the constituents is strikingly seen in the coarser clastics and is such an obvious property that it should be incorporated in the name. A breccia or fanglomerate or tillite (as contrasted with a conglomerate) should contain no less than 25 per cent of definitely angular fragments (i.e., fragments with sharp edges).

In the medium-grained clastics angularity is a less noticeable property. As a rule, the constituents of all graywackes and almost all arkoses are relatively angular, whereas those of most quartzites are rounded. Pseudo-angularity produced by secondary silica overgrowths on the grains of quartzitic rocks should not be mistaken for original angularity.

The term "grit" is considered superfluous. It usually refers to a pebbly graywacke or a pebbly arkose, rocks in which the grains are normally angular, but where the increased grain size makes this angularity more obvious to the casual observer.

Where observable, the rounding or angularity should be noted by using approximate qualifiers before the main name.

*In Chemical Rocks*

Two main textures are possible in the chemical rocks: clastic or crystalline.

1. In the sandy chemical rocks (i.e., those containing over 50 per cent of clastic silicates) the main name, such as sandy limestone, sandy dolomite, oölitic chert, etc., should be prefaced by the terms "coarse," "medium," or "fine" to indicate grain size.

2. In the pure chemical rocks (i.e., those with less than 5 per cent of clastic silicates) the texture is also probably clastic if over 10 per cent of the rock consists of obvious fragmental material of any kind, such as fossil shells. In such a case the same terminology as above may be applied. The main name in this case will be clastic (or arenitic) limestone and so on, and these main names will be modified by the following subtextures: coarse, medium, or fine.

3. If the texture is crystalline, the main name is limestone, dolomite, gypsum, etc., and the qualifier is "coarsely grained," "medium-grained," or "fine-grained." If the crystallinity is to be emphasized or is conspicuous (as is usually the case with coarsely crystalline rocks, which, again, are easier to describe than finer-grained ones), then the term "coarsely crystalline" may be used.

### QUALIFICATIONS BY SUBTEXTURE: BONDING AGENTS

1. If the detrital rocks are loose (unconsolidated) and lack bonding, the terms "gravel," "boulder bed," "sand," "silt," or "clay" should be used.

2. If the detrital rocks are consolidated by a nonchemical matrix (either produced by simple adhesion of the original finer-grained detrital constituents or by their later reorganization), then the main name is used without additional qualification if the matrix is of the normal mineral composition for that particular rock. For instance, the normal matrix for a graywacke is micaceous or chloritic, whereas the normal arkose possesses an argillaceous, i.e., a kaolinitic matrix, and the name "arkose" presupposes such a matrix. If, on the other hand, the matrix of an arkose is abnormally, but obviously, high in fine micas or in chlorite, then the qualifier "micaceous" or "chloritic" is added to arkose.

A quartzite or a quartzitic sandstone normally has no matrix whatsoever. It is bonded exclusively by chemical cements.

Hence any matrix in a quartzitic sediment is abnormal, and in such a case the main name, "quartzite," is qualified by the term "chloritic" or "argillaceous." The chances are that such rocks will prove to be very close to graywackes and may turn out to be the so-called "winnowed" graywackes with an abnormally high quartz content (a typical and excellent type of oil reservoir). . . .

If the argillaceous, micaceous, or chloritic material is red in color, the term "ferruginous" *should not be used,* since the bonding effect is produced not by the iron oxide but by the clayey material. Since in this case the ferric oxide acts only as a pigment, the term "red" should be used instead.

3. If the detrital rock is consolidated by a chemical cement, then the main name should be prefaced by the terms "siliceous," "calcareous," "dolomitic," "ferruginous," "glauconitic," or "phosphatic." In less frequent cases the main name may be followed by such expressions as "cemented by gypsum" or "by halite."

The term "ferruginous" is definitely restricted to a chemical cement consisting of ferric oxide. Even then the term is not absolutely satisfactory, and it would be much better to employ the term "hematitic" or "limonitic" instead; but this may be asking too much of the average field geologist without a streak plate. It should be pointed out, nevertheless, that the term "ferruginous" is a gross misnomer when used promiscuously to designate red rocks in general. Indeed, many dark rocks, containing iron in the ferrous state, may have more iron than do some red rocks in which the iron is in the ferric state. In igneous rocks the term "ferruginous granite" is immediately recognizable as a patent absurdity, whereas the term "biotite or hornblende granite" indicates that the iron is there and also how it occurs. The same elementary care in definition should be employed in the description of sediments.

· · · · · ·

## Qualifications by Varietal and Accessory Minerals

The essential minerals which determine the main name of a sediment are specifically listed under the heading of "Composition." Within the detrital rocks these essential minerals are quartz-chert for the quartzitic series; quartz, chert, mica, micaceous clays, and rock fragments for the graywacke series in general and also feldspar for the high-rank graywacke subseries; and quartz, feldspar, and nonmicaceous normal clay minerals (i.e., kaolinite and bauxite) for the arkosic series of detrital rocks.

Any other mineral not specifically mentioned in this list becomes a varietal mineral if it exceeds 1 per cent in amount and hence becomes a major constituent that is readily recognizable with a hand lens. The terminology employed to indicate the presence of such varietal minerals should, theoretically at least, be different from that used to designate the occurrence of chemical cements.

A system employing a terminology such as "gypsum-bearing" or "mica-bearing" or "garnet-bearing" would have the advantage of being entirely clear but would be awkward and cacophonous and hence undesirable. As a compromise between scientific and linguistic clarity the following system is tentatively proposed:

*a*) Adjectives ending in *-ic* or *-ous* should be used for varietal minerals when no confusion is possible with chemical cements. For instance, in "micaceous arkose" it is clear that mica is a varietal detrital mineral (possibly in the matrix) rather than a chemical cement.

*b*) If confusion is possible, then the less elegant but more precise term "mineral-bearing" is to be employed. An example would be "glauconite-bearing dolomitic graywacke."

Under "accessory minerals" are included mostly the so-called "heavy" minerals. Generally these minerals cannot be studied at the megascopic level. Any mineral which occurs in amounts of less than 1 per cent in a sediment is considered to be an accessory and is not mentioned in the megascopic definition of the rock. Its presence, if determinable megascopically, is mentioned in an additional sentence when proceeding with the detailed description of the rock.

### QUALIFICATIONS BY STRUCTURE

Whereas in igneous rocks a massive structure is the rule and layered or banded structures are the exception, the opposite is true in sediments. Two possibilities may exist: (1) the structure of a sediment is simple and can be defined in one or two words (cross-bedded, thinly laminated, varved, massive); or (2) the structure is complex and needs several words or an entire sentence for its definition.

In the first case the definition can be incorporated in the description preceding the main name, and its place will be between color and subtexture (for instance, a red, cross-bedded, pebbly arkose).

In the second case the definition should follow the main name and should be prefaced by the word "showing." For instance, a "dark-greenish-blue, silty, high-rank graywacke, showing well-developed cyclic graded bedding in 4-cm bands with incipient and semimicroscopic cross-bedding within the coarser portion of each 4-cm layer." If the description of the structure begins to be too long, it can be separated into a sentence of its own following the basic definition of the rock.

The presence of fossils and recognizable organic remains is considered to be a structure and should be recorded at this state (example: white, coarse, cross-bedded, fossiliferous, dolomite-bearing quartzite).

### GENETIC AND ENVIRONMENTAL TERMS

Many rock types are produced by certain specialized sets of processes (frequently and somewhat loosely referred to as "environments"). This combination of processes may produce a certain typical combination of composition and texture and possibly structure in the resulting rock. The nomenclature of these specialized sets of processes ranges from such generalized terms as "marine" or "continental" to much more definite terms, such as "eolian," "glacial," or "of alluvial-fan origin," etc. In the last three instances the products of these processes have been frequently called "loess" (a somewhat loose usage), "till," and "fanglomerate." Theoretically and in the abstract, any kind of mineral composition should be possible for a till or a fanglomerate. Actually this is not so because genetic processes, formative conditions, and so-called "environments" do not exist in a geologic vacuum but operate against a certain dominant diastrophic background which not only determines the probable relative intensity and effectiveness of any one process but also the type of material that it will have to work with.

For instance, the rigorous climatic or topographic conditions which produce a fanglomerate, a tillite, or a loess (deflated material of a glacier or of a dried-up fluvial basin) are all very typical of the large-scale emergence of continents and of periods of relatively intense orogeny and hence are characterized by arkosic sediments, possibly diluted by some graywacke-like material. The validity of this conclusion has been pragmatically verified by a petrographic study of numerous assorted loesses, tillites, and fanglomerates. For these reasons loess and fanglomerates are tentatively defined not only as eolian or alluvial-fan type sediments but also as highly feldspathic ones.

Tillites are also normally defined as basically arkosic and hence in special cases should be qualified as graywacketillites. Hence these genetic terms are elevated to the rank of main names, characterized by composition, texture, and also in this case formative agents. An igneous analogy is the term "pegmatite," which also has a definite genetic meaning.

Other genetic terms, such as "eolian," "flood-plain" (deposit), "glacial," "continental," "marine-beach" (deposit), "desert" or "desertic" (deposit), "paludal," "lacustrine," etc., if considered necessary and if conclusively known to be *correct* for the particular sediments under study, can be used as qualifiers to redefine the main name. These terms should be placed before the main name if they are brief or after the main name if they are lengthy. In the latter case the main name should be followed by a statement that the specimen is a clayey graywacke-breccia (or boulder clay) probably of late glacial origin.

Such dubious terms as "silicified" or "recrystallized" (both great favorites in stratigraphy) and similar pseudo-genetic terms which imply a knowledge that the observer at the megascopic level does not (and cannot) possess, should be avoided. Use, instead, the terms "siliceous" or "crystalline," which are correct, truthful, and adequate.

### USE OF PROPOSED TERMINOLOGY AND CLASSIFICATION TABLE

In summary, the following step-by-step procedure is suggested for the adequate megascopic description and classification of a sedimentary rock:

1. The rock is classified as a detrital or chemical rock, depending on the relative proportion of detrital material (in practice almost entirely restricted to *clastic* silicates) and chemical material.

2. The rock is classified further as belonging to the quartzite, graywacke, or arkosic series, depending upon the composition of the clastic silicate fraction. . . .

3. Such a division may not be possible when dealing with fine-grained clastic rocks (detrital rocks or sandy chemical rocks) or with pure chemical rocks with no recognizable silicate fraction. Then the terms "limestone," "siltstone," and "shale" are to be used in the same way as the term "felsite" is used in igneous rocks.

4. If the rock is a detrital one, after placing it in the proper series, determine whether it is bonded by a fine-grained matrix or a chemical cement. This can be accomplished, again without undue difficulty, by observing the clastic and grained character of a matrix as compared with the densely crystalline character of a chemical cement. At this stage the plus and minus signs will serve as a guide to the probability of the identification's being a correct one.

5. If the rock is chemical, note whether it is sandy (over 5 per cent of clastic silicates) or pure. If it is pure, determine whether the texture is arenitic (clastic) or crystalline.

6. If the chemical rock is sandy, determine the detrital series to which the sandy fraction belongs. This can be done with little effort in many, or most, sandy chemical rocks if they are medium- or coarser-grained. If the chemical rock is pure, this may prove to be impossible; but the attempt should always be made. Again the plus and minus signs will serve as a guide. If necessary, dissolve a small amount of the rock in acid and examine the insoluble residue with a hand lens.

7. Proceed with the complete identification and description of the rock as suggested in the preceding paragraphs by following the scheme of: color—structure—subtexture—varietal minerals—cement and bonding (or, conversely, detrital material in a chemical rock)—genetic affinity—main name.

# GRIM

Ralph Early Grim (1902–    ), American geologist, graduated from Yale in 1924 and after further studies there and four years of teaching at the University of Mississippi he received his Ph.D. degree from the University of Iowa in 1931. He then joined the Illinois Geological Survey as petrographer, and since 1948 he has been Research Professor of Geology at the University of Illinois. Specializing in the structure and composition of clays, his research has shed much light on many problems of sedimentation and stratigraphy.

## MODERN CONCEPTS OF CLAY MINERALS *

### CLAY-WATER SYSTEM

The most important properties of clays are plasticity, green bonding strength, drying shrinkage, compaction, thixotropy, and viscosity of clay and water suspensions—that is, properties of clay material in the presence of water. . . .

F. Grout[1] early indicated that the most satisfactory explanation of the plastic properties of clays was based on the concept of a film of water enclosing the particles making up the clay. Many workers[2] have emphasized the importance of flake-shaped constituent particles of clays in explaining their plastic properties; and later work, particularly on the clay minerals, has substantiated both the existence of flake-shaped particles in clay materials and their importance in explaining the physical properties of these materials.

At the present time there are few students of clays who would dispute the premises that clays are composed of flake-shaped particles, that these flake-shaped particles are encased in water envelopes when the clay is in the plastic state, and that the plastic properties of clays depend to a very large degree on the characteristics of the water envelopes. By "characteristics" are meant such things as thickness, density, and orientation of the water molecules. Plasticity may be considered as a consequence of a binding force between particles tending to hold the whole mass together and a water film that separates the flakes, thereby weakening the binding force and acting as a lubricant between them. Plastic deformation is the sum total of the movement of flakes with respect to each other, the actual movement taking place in the water film.

*From *Journal of Geology 50* (1942), 225–275. The excerpt begins on page 263.
[1] F. Grout, "The plasticity of clay," *Trans. Am. Ceram. Soc. 14* (1912), 72.
[2] C. Terzaghi, "The physical properties of clay," *Tech. Eng. News 9* (1928), 10, 11, 36.

*State of the Water in the Envelope*

Based on the work of I. Langmuir,[3] who investigated the orientation and packing of polar molecules in adsorptive films, Terzaghi[2] and others have conceived of the water envelope as being built up of layers of uniformly oriented water dipolar molecules. Slippage within the water film was postulated as occurring in the planes of the dipole ends. The idea has been held that the water of the envelope immediately adjacent to the clay-particle surface had a higher density than ordinary water, and some data in support of such increased density have been presented. On the basis of the oriented dipole concept and the increased density at the surface it was postulated that the innermost layers of dipoles were very closely packed and that the closeness of packing decreased outward.[4] . . .

Investigations of the hydrogen bond have led recently to a better understanding of the structure of the water molecule.[5] On the basis of this work Hendricks and Jefferson[6] have presented a concept of the structure of the water in the films. In the language of Hendricks and Jefferson a water layer is composed of water molecules joined into hexagonal groups of an extended hexagonal net as shown in projection in Figure 11. The arrangement is partly a result of a tetrahedral distribution of charge about a water molecule, two corners of the tetrahedron being occupied by hydrogen atoms and the other two corners by an excess of electrons. Each side of the hexagon (Fig. 11) must correspond to a hydroxyl bond, the hydrogen-oxygen bond of one water molecule being directed toward the negative charge of a neighboring molecule. One-fourth of the hydrogen atoms, or a hydrogen atom of half the water molecules, are not involved in bonding within the net ($K$, $M$, and $O$ of Fig. 11). Hendricks and Jefferson[6] visualize the net as being tied to the silicate sheet of the clay mineral by the attraction of those hydrogen atoms not involved in binding within the net and the oxygen atom of the neighboring silicate sheet (Fig. 12). When the surface of the clay mineral contains hydroxyl groups (e.g., kaolinite),

[3]I. Langmuir, "The constitution and fundamental properties of solids and liquids," *J. Am. Chem. Soc. 39* (1917), 1848–1906.

[4]R. E. Grim, "Relation of composition to properties of clay," *J. Am. Ceram. Soc. 22* (1939), 141–151.

[5]J. D. Bernal and H. D. Megaw, "The function of hydrogen in intermolecular forces," *Proc. Roy. Soc. London* [A] *151* (1935), 384–420. J. M. Burgers, "Introductory remarks on recent investigations concerning the structure of liquids," *Second Report on Viscosity and Plasticity* (Amsterdam, 1938).

[6]S. B. Hendricks and M. E. Jefferson, "Polymorphism of the micas," *Am. Mineral. 24* (1939), 729–771.

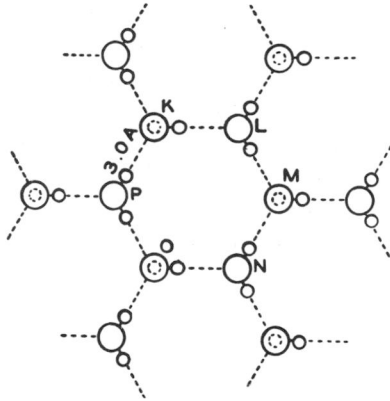

Fig. 11. Hexagonal net of water molecules. Large spheres represent oxygen atoms and small spheres hydrogen atoms; dotted lines indicate bonding through hydrogen. (After Hendricks and Jefferson.)

part of the hydroxyls are free for binding through hydrogen to oxygen atoms in the water layer.

The net has just the $a$ and $b$ dimensions of the silicate layer minerals if the separation of the oxygen atoms of the water molecules is about 3.0 A in projection. It is assumed that the oxygen atoms are in one plane. In this configuration there are four molecules of water for each layer in the unit structure instead of six, as in the closepacking arrangement of the older concept.[7]

The stability of the layer arises from its geometrical relationship to oxygen ions of the silicate framework (Fig. 12). Presence of the first

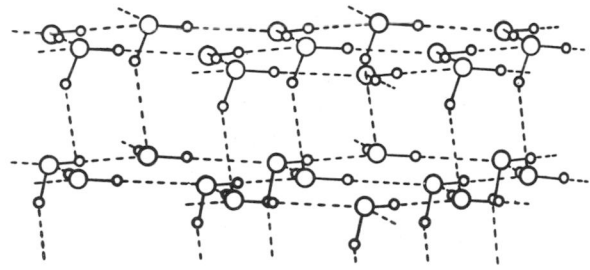

Fig. 12. Probable structure of multiple water layers. (After Hendricks and Jefferson.)

[7]W. F. Bradley, R. E. Grim, and G. L. Clark, "A study of the behavior of montmorillonite upon wetting," Z. Krist. 97 (1937), 216–222. Nagelschmidt, "On the lattice shrinkage and structure of montmorillonite," Z. Krist. 93 (1936), 481–487.

layer favors the formation of a second, and the structure is then propagated away from the surface. The dissociation pressure of successive layers considered as hydrates would finally approach the vapor pressure of water at the temperature of observation.

Kelley and his colleagues[8] have developed the concept that there are two types of adsorbed water in clays. One type, designated as "planar water," coats the plane surfaces of the flakes, is loosely held, and, as a consequence, is lost at low temperatures ($-150°$ C.). The other type, known as "broken-bond water," is more tightly held at the edges of the sheets. Strong evidence has been presented for this concept, and it seems to fit into explanations of the plastic properties of clays.

Planar water could well have the configuration described by Hendricks and Jefferson,[6] whereas broken-bond water would be expected to have such a regular molecular orientation to a much less degree. In montmorillonite, planar water would be the dominant type; but in kaolinite and illite, broken-bond water, although not necessarily dominant, would play a more important role than in montmorillonite.

### Factors Determining the State of Water in the Envelope

Many investigators, but particularly Wiegner[9] and Endell, his colleague,[10] have considered that the adsorbed cations are hydrated and that a union of the solvation hulls forms the water envelope around clay-mineral particles. According to this idea, the thickness and other characteristics of the water film are a direct consequence of the hydration of the adsorbed cations that are present. This idea has become so prevalent that it has been widely accepted without critical study of the evidence for and against it. . . . Hendricks and others have recently presented strong evidence that certain of the cations ($Na^+$) that were thought to be highly hydrated are probably not hydrated at all. In addition, Houwink[11] has stated that the thickness of the water film ($10^2$–$10^3$ A) is too great to be accounted for by the hydration of adsorbed cations, and Speil[12] has concluded that solvation of the adsorbed cations cannot explain fully the presence of water films. It seems, therefore, that the general conclusion is not justified that all the common

[8] Kelley and others, "Hydration of minerals and soil colloids in relation to crystal structure," *Soil Sci. 41* (1936), 259–274.

[9] G. Wiegner, "Some physico-chemical properties of clays," *J. Soc. Chem. Ind. 50* (1931), 65–71, 103–112.

[10] K. Endell and P. Vageler, "The cation and water hull of ceramic clays in the unfired state," *Ber. Deut. Keram. Ges. 13* (1932), 377–411.

[11] R. Houwink, *Elasticity, plasticity, and structure of matter,* Cambridge University Press, 1937.

[12] S. Speil, "Effect of adsorbed electrolytes on properties of monodispersed clay-water systems," *J. Am. Ceram. Soc. 23* (1940), 33–38.

adsorbed cations are hydrated, and that some other cause for the development of the water film around the clay particles must be sought.

The lattice structures of the clay-mineral particles are continuous in the $a$ and $b$ crystallographic directions, so that the edges of the flakes would contain broken bonds or unsatisfied valence charges that would serve to hold water perhaps through a hydrogen bond. The explanation of the planar water is not so simple. For example, in montmorillonite, according to the structure of Hofmann and others, the basal planes are oxygens without any unsatisfied charges, and there is no obvious good reason why thick films of water should develop on them. Substitutions may occur within the lattice that develop charges on the surface, but it is believed that they are satisfied with adsorbed cations. Kelley and others[8] have suggested that planar water is due to the existence of stray forces without accounting for their source. It does not seem likely that stray forces are entirely adequate to account for the thicknesses of water films that are known to form.

According to the structure of the water sheet worked out by Hendricks and Jefferson,[6] the water is held to the clay minerals through hydroxyl bonds to oxygens or hydroxyls, and it propagates itself because of its configuration. This provides a reason for the development of a water film, but it does not explain the difference in the development of the water layers in different minerals. For example, it does not explain why montmorillonite develops such thick water sheets and pyrophyllite does not.

If one assumes that the correct structures of montmorillonite and halloysite are those suggested by Edelman and Favejee,[13] that the concept of the structure of the water layers of Hendricks and Jefferson[6] is correct, and that the oriented layers can only develop when the surface of the flakes carry projecting (OH) ions, a general concept of clay-mineral-water can be worked out that seems eminently satisfactory.

According to this idea, the oriented sheets of water are tied to the projecting (OH) ions of the basal sheets in montmorillonite. Montmorillonite swells because the units of the clay mineral are pushed apart by the growth of additional sheets of water (unless *certain* adsorbed cations are present that bind the sheets together, as will be discussed presently). Similarly, a water sheet develops between the layers of halloysite. In this mineral a plane of (OH) ions is adjacent to the projecting (OH) ions in the next structure unit, and this may explain why the sheet is restricted to a single layer. It must be confessed, however, that this explanation of the extra water in halloysite is no more

[13] C. H. Edelman and J. Ch. L. Favejee, "On the crystal structure of montmorillonite and halloysite," *Z. Krist. 102* (1940), 417–431.

satisfactory than those based on other concepts. Further study is necessary before the structural attributes of the halloysite minerals become well known.

Kaolinite does not develop a sheet of water between the unit cells because it does not have projecting (OH) ions.

In the case of illite, as in that of kaolinite, there are no projecting (OH) ions, and the mineral does not develop planar water between the unit cells. In natural clay materials flake-shaped particles of illite and kaolinite exist that are many unit cells thick. On the flat surfaces of these particles a water film develops. According to the suggested concept, this water would be expected to differ from water held on the flat surfaces of montmorillonite particles. For illite and kaolinite the water molecules would be oriented little or not at all, and, as a consequence, the water sheet would not develop to any considerable thickness. Stray forces that are a consequence, perhaps, of slight distortions or irregularities of the lattice may serve to hold such water.

It follows from this concept that the water envelope of a single clay mineral consists of parts held by forces of varying intensity in which the water molecules are arranged differently, and also that the amount of water molecule orientation and the binding forces vary for the different clay minerals. Thus, for kaolinite and illite there is relatively more broken-bond water than for montmorillonite. In addition, the planar water for montmorillonite differs from that of kaolinite and illite because it is made up of oriented water molecules, because it is more tightly held, and because it may extend greater distances from the flake surfaces.

### Influence of Adsorbed Cations on the Water Film

. . . Data from investigations of the relation of exchangeable bases to plastic properties indicate that in some way the character of the adsorbed cation affects the thickness of the water film. In the absence of hydration of the cations it seems likely that the effect is produced by a binding action of the cations. That is to say that cations act as bridges to bind the clay-mineral sheets together. The action is analogous to the effect of $K^+$ in holding together the unit cells of muscovite in the direction of the $c$-axis. This idea does not preclude a slight hydration of certain ions, but it postulates the adsorbed cations as controlling the thickness of the film water primarily by means of the force with which they hold the sheets together.

In applying this idea to montmorillonite it follows that the thickness of the water film is the result of two opposing forces: ($a$) the tendency of layers of water to develop on the basal planes, for reasons already discussed; and (b) the tendency of the adsorbed cations to hold the sheets together. The resulting thickness of the film is chiefly dependent on the cation. The bonding action of the adsorbed cations is not a new concept, but its significance has perhaps not been appreciated fully.

It may be postulated that the bridging action of the adsorbed cations varies with their valence and parhaps also with their size. With regard to the latter factor, the work of Page[14] suggests that, for ions of equal valence, those with a diameter about equal to that of the hole in the hexagonal net of the silica sheet would exert the greatest bonding action.

It is a well-known fact that Na-montmorillonite expands greatly in the presence of abundant water, whereas under similar conditions Ca-montmorillonite expands very little. According to this concept, the great swelling of the Na-montmorillonite is due not to the hydration of the Na[+] serving as a wedge to force the layers apart but to the absence of a strong bridge because of the univalent character of Na[+] and perhaps also because of its small size enabling it to fit well in the hole of the silica sheet. The Ca-montmorillonite does not expand greatly because of the slight hydration of Ca[++] but because the divalent ion holds the layers together so that a thick series of water sheets cannot form between them.

It is also a well-known fact that completely electrodialyzed montmorillonite expands only very slightly. On the basis of the above concept, it would seem at first that the H-montmorillonite should swell more avidly than Na-montmorillonite. That, perhaps, would be true if H-montmorillonite contained only H[+] as the adsorbed cation. There is a considerable body of data to indicate that, before all the adsorbed cations are replaced by H[+], some Al[+++] is removed from the lattice to occupy exchange positions. Many workers have presented experimental evidence for this point. An explanation for the nonswelling of so-called "H-montmorillonite clays" is that they are not pure H-montmorillonites but also contain multivalent cations that serve to bind the layers together.

What has been said has been developed with particular reference to montmorillonite clay materials. It can also be applied to clay materials composed of other clay minerals. In illites and kaolinites the water does not penetrate between the basal planes of the unit cells. The planar water occurs on aggregates and, as pointed out before, is probably held by weaker forces than those operating in montmorillonite. Likewise, illite and kaolinite have low capacity for holding adsorbed cations, so

[14] J. B. Page, "The relation of ionic state to the fixation of potassium and other cations by colloidal clay," unpubl. diss., Ohio State University, 1940.

that the forces holding the clay-mineral aggregates to each other would be less than in montmorillonite clay materials. It may be concluded that the total area encased by water in illite and kaolinite clay materials would be less than in those composed of montmorillonite. It can also be concluded that a smaller part of the total water of illite and kaolinite clay materials would show a definite configuration than of montmorillonite clay materials and that the configuration would be less regular in the former types of materials than in the latter types.

### Plastic Properties of Clay Materials on the Basis of the Foregoing Concept

Clays composed of illite and kaolinite clay minerals tend to adsorb less water, to have lower green bonding strength, as expressed in terms of modulus of rupture of the clay alone or when determined for sand-clay mixtures, to be more permeable to water, and to shrink less and more rapidly than clays composed of montmorillonite. These differences in properties would be expected on the basis of the concept outlined. . . .

Extensive data regarding the effect of exchangeable cations on bonding strength are not yet at hand. Available data suggest that the strength in the green (i.e., moist) condition is greater for Ca- and H-clays than for Na-clays and that the reverse relationship is true for strength in the dried but unfired condition. The green-strength relationship is clear on the basis of the low bonding power of $Na^+$, but the explanation for the dry-strength relationship is not entirely clear, unless it is considered that dry strength is a function of the total available surface area of the clay-mineral particles. With the low bonding power of the particles for each other in the Na-clay the tendency would be for the component clay-mineral particles to disaggregate and form a huge surface area per volume of clay.

It is well known that Na-clays dry more slowly than Ca- or H-clays. An explanation is that the water in the Na-clay penetrates more completely between sheets; or, stated another way, the clay-mineral units separated by the water are smaller and the water itself occurs in smaller spaces. A further factor that may be of importance is that in Na-clays there is little binding force between the clay-mineral flakes to speed up drying by squeezing action on the water.

Speil[12] has shown that substitution of $Na^+$ for $H^+$ on a kaolinite clay tends to decrease both the pore water and shrinkage water. The suggested explanation, in addition to that already given, is that particles with low attractive forces between them (Na-clay) could come into a more compact arrangement, whereas particles with high attractive forces

334

between them would be pulled together into a random arrangement before they reached the most compact positions. The random arrangement would be expected to give a relatively higher pore-water value.

Na-montmorillonite adsorbs water and is much less permeable than Ca-montmorillonite. The high water adsorption of Na-montmorillonite is expected because the flakes are held together loosely, so that a large amount of water can enter between them. The low permeability is in accordance with the discussion of rate of drying.

It would seem, therefore, that the suggested concept agrees with certain important plastic properties of clays. Whether it is successful in explaining all or even most of the plastic properties of clays remains to be determined by future work.

# BUERGER
Martin Julian Buerger (1903– ), American crystallographer and mineralogist, has been associated with the Massachusetts Institute of Technology throughout most of his life, first as a student, receiving the baccalaureate degree in 1925 and the doctorate in 1929, then as a teacher, becoming Professor of Mineralogy and Crystallography in 1944 and an Institute Professor in 1956. He was the recipient of the Arthur L. Day Medal of the Geological Society of America in 1951 and the Roebling Medal of the Mineralogical Society of America in 1958 and served as Director of the School for Advanced Studies at M.I.T. from 1956 to 1963. The following excerpt is from his address as President of the Mineralogical Society, delivered in Ottawa, Canada, December 29, 1947.

## THE ROLE OF TEMPERATURE IN METAMORPHISM *

Metamorphism involves many factors which we cannot consider in any detail. Specifically, it often involves pressure, a discussion of which is outside the range of this discourse. I do wish, however, to point out that the really essential factor in metamorphism is temperature, and that without an adequate temperature level there is no metamorphism.

Consider one of the simplest instances of metamorphism, the matter of the recrystallization and grain growth of a monomineralic rock, such as a limestone. To drive recrystallization, some kind of energy difference is required. This is ordinarily supplied in the form of strain energy consequent upon plastic deformation. The energetics are then somewhat analogous to those involved in a polymorphic transformation. The strained material is, in effect, a metastable polymorph, and the energy

*From "The Role of Temperature in Mineralogy," *American Mineralogist 33* (1948), 101–121.

difference between the strained and unstrained mineral is the potential which drives the transformation. It is opposed by a structural barrier which prevents the transformation unless temperature provides the required activation energy. During the recrystallization, the crystalline matter at points of greatest strain transforms into small strain-free nuclei. The process probably takes place by essentially a semi-reconstructive transformation. The temperature of recrystallization is known to be lowered with increasing strain energy, but it would not occur at all if it were not for the existence of temperature, for the energy associated with the temperature is required to supply the activation energy necessary for the transformation. Nor would the subsequent growth of crystal dimensions occur in metamorphism unless thermal energy supplied the activation energy necessary to remove atoms from one crystal and implant them on the growing crystal. Thus, no limestone would ever recrystallize at absolute zero, nor would it recrystallize in geologically available time unless the temperature is above a certain level characteristic of the mineral and its strain. Of course, this is why unmetamorphosed limestones exist in very old rocks.

It is known that the activation energy of grain growth in metals is about twice the activation energy required to make the metal atoms diffuse through their own solid structure. The reason for this, evidently, is that more bonds must be broken to transport an atom across a crystal boundary than to merely pass it along in the same structure. *There is an important geological significance to this relation, for it implies that whenever the temperature is sufficiently high to cause spontaneous growth of the crystals, it is already maintaining a very high level of diffusion.* In this condition, the smaller atoms, at least, may be expected to be rather freely migrating through the remainder of the structure of the crystal. Thus, whenever the rock is in a condition to recrystallize, it is also something of a blotter for available atoms, thanks to temperature. It is, therefore, evident that wholesale diffusion must play an important role in the transfer of chemical material in metamorphism.

Not only must diffusion play an important role in metamorphism, but it appears that sulfide replacement in ore deposits is on a similar footing, for such features as unmixing bespeak free diffusion. The process occurs at lower temperatures in sulfides than in the rock minerals because the tetrahedral coordination of sulfur imposes a rather open structure on its minerals. Thus, at moderate temperatures a sulfide can hardly avoid blotting up the atoms supplied to it by the surrounding solutions. As the atoms are passed along, a wave of replacement ensues.

Lindgren long ago pointed out that replacement occurs on approximately a volume-by-volume basis. While the field evidence for this has been obvious, the mechanism for accomplishing it has been obscure. Diffusion suggests the mechanism. There is a tendency on the part of crystals to have their volumes determined by their largest atoms. Thus, the volumes of the rock minerals are dominated by their oxygen atoms and the volumes of the sulfides are dominated by the packing of the sulfur atoms. Replacement is, therefore, substantially a matter of the diffusion of new metals into the volumes dominated by oxygen or sulfur atoms. Thus diffusion supplies a mechanism for approximately maintaining volume during replacement.

In studying metamorphism, it is customary to consider that some oxide, such as silica or alumina, has remained constant while other oxides have varied in the process. Evidently a closer approximation would be that the *oxygen* content has remained nearly constant while the wandering interstitial metals themselves have varied with the change. . . .

*Melting and Reaction Relations*—There is an interesting relation between the arrangement of minerals in Bowen's discontinuous reaction series and the order of increased sharing of oxygen atoms by silicon atoms in the silicates. In all silicates, the silicon atom is surrounded by four oxygen atoms in tetrahedral coordination (see table). Each oxygen atom may belong to one silicon atom only or it may be shared between two neighboring silicon atoms. If it is shared, then the oxygen:silicon ratio is reduced, and the formula of the silicate departs from the formula of the pure tetrahedron, namely $SiO_4$. Since each silicon tetrahedron may share any number up to four oxygen atoms with its neighbors, several silicate formulae are possible which depart the more from $SiO_4$ the greater the number of the four possible oxygen atoms shared. The

| Number of oxygen atoms shared per silicon tetrahedron | Type | Example | Bowen's discontinuous reaction series |
|---|---|---|---|
| 0 | orthosilicates | olivine | olivine |
| 1 | pyrosilicates | melilite | — |
| 2 | metasilicates | pyroxene | { Mg pyroxenes<br>{ Mg, Ca pyroxenes |
| half 2, half 3 | double chain silicates | amphiboles | amphiboles |
| 3 | sheet silicates | micas | { biotite<br>{ muscovite |
| 4 | network silicates | quartz | quartz |

general sharing schemes which have been found by crystal structure studies of the silicates are shown in comparison with Bowen's reaction series, in the accompanying table. The comparison between Bowen's reaction series and the number of shared oxygens in the silicon tetrahedron is striking. What is its significance?

Two factors appear to be involved. In the first place, it must be evident that thermal agitation sufficient to disintegrate a structure of linked tetrahedra must leave fragments of simpler linking. Thus a mica sheet could conceivably be disintegrated into amphibole double chains, pyroxene single chains, melilite pairs, or single unshared tetrahedra, all plus a residue. In a similar manner any of the linked structures higher in the series can be disintegrated into fragments of structures having less sharing. Thus with increasing temperature the breakdown sequence is networks, multiple chains, single chains, tetrahedron pairs, and single tetrahedra, all plus a residue which appears as a glass. This corresponds very well with Bowen's up-temperature sequence, except for the presence in the theoretical sequence of the pyrosilicates which are absent in Bowen's series.

This is a purely geometrical picture. A bond picture is also involved. As an obvious consequence of Pauling's rules, the number of atoms which bond together the silicate units depends on the number of *unshared* oxygen atoms. Thus, the greater the sharing, the fewer the bonding atoms, the looser the binding of silicate units to one another, per silicon atom, and the lower the temperature of disintegration of the structure.

Consider, now, the effect of aluminum. If the aluminum proxies for silicon in certain tetrahedra, the saturation of the oxygens of those tetrahedra is reduced and they are capable of contributing to stronger bonding between silicate units than without the aluminum. In this way, the presence of aluminum proxying for silicon in a silicate increases its disintegration temperature and consequently raises its position in the reaction series. This is true for both discontinuous and continuous reaction series. The effect of aluminum in a discontinuous reaction pair can be seen in the higher position of leucite (Al: Si = 1:2) with respect to orthoclase (Al: Si = 1:3). The effect of aluminum in a continuous reaction series is illustrated by the higher position of anorthite (Al: Si = 1:1) with respect to albite (Al: Si = 1:3). . . .

I hope that in this sketchy account I have been able to convince you that it is important for a mineralogist to have a background of dynamic structural crystallography, and that such a background provides a rational frame for understanding and filing away his knowledge of the temperature relations of minerals.

# HUBBERT

Marion King Hubbert (1903–    ), American geologist, received his B.S. degree in 1926 and his Ph.D. degree in 1937 from the University of Chicago. From 1931 to 1940 he was Instructor of Geophysics at Columbia University and after service on the Board of Economic Warfare in Washington as Senior Analyst of world mineral resources he became in 1943 a Research Geophysicist with the Shell Oil Company in Houston, Texas. Continuing his research in all phases of geology that might have bearing upon the occurrence of petroleum, he has been Chief Consultant (General Geology) to the Shell Development Company since 1956.

## ENTRAPMENT OF PETROLEUM UNDER HYDRODYNAMIC CONDITIONS *

### INTRODUCTION

During the first five years following Colonel Drake's discovery of oil at Titusville, Pennsylvania, in 1859, the idea that oil and gas in a groundwater environment are impelled by the forces of buoyancy into a stable stratified arrangement in porous or fractured strata on the crests of anticlines was clearly formulated; and by 1890 the "anticlinal theory" had become firmly established as the controlling principle of oil accumulation. (For a review of early literature see J. V. Howell.[1]) Other geometrical arrangements such as fault and stratigraphic traps have subsequently been added, but these have mostly been in accord with the basic principle that oil and gas accumulations occur in a normally water-saturated environment in the highest local position to which these fluids can migrate. As a special case the possibility of a "dry" or water-free sand has also been admitted wherein the oil would occur in the lowest positions.

Implicit in this formulation, although rarely expressed, is the assumption that the environmental ground water is at rest and the resulting fluid equilibrium is one of complete hydrostatics with the interfaces between separate fluids, except as modified by capillary forces, forming horizontal surfaces.

The only notable departure from this line of thought was that represented by a minority literature extending from 1909 into the 1930's . . . in which the "hydraulic theory" of oil and gas accumulation was developed. Beginning with the basic premise that the migration of oil and gas in a hydrostatic environment is inhibited by capillary impediments,

*From *American Association of Petroleum Geologists Bulletin 37* (1953), 1954–2026.
[1] J. V. Howell, "Historical development of the structural theory of accumulation of oil and gas," *Problems of Petroleum Geology,* Am. Assn. Petrol. Geol. (1934), 1–23.

the flow of water was invoked as an essential condition for oil and gas migration and accumulation, the migration occurring always, except for an oblique upward drift, in the direction of the flow of the water. Entrapment of oil, according to this theory, would occur in any position where resistance to further migration exceeded the propulsive force exerted by the flowing water. Accumulations might thus be formed in anticlines where the oil could be dragged up the dip on one side but not down the dip on the other. They might occur by filtering action with the water flowing from coarse sands into silts or shales; or on unclosed structures such as noses or structural terraces where, with the water flowing up the dip, the oil might be arrested by the increased drag produced by a decrease in the angle of dip.

During the 1920's the hydraulic theory, although never completely accepted, exercised considerable influence on contemporary geologic thought. This rapidly subsided, however, and by the mid-1930's geologic thinking had reverted largely to the premises of hydrostatics. Recently the hydraulic theory has shown signs of revival, and has in fact been accepted as the basis of petroleum migration and accumulation in one recent textbook of petroleum geology.[2]

The present inquiry stems from a study of some years ago[3] in which during an investigation of the motion of underground fluids—particularly ground water—it became necessary to determine the behavior of any fluid in an environment dominated by the presence of another in some state of motion. In particular it was determined that, whereas under hydrostatic conditions two fluids will arrange themselves with a horizontal interface and the less dense fluid uppermost, under dynamical conditions with one or both fluids in motion, the steady-state interface would in general be inclined at an angle which might assume any value up to the vertical.

Since oil and gas are minority fluids in a ground-water-dominated environment, with the ground water commonly in some state of motion, it is evident that the foregoing results should apply to problems of petroleum geology. In what follows, therefore, an endeavor will be made to establish the general theory of migration and entrapment of oil and gas under hydrodynamic conditions in which the more familiar hydrostatic relationships will emerge as but special cases.

## General Principles

Present-day accumulations of petroleum and natural gas are found invariably in or adjacent to sedimentary rocks. According to all available

[2] E. N. Tiratsoo, *Principles of Petroleum Geology* (New York: McGraw-Hill, 1952), pp. 45–90.

[3] M. King Hubbert, "The theory of ground water motion," *J. Geol.* 48 (1940), 785–944.

evidence, these fluids have originated from the organic matter deposited in sediments—principally marine—at the time of their deposition.[4] The organic-rich, sediments are usually the fine-textured rocks, shales, and limestones of great areal and volumetric extent; whereas the present-day accumulations are usually found in highly restricted volumes in the coarse-textured rocks, sandstones, and porous or fractured limestones. The term organic-rich applied to a shale is of course relative; the amount of organic matter present is small compared to the great porosity (up to 80 per cent) of such a rock at the time of its deposition. It is inferred, therefore, that oil and gas must have originated in a highly dispersed state, from which they have been impelled to their present positions of concentration and entrapment.

In general, the sedimentary rocks are porous, with the pore space forming an intricately branching three-dimensional network. Furthermore, below shallow depths from the earth's surface the pore spaces of the rocks are normally filled with water, so that the origin, migration, and final accumulation of petroleum must take place in an otherwise water-saturated environment. We envisage, therefore, petroleum in its initial dispersed state as consisting of numerous discontinuous volume elements, each entirely surrounded by water and the solid framework of the rock in which it occurs.

We now make use of one of the fundamental principles of mechanics applicable to all manner of mechanical systems of whatever degree of complexity: namely, that if such a system is at rest and not already in a configuration for which its potential energy is a minimum it will move spontaneously until such a configuration is achieved. Mechanical equilibrium therefore is characterized by a configuration for which the kinetic energy is zero and the potential energy of the system for all small displacements compatible with the constraints of the system either remains constant or increases. The equilibrium positions of a marble in a bowl, or of a mass suspended by a spring, are familiar illustrative examples.

Applying this principle to petroleum in its dispersed state, we recognize that each element possesses an amount of mechanical potential energy with respect to its environment which, in general, will vary with position. The element will accordingly be acted upon by an unbalanced force tending to impel it from regions where its energy is higher to those where it is lower. It will therefore tend to migrate from higher- to lower-energy regions and will come stably to rest in any region which is surrounded entirely by higher energy levels, or jointly by higher energy levels and impermeable barriers (see Fig. 1). A petroleum trap is therefore such a low-energy region, and the search for petroleum reduces in

[4]Paul V. Smith, Jr., "Preliminary note on origin of petroleum," *Bull. Am. Assn. Petrol. Geol. 36* (1952), 411–413.

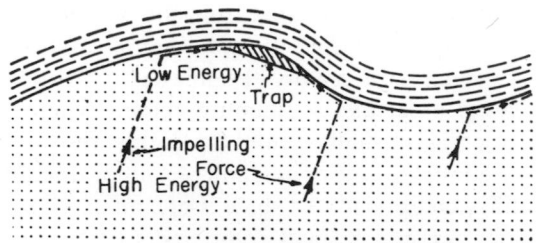

Fig. 1. Dispersed oil in water environment migrating from region of high energy to one of low energy where impermeable barrier forms trap and accumulation is being built up.

large part to the determination in underground space of the positions of these local low-energy regions.

## FLOW OF GROUND WATER

Since petroleum migration occurs in a ground-water environment, the determination of the energy field for petroleum can most effectively be done in terms of that of the ambient ground water. We shall direct our attention, therefore, to the general behavior of ground water which initially we shall regard as a homogeneous fluid.

The water which saturates the pore spaces of the rocks of the earth below shallow depths possesses potential energy in the earth's gravitational field and can be in static equilibrium only when at a configuration for which this energy is a minimum. Since the pore spaces of the rocks form a three-dimensional interconnected network, those rocks are to some degree permeable to the flow of water. Ultimate equilibrium of water would therefore occur only if the upper surface of the ground water, or more strictly the water table, were a horizontal surface. Actually, the water table follows closely the earth's topographic variations, with the result that the water is not in equilibrium and so must flow continuously, descending into the ground in regions where the topography is high and emerging in areas where the topography is low. If no water were added to such a system and none withdrawn except by flow, movement would continue until the ground-water table was everywhere at the same level. Actually, water is repeatedly added to the system at the higher elevations by precipitation, keeping it perpetually out of equilibrium, and thus maintaining a general ground-water circulation.

If the ground water is of constant density and in motion in one region of underground space, it will be shown later that it must also be in motion throughout all space not isolated by impermeable barriers. If, on the contrary, the water is inhomogeneous and consists of different bodies of contrasting density, such as fresh water and salt water, it is possible for one kind of water, say fresh water, to be flowing while a contiguous body of salt water remains in hydrostatic equilibrium. Since water upon entering the ground is fresh and is not in equilibrium, it follows from the foregoing that fresh water at whatever depth, unless isolated by impermeable barriers, should be in some degree of motion. Hence, in the absence of more positive evidence, the occurrence of fresh or brackish water underground is presumptive of a dynamic state. Saline water, on the contrary, may or may not be in equilibrium.

. . . . .

## Types of Hydrodynamic Traps

The types of accumulation of oil and gas to be expected under hydrodynamic conditions are influenced by all of the structural and stratigraphic complexities which are already familiar in the case of hydrostatic traps, but with the additional complication that these also influence the flow pattern of the water which in turn determines the angle of tilt and hence the positions of the hydrodynamic traps. As illustrative examples of the types of hydrodynamic traps that may be expected, only a few of the simplest cases will be cited.

The most obvious is an anticlinal or domal structure. If water is flowing through a regional sand in such a structure, the oil and gas equipotential surfaces will each be tilted downward in the direction of the flow, those for oil by an angle greater than those for gas. If the dip on the downstream side of the structure is steeper than the tilt of the oil equipotential surface, then the structure will serve as a trap for both oil and gas. Gas or oil separately may then be trapped in the structure with a tilted water interface, high on the upstream and low on the downstream side. If both fluids are trapped together, the oil may rest upon the water with a tilted interface, while a gas cap may rest entirely upon the oil with a static, horizontal gas-oil contact [Fig. 24 (a)]; or, the gas cap may rest partly upon the oil on the downstream side and partly upon water on the upstream side, as shown in Figure 24 (b). In this case the gas-water contact will be tilted at a small angle, the oil-water contact at a greater angle, while the gas-oil contact will be horizontal. It is also possible that the gas may be entirely underlain by water with a gently tilted interface, with the oil in a completely separate trap in a down-structure nose, as shown in Figure 24 (c).

These three configurations, (a), (b), and (c), could represent the conditions under which an oil of given density would be trapped by (a) weak, (b) moderate, or (c) strong flow of ground water. Alternatively,

343

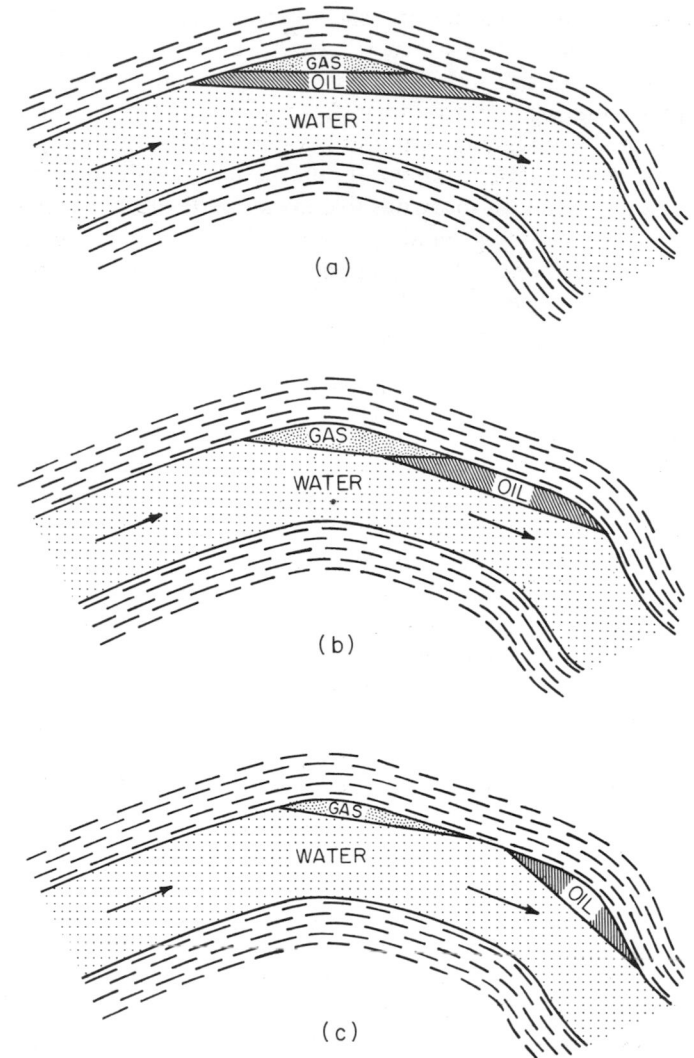

Fig. 24. Types of hydrodynamic oil and gas accumulation in gently folded thick sand: (a) gas entirely underlain by oil; (b) gas partly underlain by oil; (c) gas and oil traps separated.

with the same flow of ground water in each case, they could also represent the conditions under which (*a*) light, (*b*) medium, or (*c*) heavy oil would trap.

· · · · ·

## CONCLUSION

At the outset of the present paper we proposed to investigate the forces which cause petroleum to migrate and the characteristics of the positions in which it will become entrapped under the general conditions when the environmental ground water is in some state of motion. This we have done and our formulations reduce, as they should, in the special case for which the water is at rest, to the results with which we are already familiar: vertical and parallel impelling forces, and traps for both oil and gas in the spaces between downwardly concave impermeable barriers and horizontal surfaces.

If the water is in motion, however, in a nonvertical direction, which often is the case, our formulation leads to consequences which are by no means familiar. Oil and gas equipotentials are no longer horizontal but are inclined, with the angle of inclination of the equipotentials for oil greater than that of the equipotentials for gas. The paths of migration for oil and gas in the same space are no longer vertical, nor are they parallel, the paths for oil being deflected away from the vertical by an angle greater than that of the paths for gas. Likewise the traps for oil and gas no longer coincide and may in fact be separated entirely. In the latter event a trap for oil will not hold gas nor a trap for gas, oil; the fluids will migrate to their respective traps instead.

The oil- and gas-water interfaces will not be horizontal but inclined at an angle given by

$$\tan \theta = \frac{dz}{dx} = \frac{\rho_w}{\rho_w - \rho_0} \frac{dh}{dx},$$

where $\rho_0$ is the density of the oil or gas, respectively.

Under such circumstances oil or gas entrapments will not occur in the conventional positions. They may occur in anticlines in asymmetrical positions with the water high on one side and low on the other, or in completely unclosed structures such as noses or terraces, with the water flowing down the dip. Again, if the closing dip of an anticline in the downstream direction is less than the angle of tilt, this structure will not hold the specified fluid under the conditions prevailing.

These theoretical deductions have been confirmed experimentally, and the predicted phenomena have also been sought in the field. Not only have they been found, but the frequency of their occurrence has exceeded expectations, and in every major oil-producing area so far examined, hydrodynamic conditions in at least some reservoir formations, with oil-field tilts ranging from tens to hundreds of feet per mile, have been observed. We are thus led to the suspicion that many off-structure accumulations of oil and gas, which, on the basis of hydrostatic premises, have been classified as fault or stratigraphic traps, may in fact be hydrodynamic traps instead.

From such considerations it becomes evident that in the prospecting for petroleum in any area, as complete a knowledge as possible, in three-dimensional space, of the ground-water hydrology is of importance comparable with a knowledge of the stratigraphy and the structure. If conditions can be demonstrated to be very nearly hydrostatic, then our customary procedures are appropriate; if hydrodynamic conditions prevail, it is important that these be determined in detail, stratum by stratum, over the given basin in order that the positions of the traps may better be determined.

For this purpose regional geology and topography constitute the initial and most readily available information. Next comes the information obtainable from wells of which the most informative are widely spaced wildcats. Water samples for analysis and density determination should be taken in such wells in every regional sand or permeable formation. In addition, in the same formations, accurate shut-in pressures, together with the precise elevation of the point of measurement, should also be taken. This information is essential for the computation of the potential $\Phi_w$, or the head $h_w$, by means of the equations

$$
\left.
\begin{aligned}
\Phi_w &= gz + \frac{p}{\rho_w}, \\
h_w &= z + \frac{p}{\rho_w g},
\end{aligned}
\right\}
$$

where $p$ is the undisturbed pressure in the formation and $z$ the elevation of the point of measurement.

The systematic assembling of data of this kind is appropriately a cooperative enterprise for the whole petroleum industry, and such data should be taken and exchanged between various groups in the same manner that well-log information is now exchanged. It will be found that our present procedures in taking pressure measurements in wildcat wells are inadequate, both as to frequency and accuracy. Since pressure measurements are most often made incidental to drill-stem tests, there is need for an improvement in the pressure measurements and procedures in making such tests. This includes both an improvement in the precision of pressure measurements, and also a change of the routine so that shut-in pressures may be taken prior to the drastic disturbance produced by the withdrawal of fluids, rather than afterward.

In the light of the evidence before us it appears essential that in addition to our customary procedures in petroleum geology, involving principally stratigraphy and structure, we must now add regional ground-water hydrology if many otherwise obscure accumulations of petroleum are not to be overlooked.

# MARSHALL KAY
George Marshall Kay (1904–     ), American geologist, received his B.S. degree from the University of Iowa in 1924 and his Ph.D. degree from Columbia University in 1929. Continuing at Columbia as a member of the faculty, he became Professor of Geology in 1944 and from 1953 to 1956 was Executive Officer of the Department of Geology there. Associated at various times with the New York State Museum and the U. S. Geological Survey, his interests have focused especially on Paleozoic stratigraphy and the history and classification of geosynclines.

## GEOSYNCLINAL NOMENCLATURE AND THE CRATON *

### INTRODUCTION

Geosynclines are the largest stratigraphic units, comprising rocks of relatively great thickness and extent laid in sinking areas in the earth's surface. Classification is based on the rocks, rather than on the form of the original surface of deposition, or on subsequent tectonic or vulcanic history. Some have referred to oceanographic "troughs" and structural synclinoria as geosynclines. Though the etymology of the word, earth down-fold, does not exclude them, the original definition gives rocks as representatives, considers geosynclines to be potential sites of orogeny though including unfolded examples, and definitely excludes synclinoria.

### CRATON

North America had a comparatively stable interior in the early Paleozoic, bordered by more mobile geosynclinal belts. A consolidated, rather immobile area such as this central shield is a *craton* (kră-tŏn), the adjoining geosynclines are *orthogeosynclines* (that is, straight), geosynclines lying between cratons, whether higher continental or lower oceanic cratons.[1] The monoclinal flexure or hinge delimiting the North American early Paleozoic craton trended on present geography from Labrador toward Quebec City, thence through northeastern New York, south-cen-

---

* From *American Association of Petroleum Geologists Bulletin 31* (1947), 1289–1293.
[1] Hans Stille, "Wege und Ergebnisse der geologisch-tektonischen Forschung," *25 Jahres Kaiser Wilhelm Ges. Förd. Wissensch. 2* (1936), 84–85.

tral Pennsylvania, northwestern Virginia, and eastern Tennessee, to central Alabama; the medial Ordovician position is the Adirondack line. . . . That on the west, along the Wasatch line, extended from western Mackenzie through western Alberta, Montana, and Wyoming to central Utah, southeastern Nevada, and western Sonora. A craton is transitory, expanding as orogenies add rocks of former orthogeosynclines, contracting as new orthogeosynclines reduce its area.

North America is perhaps peculiar in that the early Paleozoic craton has had persisting influence on continental development, and has close correlation with present structure. Although the eastern side lost the initial bordering geosyncline by the middle Paleozoic, the western flexure endured into late Mesozoic. The area of this early Paleozoic North American craton is designated as an *hedreocraton* (steadfast),[2] one having long continuing influence.

## ORTHOGEOSYNCLINES

The classification of geosynclines is based on their form, the character and derivation of their rocks, and in the principal classes, on their position relative to a craton. The linear orthogeosynclines between cratons are of two types, *miogeosynclines* (less) and *eugeosynclines* (truly).[3] Those nearer the craton, the miogeosynclines, were rather regularly sinking as deposition progressed and lack appreciable volcanic material; North American early Paleozoic miogeosynclines derived their initial detritus from erosion of the hedreocraton. The more distant eugeosynclinal belts had rapidly sinking linear geosynclines with locally thick and abundant volcanic rocks, as well as sediment eroded from rising narrow intervening lands, like island arcs. The early Paleozoic rocks in the eastern eugeosynclinal belt of North America extend from central Newfoundland through New Brunswick, Maine, New Hampshire, and central Massachusetts to the Atlantic Piedmont; possibly eastern Newfoundland and Nova Soctia lie in an opposite miogeosynclinal belt. Devonian orogeny with accompanying intrusion closed the eugeosynclinal history. Paleozoic and early Mesozoic rocks in the western eugeosynclinal belt extend westward to the Pacific from central Alaska, Yukon

---

[2] Pre-Paleozoic cratons had quite different disposition; thus the pre-Algoman rocks north of Lake Superior and east to western Quebec formed in an orthogeosynclinal belt (F. J. Pettijohn, "Archean sedimentation," *Bull. Geol. Soc. Am.* 54 [1943], 968); and the late pre-Cambrian Beltian sediments of the west (N. E. A. Hinds, "Uncompahgran and beltian deposits in western North America," *Carnegie Inst. Washington Pubs.* 463 [1936], 53–136) formed in a great geosyncline extending far into the hedreocraton.

[3] Marshall Kay, "Stratigraphy of the Trenton Group," *Bull. Geol. Soc. Am.* 48 (1937), 290.

and British Columbia, western Idaho and central Nevada, occupying all but southeastern California; eugeosynclinal development ended with the late Jurassic Nevadian orogeny.

The present areas of the early Paleozoic eastern miogeosynclinal and eugeosynclinal rocks have been called the Champlain and Magog belts.[4] It is proposed that the corresponding western belts of miogeosynclinal and eugeosynclinal rocks be called the Millard and Fraser belts, after Millard County, Utah and Fraser River, British Columbia. The Millard belt had exceptionally broad and long continuing miogeosynclinal development in Paleozoic and earlier Mesozoic, submarine volcanic rocks being almost absent; it is not now a miogeosyncline, and the rocks were so distorted by post-miogeosynclinal orogenies as to require restoration to their original relative geographic positions on palinspastic base maps[5] to give true paleogeography. The eastern margin has major Laramian thrusts, and plutons are present in limited areas. The Fraser belt contains rocks of Paleozoic and earlier Mesozoic eugeosynclines and intervening narrow lands; the rocks in the belt are of types characteristic of eugeosynclines interruptedly in place and time. It contains the principal late Jurassic Nevadian plutons, and its eastern margin is a zone of major thrusts.

## Geosynclines within Cratons

Three types of geosynclines lie outside the orthogeosynclines and within the cratons. A geosyncline invading the margin of a craton, having detritus gained principally from orogenic highlands in the adjacent belts of orthogeosynclinal rocks, was called by the writer a deltageosyncline. The term was ill chosen and confusing, for it has been supposed to include deposits in various stream deltas. Therefore, it is proposed that *exogeosyncline* (outside) replace the term deltageosyncline, in reference to the principal source of detritus being outside the craton; the Upper Ordovician, earlier Silurian, and later Devonian of Pennsylvania and adjacent states are typical; stratigraphic units commonly diverge until they closely approach the source. The second type, the *autogeosyncline*[6] has in the typical Upper Silurian and Devonian of lower Michigan, non-detrital carbonates and salines, and detritus from low near-by land and from orogenic mountains in a distant orthogeosynclinal belt; stratigraphic units generally converge gradually from the center or axis

[4] Hans Stille, *Einführung in den Bau Amerikas* (Berlin: Borntraeger, 1940, 1941), p. 15.
[5] Marshall Kay, "Paleogeographic and palinspastic maps," *Bull. Am. Assn. Petrol. Geol. 29* (1945), 426–450.
[6] Marshall Kay, "Development of the Northern Allegheny synclinorium and adjoining regions," *Bull. Geol. Soc. Am. 53* (1942), 1643.

of the deposit. Autogeosynclines may trend toward orthogeosynclinal belts, but seem essentially independent of them; the structure of the base changed from a plane to a basin or trough as the geosyncline developed. An exogeosyncline tends to diminish gradually and regularly within the craton or to pass into autogeosynclinal patterns, as in the earlier Upper Cretaceous of the western hedreocraton, whereas a miogeosyncline tends to meet the craton in a distinct flexure. American Paleozoic and Mesozoic exogeosynclines enter the margin of the hedreocraton. A third type, the *zeugogeosyncline*[7] (yoked), has detritus from nearby uplifts within the craton, as in the late Paleozoic of northwestern Colorado.

## OTHER GEOSYNCLINES

There are other geosynclinal types whose definition does not depend on their relations to the hedreocraton. A *taphrogeosyncline*[8] (trench) is bounded by high-angle faults, as in the late Triassic geosynclines of the Atlantic Coast. An *epieugeosyncline*[7] (above) has elongate, relatively nonvolcanic deposits derived from adjoining rising swells in areas of former eugeosynclines, as in the Carboniferous of Nova Scotia, and the Tertiary of California. The *idiogeosyncline*[9] (distinct), based on the Tertiary of central Sumatra and Java, has not been defined on a comparable basis, but suggests a late-cycle miogeosyncline. A *paraliageosyncline*[7] (coastal) is one such as the Tertiary of the northern Gulf of Mexico coast, a linear geosyncline along the present continental margin, having flexures on the foreland similar to those delimiting miogeosynclines.

## GEOSYNCLINAL DURATION

Geosynclines have temporal as well as geographic limits. Deformation in a single cycle commonly but not invariably progresses from orogenies in the eugeosynclinal belts to those in the miogeosynclinal belts, with development of exogeosynclines on the cratonal border, and consolidation in an enlarged craton. Subsequent cycles may have quite different positions and trends. Thus, there are belts of pre-Cambrian eugeosynclinal rocks that trend across the early Paleozoic cratons of North America and Fennoscandia. Moreover, eugeosynclines can overlie miogeosynclines, and there are instances of eugeosynclines that closely approach a craton. Though many geosynclines have the characters of a

[7] Marshall Kay, "North American geosynclines—their classification" (abstract), *Bull. Geol. Soc. Am. 56* (1945), 1172.

[8] Marshall Kay, "Geosynclines in continental development," *Science 99* (1943), 462.

[9] J. M. B. Umbgrove, "Verschillende typen von tertiaire geosynclinalen in den Indischen Archipel," *Leidsche Geol. Mededeel. 6* (1933), 33–43.

single class others are compound in their attributes. The late Upper Cretaceous of the western part of the North American hedreocraton is principally exogeosynclinal, but has independently sinking autogeosynclinal areas, and others of zeugeosynclinal nature adjoining rising swells in the earlier exogeosynclinal belt.

# ZOBELL
Claude Ephraim ZoBell (1904–    ), American microbiologist and oceanographer, graduated from the Southern Idaho College of Education in 1924 and received his M.S. degree from Utah State University in 1929 and his Ph.D. degree from the University of California in 1931. He joined the staff of the Scripps Institution for Oceanography, La Jolla, California, in 1932 and since 1948 he has been Professor of Microbiology there. He was a "distinguished lecturer" for the American Association of Petroleum Geologists in 1943, and from 1944 to 1950 he was a member of that organization's committee on research. The experiments and observations upon which the paper excerpted here was based were financed in part by the American Petroleum Institute.

## STUDIES ON REDOX POTENTIAL OF MARINE SEDIMENTS *

### INTRODUCTION

The oxidation-reduction or redox potential is believed to have a pronounced effect upon the composition, chemical reactivity, diagenesis, color, biological population, and other properties of recent sediments. Being a quantitative measure of the tendency of a given system to oxidize or reduce susceptible substances, the redox potential of sediments provides a criterion as to whether certain constituents occur in an oxidized or a reduced state. For example, iron could be expected to occur in the metallic or ferrous state in a highly reducing environment, whereas it ordinarily would occur in the ferric state in an oxidizing environment. This applies to a large number of other reversibly oxidizable or reducible constituents of marine sediments, both organic and inorganic.

Besides indicating the state of such constituents, the redox potential of sediments indicates whether new materials being deposited are more likely to be oxidized or reduced. The solubility of such substances as iron, manganese, copper, and certain other reversibly oxidizable minerals is influenced by the redox potential. The state of both manganese and iron in marine sediments was found by Brujevicz[1] to be a function of

*From *American Association of Petroleum Geologists Bulletin 30* (1946), 477–513.
[1]S. W. Brujevicz, "Oxidation-reduction potentials and pH of sea bottom deposits," *Verhandl. Intern. Vereinigung Theor. Angew. Limnologie 8* (1937), 35–49.

the redox potential. Pearsall and Mortimer[2] report that the state of iron, sulphur, and certain nitrogen compounds in water-logged soils is influenced by the redox potential. Allgeier *et al.*[3] find that the principal effect of the redox potential of lake deposits is on the content of ferrous iron, hydrogen sulphide, and organic matter. The redox potential of sediments is a most important factor in determining the stability and biochemical transformation of organic matter.

A good many chemical reactions which influence the diagenesis and morphology of sediments are influenced by the redox potential. According to Keaton and Kardos,[4] the redox potential of a soil may be used in the study and interpretation of the general nature of the chemical processes in the soil and the changes in these processes as affected by some external factor. Any chemical reaction which involves the exchange of electrons (and this is generally true of all oxidation and reduction reactions) will be influenced by the redox potential. . . .

The redox potential has much to do with determining the kinds, distribution and physiological activities of bacteria and allied microorganisms in sediments and there are many ways in which the activities of microorganisms influence the diagenesis of sediments.[5] Bacteria themselves appear to be the principal dynamic agents which affect the redox potential of soil and sediments. . . .

In addition to its multiple effects on the diagenesis of sediments, the redox potential is believed to influence the formation and preservation of petroleum. Highly reducing conditions favor the biochemical hydrogenation or reduction of organic matter, a process which tends to convert certain kinds of organic matter into petroleum hydrocarbons or substances which are more hydrocarbon-like than the parent substance. In oxidizing environments, organic matter is more likely to be carbonized or oxidized by microorganisms to carbon dioxide and water.

Porfiriev[6] expressed the view that the same organic matter could have been converted into either coal or petroleum, depending on the mode of fossilization and whether conditions were oxidizing or reducing. According to Stutzer and Noé[7] the redox potential of peat, which gives

[2] W. H. Pearsall and C. H. Mortimer, "Oxidation-reduction potentials in water-logged soils, natural waters and muds," *J. Ecol.* 27 (1939), 483–501.

[3] R. J. Allgeier, B. C. Hafford, and C. Juday, "Oxidation-reduction potentials and pH of lake waters and of lake sediments," *Trans. Wisconsin Acad. Sci.* 33 (1941) 115–133.

[4] C. M. Keaton and L. T. Kardos, "Oxidation-reduction potentials of arsenate-arsenite systems in sand and soil mediums," *Soil Sci.* 50 (1940), 189–207.

[5] C. E. ZoBell, "Changes produced by microorganisms in sediments after deposition," *J. Sed. Petrol. 12* (1942), 127–136; "Influence of bacterial activity on source sediments," *Oil Weekly 109* (1943), 15–26.

[6] V. B. Porfiriev, "The mode of formation of oil fields in the Central Asiatic part of the Thetis," *Abstract of Papers, Intern. Cong., 17th Sess.* (Moscow, 1937), p. 7.

[7] O. Stutzer and A. C. Noé, *Geology of Coal*, University of Chicago Press, 1940.

rise to coal, is quite different from that of the sapropel from which petroleum is believed to be derived. Since preliminary observations indicate that petroleum occurs only in highly reducing environments, it is believed that the redox potential may prove to be a significant characteristic of source sediments. Detailed data on the redox potentials of sediments may make it possible to determine the more exact nature of the diagenetic processes in general.

The potential differences across the contacts of sandstone and shale, which Dickey[8] calls "natural potentials" as differentiated from the potentials caused by electro-endosmosis and concentration differences, may be due in part to the redox potential of sedimentary rocks. While it may be far easier to measure the redox potentials of sediments (and such measurements are attended by many pitfalls) than to interpret the results, detailed studies of the redox potentials of source sediments seem to be indicated. This paper is devoted primarily to a discussion of the concepts of redox potentials and the methods of determining such potentials of sedimentary materials.

## DEFINITIONS

Oxidation-reduction potential may be defined as a quantitative measure of the energy of oxidation or the electron-escaping tendency or fugacity of a reversible oxidation-reduction system. For short, it is often referred to as the *redox* potential and is commonly abbreviated $O/R$ potential. It is sometimes called the *reduction* potential, the *oxidation* potential, or the *electrode* potential, although these terms are not necessarily synonymous. Throughout this paper, redox potential is used as synonymous with oxidation-reduction or $O/R$ potential.

The redox potential is the degree of oxidation or reduction of a reversible $O/R$ system, or it is a measure of how reducing or how oxidizing the system is with reference to some standard. When referred to hydrogen, the redox potential is commonly expressed as $E_h$ in terms of volts, $E_h$ being the potential difference between the standard hydrogen electrode and the system of which the redox potential is being measured. In some respects the $E_h$ of a system is analogous to the $pH$, and the two are closely related. Whereas the $pH$ is an expression of the hydrogen-ion ($H^+$) concentration, or the relative acidity or alkalinity of a system, the $E_h$ is an expression of the tendency of a reversible redox system to be oxidized or reduced.

Unlike the $pH$ scale, on which neutrality is defined as $pH$ 7.0, there is no true neutrality on the $E_h$ or redox potential scale. Likewise there are no readily definable upper or lower limits on the $E_h$ scale as there

[8]P. A. Dickey, "Natural potentials in sedimentary rocks," *Am. Inst. Min. Met. Eng. Tech. Publ. 1625* (1943), pp. 1–10.

are on the $pH$ scale. While it is customary to regard the $E_h$ values of the theoretical hydrogen and oxygen electrodes as the lower and upper limits respectively on the redox potential scale, there are numerous oxidizing agents such as acidic bichromate and persulfate, for example, which are more oxidizing than $O_2$, and there are numerous systems which are more reducing than $H_2$.[9]

The redox potential of a standard normal hydrogen electrode ( a solution of $H_2$ at one atmosphere pressure and $pH$ 0) is $E_h = 0$ at 25° C. The theoretical oxygen electrode at $pH$ 0 has been shown to be $E_h = 1.23$ volts. As discussed later, the $E_h$ is partly a function of the $pH$. At $pH$ 7.0 the redox potential of the hydrogen electrode is $E_h - 0.41$ volt. At $pH$ 7.0 the redox potential of the oxygen electrode is $E_h + 0.81$ volt.

According to early concepts, oxidation was regarded as a chemical reaction involving the addition of oxygen to an oxidizable substance such as ferrous oxide; for example:

$$2FeO + O \rightarrow Fe_2O_3.$$

The reverse process, or the removal of oxygen, is reduction. Later it was learned that certain substances could be oxidized or reduced without oxygen being involved. For example, on heating in the absence of oxygen, ethane is oxidized to ethylene and hydrogen:

$$\begin{matrix} CH_3 \\ | \\ CH_3 \end{matrix} + heat \rightarrow \begin{matrix} CH_2 \\ \| \\ CH_2 \end{matrix} + H_2.$$

In this case oxidation involves the loss of hydrogen. The reverse process, or the addition of hydrogen, is reduction. Thus reduction may be defined as the addition of hydrogen or the removal of oxygen, and oxidation may be defined as the addition of oxygen or the removal of hydrogen. However, certain substances may be oxidized or reduced without either oxygen or hydrogen being involved. For example, when treated with chlorine, ferrous chloride is oxidized to ferric chloride:

$$Fe^{++}Cl_2^- + Cl \rightarrow Fe^{+++}Cl_3^-.$$

When written in the ionized form, it is observed that the oxidation of iron has involved the exchange of an electron. An inspection of other oxidation or reduction reactions reveals that such reactions always involve the exchange of electrons regardless of whether oxygen or hydrogen is involved. If the iron system is considered alone, the reaction may be written:

$$Fe^{++} \rightarrow Fe^{+++} + e$$

[9] C. D. Hodgman, *Handbook of Chemistry and Physics,* 27th ed. (Cleveland: Chemical Rubber Publ. Co., 1943), p. 1345.

where $e$ represents an electron. It should be borne in mind that an electron is a negative charge. Substances or systems undergoing oxidation lose electrons while those undergoing reduction gain electrons. For every oxidation there must be a corresponding reduction.

### PHYSICOCHEMICAL CONSIDERATIONS

Since oxidation and reduction reactions are electronic migrations involving the exchange of electric charges, the intensity of redox reactions can be measured in terms of e.m.f., or electric potential differences. When an unattackable electrode (such as platinum or gold metal) is immersed in a reversible redox system, a potential difference is set up at the electrode which can be measured potentiometrically. The more highly oxidized a system is the higher will be the electrode potential, and the more reduced a system is the more negative will the potential be. Since we are dealing with reversible systems, the electrons may flow in either direction, depending on prevailing conditions. Consider the system of ferrous-ferric ions, for example:

$$Fe^{++} \rightleftarrows Fe^{+++} + e_s. \tag{1}$$

Applying the mass action chemical equilibrium equation, we get

$$\frac{(Fe^{+++}) \times (e_s)}{(Fe^{++})} = k \tag{2}$$

where $e_s$ is the concentrations of free electrons in the system and $k$ is a constant. The parentheses indicate activity concentrations. If $e_s$ is increased, reaction (1) proceeds from right to left, or ferric iron will be reduced to ferrous iron until equilibrium is established. If $e_s$ in reaction (1) is decreased, there is a tendency for ferrous iron to be oxidized to the ferric state.

An unattackable electrode immersed in the reversible redox system does not participate in the reaction but acts merely as an inert conductor of electrons to or from the system. Such an electrode can be considered to be a store of electrons of fixed concentration, $e_m$. Since the concentration or escaping tendency of electrons in the unattackable electrode, $e_m$, is different from that in the reversible redox system, $e_s$, a potential difference is set up at the electrode. It can be shown from physicochemical considerations that the work done in transferring an equivalent of electrons from the redox system to the electrode is:

$$\text{Osmotic work} = RT \ln (e_m) + RT \ln \frac{1}{(e_s)} \tag{3}$$

where $R$ is the gas constant equal to 1.99 calories per degree, $T$ is the absolute temperature and ln is natural logarithms. The work is equal to the quantity of electricity transferred multiplied by the potential at which the transfer is made:

$$\text{Electrical work} = nEF \tag{4}$$

where $n$ is the number of equivalents transferred, $E$ is the potential at which the transfer is made, and $F$ is the conversion factor, a faraday of electricity. Now combining equations (3) and (4), we get:

$$EF = RT \ln (e_m) + RT \ln \frac{1}{(e_s)} \tag{5}$$

and solving for the redox potential, $E$:

$$E = \frac{RT}{F} \ln (e_m) + \frac{RT}{F} \ln \frac{1}{(e_s)}. \tag{6}$$

Since the concentration of electrons $(e_m)$ in the unattackable electrode is a constant, $k_1$, equation (6) may be written:

$$E = k_1 + \frac{RT}{F} \ln \frac{1}{(e_s)}. \tag{7}$$

Now returning to equation (1) and making it applicable to reversible redox systems in general, rather than merely to the ferrous-ferric iron system, we may designate the reduced form of a system by Red. and the oxidized form by Ox. so that:

$$\text{Red.} \rightleftarrows \text{Ox.} + n, \tag{8}$$

where $n$ is the number of electrons. Making similar substitutions in equation (2) we get:

$$\frac{(\text{Ox.}) \times (e_s)}{(\text{Red.})} = k. \tag{9}$$

Equation (9) may be rewritten:

$$(e_s) = k \frac{(\text{Red.})}{(\text{Ox.})} \tag{10}$$

and substituting this value for $e_s$ in equation (7), we obtain:

$$E = k_2 + \frac{RT}{nF} \ln \frac{(\text{Ox.})}{(\text{Red.})} \tag{11}$$

where $k_2$ is a constant.

It is not possible to measure a single potential difference, $E$, at an electrode because this constitutes only a half-cell, but if the circuit is completed by including a standard half-cell, the e.m.f. of the completed cell may be measured. If the standard half-cell is fixed as a solution containing one atmosphere of hydrogen ($H_2$) and one normal hydrogen-ion ($H^+$) concentration, we have a normal hydrogen electrode which is the standard of reference. Electrode potentials referred to this standard are measured in volts and designated $E_h$.

$E_h = E - k_3$, where $k_3$ is the potential of the normal hydrogen electrode. Then by substituting this value for $E$ in equation (11):

$$E_h = k_2 + \frac{RT}{nF} \ln \frac{(\text{Ox.})}{(\text{Red.})} - k_3. \tag{12}$$

Now let $k_2 - k_3 = E_0$, a constant for the system:

$$E_h = E_0 + \frac{RT}{nF} \ln \frac{(\text{Ox.})}{(\text{Red.})}. \tag{13}$$

This is the general electrode equation of Peters. According to Clark, $R = 8.31507$ volt coulombs, $T$, the absolute temperature at $30°$ C. $= 303°$, and $F = 96,500$ coulombs. Substituting these values for a system in which two electrons are concerned ($n = 2$), at constant $pH$ the equation becomes:

$$E_h = E_0 + 0.03 \log \frac{(\text{Ox.})}{(\text{Red.})} \tag{14}$$

in which log represents Briggsian logarithms ($\ln x = 2.302585 \log x$). $E_h$ is measured in volts and $E_0$ is a constant for the system. (Ox.) and (Red.) are the concentrations of the oxidized and the reduced forms respectively of the redox substance. From equation (14) it is evident that the $E_h$ increases as (Ox.) increases and as (Red.) decreases. When the redox substance or system is 50 per cent oxidized (Ox.) = (Red.) and $E_h = E_0$. In other words, $E_0$ is the redox potential of a system which is 50 per cent in the oxidized form and 50 per cent in the reduced form.

.   .   .   .   .

## DISCUSSION

These studies, which are more exploratory than intensive or extensive in nature, indicate that with proper precautions it is possible to estimate the redox potential of recent marine sediments with sufficient precision to be of descriptive significance in characterizing and studying sediments. The range of redox potentials found in sediments is far greater than the range of experimental error in estimating the potentials. Redox potentials ranging from $E_h$ $+0.350$ to $-0.500$ volt have been observed in bottom deposits, homologous samples of which give $E_h$ values that are reproducible to within $\pm 0.01$ to 0.05 volt.

One of the most disconcerting features of redox potential measurements of recent marine sediments is that the redox potential of such material is a dynamic property which is in a state of constant flux. The $E_h$ of poorly poised sedimentary materials changes rapidly and appreciably with oxygen tension, bacterial activity, dilution with water, temperature, and other factors. Bacterial or enzymatic activity appears to be the most important dynamic factor which affects the redox potential of bottom deposits.

The negative drift in the redox potential of soil samples has been attributed by Heintze[10] to the organic content. It has been shown by Burrows and Cordon,[11] however, that the drift is primarily a function of bacterial activity and that the potential may be influenced by both the numbers and kinds of bacteria present. Bacterial activity is influenced by the concentration and decomposability of organic matter.

Bacterial activity in marine muds and the attendant changes in $E_h$ are appreciably accelerated by certain changes which occur during the collection of samples. A ten-fold increase in bacterial population was observed by ZoBell (1938) in mud samples stored for 7 days at 4° C., and much greater and more rapid changes occurred in mud stored at higher temperatures. This is a commentary on the necessity of making $E_h$ measurements on mud samples as soon as possible after their collection in order to obtain values which are representative of $O/R$ conditions *in situ.*

To date our efforts to find a means of stabilizing the redox potential of sediment samples have been unsuccessful because all of the substances tried for inhibiting bacterial and enzymatic activity have had a direct effect themselves on the redox potential. Volk[12] experimented with mercury compounds, copper compounds, toluene, alcohol, heat, and refrigeration as preservatives to prevent a drift in the redox potential of soil samples by bacterial activity from the time the samples were collected until $E_h$ measurements could be made. Cooling the samples to just above the freezing point and excluding atmospheric oxygen by means of nitrogen proved to be the only procedure which was at all satisfactory.

In view of the multiplicity and complexity of the factors which in-

[10] S. G. Heintze, "The use of the glass electrode in soil reaction and the oxidation-reduction potential measurements," *J. Agric. Sci. 24* (1934), 28–41.

[11] W. Burrows and T. C. Cordon, "The influence of the decomposition of organic matter on the oxidation-reduction potentials of soils," *Soil Sci. 42* (1936), 1–10.

[12] N. J. Volk, "The determinaton of redox potentials in soils," *J. Am. Soc. Agron. 31* (1939), 344–351.

fluence the redox potential of sediment samples, it is noteworthy that values characteristic for each type of sediment are obtainable. The results probably would be viewed with considerable skepticism by the physical chemist, though, because of the large experimental errors involved and particularly because the interpretation of redox potentials of sediments is affected by so many unknown factors. Wartenburg, for example, claims that any correlations between redox potentials and soil properties that have been reported are due to special circumstances and to particular methods employed, and are not explainable by the physical chemist on a basis of true theoretical considerations. The purpose of this paper, however, is to point out that while the $E_h$ values obtained for sediment samples are more descriptive than physicochemically exact, such values may prove to be a useful means of characterizing sediments, since so many chemical and biological processes which affect the diagenesis of sediments are influenced by the redox potential. The capacity factor (poise) as well as the intensity factor ($E_h$) must be taken into consideration in the characterization of sediments.

Since exploratory observations have shown oil-bearing sands and other petroliferous sediments to have a relatively high reducing intensity and a rather low reducing capacity as compared with other sediments, it is believed that these properties may be proved a significant characteristic of source beds of petroleum or producing horizons. . . .

Bacteria have a pronounced effect on the $E_h$ of the medium in which they are growing, and in turn the $E_h$ of the medium influences the growth and metabolism of bacteria. It is claimed by many workers that the growth of anaerobic bacteria is determined by the $E_h$ and not by the oxygen tension. It is a commonly reported observation that growth of anaerobes is possible in the presence of air when the $E_h$ is sufficiently low. If the $E_h$ is above the critical point, free oxygen interferes with the oxidation-reduction processes of anaerobes.

Whether the predominating type of bacterial activity is aerobic or anaerobic has a marked effect on the transformation of organic matter and certain inorganic constituents in sediments. Carbon dioxide is the principal product resulting from the aerobic attack of organic matter; anaerobic processes produce hydrogen, hydrogen sulphide, and methane along with lesser quantities of carbon dioxide. As far as is known, hydrogen, hydrogen sulphide, and methane are produced only under anaerobic conditions or at a low $E_h$. The formation of these gases is believed to be associated with petroleum genesis. Moreover, there is accumulating evidence that petroleum hydrocarbons will be produced by bacteria or accumulate in recent sediments only when the $E_h$ is low. Nearly all kinds of hydrocarbons are susceptible to bacterial oxidation under aerobic conditions, according to ZoBell *et al.*,[13] but under anaerobic conditions hydrocarbons are attacked very slowly by bacteria or not at all. For purposes of this discussion conditions may be regarded as anaerobic when the redox potential is negative to $E_h$ −0.1 volt.

． ． ． ． ．

## CONCLUSIONS

The $E_h$ of recent marine sediments ranges from +0.350 to −0.500 volt and $p$H ranges from 6.4 to 9.5. Each type of sediment appears to have its own characteristic $E_h$ and $p$H. Bottom deposits rich in organic matter and bacteria are generally reducing. Negative $E_h$ values or reducing conditions are also a property of fine sediments; coarser sediments are generally less reducing. Positive $E_h$ values are found in well-oxygenated bottoms. As a very general rule the $E_h$ and redox capacity decrease with core depth; the $p$H increases. The reducing conditions found in bottom deposits are attributed to the activity of bacteria which oxidize organic matter. Once created, the reducing conditions are maintained by certain organic compounds, ferrous iron, reduced manganese, hydrogen sulphide, and other inorganic constitents in sediments.

It is believed that detailed data on the redox potential of sediments will contribute to an understanding of the morphology, general nature, and diagenesis of sediments. Such data may find their most important application in the study and characterization of source sediments of petroleum.

# MACKIN
Joseph Hoover Mackin (1905– ), American geologist, received his baccalaureate degree from New York University in 1930 and his doctorate from Columbia University in 1937. He has been a member of the faculty of the University of Washington (Seattle) since 1932 and Professor of Geology there since 1947. From 1943 to 1954 he was also on the staff of the U. S. Geological Survey. His training as an engineer and his interest in engineering geology enable him to make an unusually perceptive approach to the problems of geomorphology, especially to those encountered in quantitative studies of the geologic work of rivers.

## CONCEPT OF THE GRADED RIVER *

The concept of grade, as a condition of equilibrium in streams as agents of transportation, has been the fundamental basis for the understanding of fluvial landforms for the last half century. The geologic lit-

[13]C. E. ZoBell, C. W. Grant, and H. F. Haas, "Marine microorganisms which oxidize petroleum hydrocarbons," *Bull. Am. Assn. Petrol. Geol. 27* (1943), 1175–1193.
*From *Geological Society of America Bulletin 59* (1948), 463–512.

erature contains, however, a number of markedly different definitions of the concept, and many geologists have been troubled by its defects and inconsistencies. An analysis of some of these difficulties leads Kesseli,[1] to conclude that the views of Gilbert[2] and Davis[3] regarding the equilibrium relationship are untenable and that the concept of grade must be abandoned. This article is an outgrowth of studies of stream planation surfaces in Wyoming,[4] was started several years before Kesseli's critique was published, and is a revision of the concept rather than a defense of the writings of Gilbert and Davis.

The engineering literature provides a counterpart for the concept of grade in the idea of the "adjusted" or "regime" condition in streams. The engineer is concerned primarily with short-term reactions of adjusted streams to damming, shortening, and deepening operations and other river training measures. The geologist sees erosional and depositional features in valleys as records of the long-term response of the graded stream to various natural changes in conditions controlling its activity. These natural changes in control are in many instances closely comparable with those introduced by man. Because they are a good test of the concept of the graded or adjusted condition, a number of paired examples of long- and short-term reactions of streams to analogous changes are brought together here; citations are drawn about equally from geologic and engineering writings.

There is much of common interest in this type of synthesis, but the geologist and the engineer differ widely in background and habits of thought, and an attempt to bridge the gap requires certain compromises in use of terms and manner of treatment. General policies are as follows:

(1) Future advances in knowledge of stream processes will certainly be based increasingly on quantitative measurement and mathematical analysis. But the quantitative aspects of transportation by running water are controversial and are not essential for an evaluation of the concept of grade; the treatment here is qualitative. If, by clarifying some of the genetic aspects of the problem in qualitative terms, or focusing attention on them, the article clears the way for more rapid quantitative advances, it will have served part of its purpose.

(2) There are two possible approaches to the study of streams as agents of transportation: (A) in terms of relationships between slope, discharge, channel form, and the size of grains comprising the load; and (B) in terms of energy transformations. Preferably, the two should not be com-

[1] John E. Kesseli, "The concept of the graded river," *J. Geol. 49* (1940), 561–588.

[2] G. K. Gilbert, *Report on Geology of the Henry Mountains,* U. S. Geog. Geol. Survey, Rocky Mountain Region, 1877.

[3] W. M. Davis, "Base level, grade and peneplain," *J. Geol. 10* (1902), 77–111.

[4] J. Hoover Mackin, "The capture of the Greybull River," *Am. J. Sci.* [5] *31,* 373–385; "Erosional history of the Big Horn Basin," *Bull. Geol. Soc. Am. 48* (1937), 813–894.

bined. But they *are* combined in most of the papers cited, and, while the thesis of this article depends wholly on the first approach, some discussion of energy transformations is necessary. The manner in which the term energy is used is well established in the literature; it may be regarded by the specialist as loose, but he will be merely irritated rather than misled.

(3) Transporting power is considered to be a function of *velocity,* rather than the *depth-slope* (tractive force) *relationship* that forms the basis for many mathematical treatments of transportation. This usage has the advantage of simplicity and, for present purposes, the differences are negligible. . . .

. . . . .

A graded stream is not then, strictly speaking, one in which there is "a balance between total energy and the work given the stream to do," or in which "energy supplied equals energy consumed"; a non-accelerating flow of water carrying no load in a flume or a bed-rock channel fulfills these requirements, but would hardly be considered graded in the geologic sense. It is not a stream in which "slope is adjusted to load"; the carrying power of a stream is a function of velocity, and slope is only one of the factors which bear on velocity. One of the attributes of a graded stream is a "balance between erosion and deposition," but definition of the condition of grade in terms of this balance, and emphasis on the "constant shifting" of the balance, is unfortunate because it focuses attention on incidental short-term changes in the activity of the stream and loses sight of the long-term balance which is the distinctive characteristic of the stream at grade. A graded stream is not a stream "loaded to capacity" because streams never carry a capacity load (by Gilbert's definition). These definitions are partly or basically sound, but all of them include half-truths that are sources of confusion.

A graded stream is not in any sense a stream which is unable to abrade its bed because "all of its energy is used in transportation," or because "transporting the load requires all the energy that was formerly (during youth) applied to downcutting." The particles comprising the load are the tools used in abrasion, and since abrasion does not involve a dissipation of energy independent of that consumed in the propulsion of the tools, abrasion may be regarded as an incidental result of the bouncing, sliding, and rolling motion of the particles.

*A graded stream is one in which, over a period of years, slope is delicately adjusted to provide, with available discharge and with prevailing channel characteristics, just the velocity required for the transportation of the load supplied from the drainage basin. The graded stream is a system in equilibrium; its diagnostic characteristic is that any change in any of the controlling factors will cause a displacement of the equilibrium in a direction that will tend to absorb the effect of the change.*

By *stream* we mean, of course, that particular segment with which we are directly concerned; many rivers have both graded and ungraded parts. The expression *over a period of years* rules out seasonal and other short-term fluctuations on the one hand and, on the other, the exceedingly slow changes that accompany the progress of the erosion cycle. *Load* and *discharge* deserve the prominence given in the definition not because they are the only or even necessarily the most important factors controlling slope, but because they are the only factors which are, *in origin,* wholly independent of the stream. *Slope* stands alone because it appears to be the only factor in the equilibrium which is automatically adjustable by the stream itself in such a direction as to accommodate changes in external controls that call for changes in velocity.

The balance involved in the condition of grade can be stated in an equation, but this method of expression is inadequate for present purposes because the terms of an equation are transposable. As set up in an equation, for example, load is a function of velocity. In answer to a query as to which is the cause and which is the effect, the average engineer will assert that velocity controls or determines the load that is carried by a stream; and he may have misgivings as to the sanity of the party who raised the question. In a flume or rock-floored torrent, velocity does, in a sense, determine the load that can be carried. But, over a period of years, the load supplied to a stream is actually dependent, not on the velocity of the stream, but on the lithology, relief, vegetative cover, and erosional processes in operation in its drainage basin, and, in the graded stream, that particular slope is maintained which will provide just the velocity required to transport all of the supplied load. In this very real sense velocity is determined by, or adjusted to, the load. In the graded stream, load is a cause, and velocity is an effect: this relationship is not transposable.

· · · · ·

It has been repeatedly emphasized that the declivity of the graded stream is controlled by load (and other factors); the declivity is adjusted to furnish just the velocity required for the transportation of all the load supplied to the stream. In the aggrading stream the supplied load does not control declivity in the same degree because, by definition, *all* of the supplied load is not transported. But it is important to recognize that the amount of material moved through any segment of the channel of the aggrading stream in any interval of time is enormously greater than the amount deposited, and that even in the aggrading stream the declivity of each segment is *approximately* adjusted to the load in transit through that segment. In general, with decrease in the discrepancy between the supplied load and the load in transit, the aggrading stream approaches the graded condition.

No generalization can be made with regard to the average steepness of the profiles of graded and aggrading streams as such; both may vary from a small fraction of a foot to hundreds of feet per mile. But an exceedingly useful generalization can be made with regard to a contrast in the *form* of the profiles of graded and aggrading streams. Since declivity is in general adjusted to caliber of load in transit, and since the downvalley decrease in caliber of load in aggrading streams (by attrition, sorting, and exchange) is much more rapid than the downvalley decrease in caliber of load in graded streams (by attrition), it follows that declivity should decrease in a downvalley direction much more rapidly in the aggrading stream than in the graded stream under otherwise similiar conditions. The profile of aggradation should be, in other words, more strongly "concave upward" than the graded profile. Thus, while the profile of the graded stream usually shows no tendency to be asymptotic with respect to a horizontal plane passing through a downvalley control point, the profile of the aggrading stream should and usually does show a definite tendency in this direction.

The writer has found two "rules" that follow from the discussion above to be useful tools in field study and interpretation of terraces of many types in stream valleys: (1) If there is any considerable length of stream upvalley from a given segment, aggradational channel deposits in that segment are so consistently finer in grain size than earlier or later deposits formed when the stream was at grade that variation in grain size and sorting serves as a criterion, for example, in distinguishing between channel deposits laid down in a valley-filling stage and the channel gravel sheet that mantles terraces cut in the fill during a subsequent degradational stage. (2) Aggradational profiles (recorded by terrace remnants) are usually steeper than earlier or later graded profiles in the upper parts of proglacial valleys, but the contrast in slope decreases in a downvalley direction and may be reversed, so that the aggradational profile is less steep than the graded profile in the vicinity of a downvalley control point. . . .

The principal conclusion, that the concept of the graded stream as a system in equilibrium is valid, is based on:

(1) Citation of broad valley floors cut by long-continued planation

at the same level by high-gradient streams crossing rock types of vary-ing resistance to corrasion;

(2) Analysis of the form of the longitudinal profile developed and maintained by the graded stream under stable conditions, demonstrat-ing by citation of cases that, in each segment, slope is adjusted to pro-vide, with available discharge and under prevailing channel conditions, just the velocity required for transportation of all of the load supplied to that segment without regard for variation in resistance to corrasion in the subjacent materials; and,

(3) an outline of the manner in which graded streams readjust them-selves to natural and man-made changes in controlling conditions of several types, demonstrating that the stream responds to such changes always so as to "absorb the effect of the stress," and thus exhibits the chief and diagnostic characteristic of the equilibrium system.

A critical point in connection with (2) is that, because in a trunk stream conditions controlling slope do not vary systematically from seg-ment to segment, the longitudinal profile cannot be a simple mathe-matical curve. This conclusion is qualitative; if, in conformity with it, we cease to smooth out real departures from uniformity and center the attack on them, with an adequate understanding of the genetic relation-ships of the independent and interdependent factors involved, then mathematical analysis of longitudinal profiles will advance our knowl-edge of streams.

A second generalization, important because it has been so generally neglected in geologic writings, is that the slope of the graded profile is adjusted to, or controlled by, not only the classic "load and discharge" but also the cross-sectional form and alignment of the channel—the more efficient the channel, the lower the slope.

In connection with (3) the present study tends to confirm the standard geologic view that streams readjust themselves to new conditions pri-marily by adjustments in slope, and only in minor degree by modifica-tion of the channel section. This statement is so phrased as to avoid any semblance of a "law"—certainly no fetish attaches to slope, and each individual case must be judged on the basis of the evidence. But it does appear that, confronted by changed conditions that call for in-creased or decreased energy for transportation, the stream usually responds by increasing or decreasing its total energy by appropriate adjustments in slope rather than by effecting economies in the energy dissipated in friction.

Additional generalizations include the distinction between "upvalley" and "downvalley" changes in control and between "upvalley" and "down-valley" reactions of the stream to a given change, the contrast between the form of the disadjusted profile during the period of readjustment and the final readjusted profile, and the effect of secondary changes in control on the slope of the readjusted profile.

With a few minor lapses, this paper does not treat the practical implications of the concept of grade. In geology these ramify widely, ranging from the power of rivers to corrade laterally to interpretation of ancient fluvial sediments and the origin of unconformities beneath and within them. In connection with control of rivers by men, a safe general implication is that the engineer who alters natural equilibrium relations by diversion or damming or channel-improvement measures will often find that he has a bull by the tail and is unable to let go—as he continues to correct or suppress undesirable phases of the chain reaction of the stream to the initial "stress" he will necessarily place increasing emphasis on study of the genetic aspects of the equilibrium in order that he may work *with* rivers, rather than merely *on* them. It is certain that the long-term response of streams to the operations of the present generation of engineers will provide much employment for future generations of engineers and lawyers.

In this connection the most important point brought out by the study may well be the striking analogy between the streams' response to the works of man and to accidents and interruptions due to geologic causes. Nature has brought to bear on streams nearly all of the changes in controlling conditions that are involved in modern engineering works; the record of the long-term reaction of rivers to past geologic changes that is revealed by terraces and in dissected valley fills should contribute much to an understanding of the future of streams that man seeks to control, and will call for changes in design. Conversely, every advance in knowledge of erosional, transportation, and sedimentation processes deriving from engineering investigations will increase the geologist's ability to interpret the record of the past. As the engineer becomes more and more concerned with the genetic aspects of his especial problems (as he must), and as the geologist learns more about the quantitative aspects of his especial problems (as *he* must), it will become evident that the problems are in large measure the same.

# SCHOTT Wolfgang Ernst Schott (1905– ), German geologist, received his doctorate from Göttingen University in 1930, taught geology at Rostock University for several years, and from 1936 to 1940 was a geologist in the Reichsamt für Bodenforschung in Berlin. Since 1953 he has been a professor at Göttingen University. His report on the bottom samples collected by

the oceanographic vessel *Meteor* on its 1925–1927 voyage is a classic document in the annals of physical oceanology.

## INTERPRETATION OF THE STRATIGRAPHIC DISTRIBUTION OF FORAMINIFERA IN BOTTOM SAMPLES FROM THE EQUATORIAL ATLANTIC OCEAN *

From the location of the faunistic zones in which *Globorotalia menardii* disappears and reappears, it becomes evident beyond doubt that we are dealing with two planes of separation that pass through all profiles of stations which penetrated the three layers. In consequence, the corresponding points in the boring samples have been connected in the profiles. The origin of these faunistic separations can be explained by the regional distribution of those Foraminifera which have chiefly caused them. The spatial distribution of those Foraminifera below the upper faunistic separation (that is, in the layer devoid of *Globorotalia menardii*) can be compared with that found on the bottom of the sea today. Below the first faunistic separation, *G. menardii* is completely absent, except for Stations 259, 279, 280, 284, and 285 where there are still traces of it. *Globigerina bulloides* and *Globigerina inflata,* on the other hand, are much more abundant in the layer devoid of *Globorotalia menardii* throughout the examined area and occur there in the individual stations more abundantly on a percentage basis than on the bottom of the sea today. . . .

The more frequent occurrence of the Foraminifera *Globigerina bulloides* and *Globigerina inflata,* which today live predominantly in cooler water, as well as the absence of the warmth-preferring *Globorotalia menardii* (widespread today) in the layer devoid of that species, permits the assumption that during the sedimentation of that layer the surface water of the equatorial Atlantic Ocean was cooler than it is today. This decline in temperature of equatorial ocean water must be attributed to the influence of the Ice Age. Diverse investigations, including those by Milankovitch of variations in solar radiation, indicate that no significantly cooler climatic conditions have prevailed during post-glacial time, relative to those of today. It must be inferred, therefore, that the layer devoid of *Globorotalia menardii* was accumulated during the Ice Age and that the reappearance of *G. menardii* indicates the warming of ocean water at the start of post-glacial time. . . .

Inasmuch as the disappearance of *G. menardii* was caused by a de-

* From *Wissenschaftliche Ergebnisse der Deutschen Atlantischen Expedition auf dem Forschungsund Vermessungsschiff "Meteor" 1925–1927,* vol. III, pt. 3, (Berlin and Leipzig, 1937), pp. 43–134. This excerpt, translated by Robert G. Wertheimer and Kirtley F. Mather, is from pp. 120–130.

cline in temperature of the equatorial surface water in the diluvial period, and the red clay under the Globigerina ooze is explained by a considerable extension of the Antarctic bottom current during the diluvial period, we can interpret the upper faunistic limit at which *G. menardii* disappears and the stratigraphic change, Globigerina ooze/red clay, as excellent examples of climatic layering in sediments.[1] . . .

During the Ice Age in the polar regions, the pluvial period prevailed in equatorial latitudes, and this caused increased erosion on land and hence a greater transport of terrigenous materials to the ocean. Thus is explained the deposition of blue clay during the Ice Age in areas distant from the coast where Globigerina ooze is today accumulating. At the end of the diluvial period there was a reverse extension of the Globigerina ooze toward the coast to cover the blue clay. Like the earlier extension of the Globigerina ooze over the red clay, this was a result of the climatic change during the transition from the diluvial period to post-glacial time; hence it could also be called a climatic transgression. It seems to have continued into post-glacial time in certain places along the African coast. At stations near that coast between Cape Palmas and Cape Verde where Globigerina ooze overlies blue clay, the upper faunistic *G. menardii* zone, indicating the end of the diluvial period, is found at a lower level than the stratigraphic contact, Globigerina ooze/blue clay. This means that the Globigerina ooze has arrived there somewhat later and during the post-glacial period.

No definitive interpretation of this delayed extension of Globigerina ooze in post-glacial time can be made from the data now available. The following two possibilities exist, of which the first is more likely the correct explanation. Perhaps, in this area between Cape Palmas and Cape Verde along the African coast, the increased transport of terrigenous material during the pluvial post-glacial period continued for some time, so that the Globigerina ooze could only later extend into this area. On the other hand, this extension of Globigerina ooze in post-glacial time could have been caused, according to Suess, by a positive shift in the shore, corresponding to a moving-back of the African coast. That speculation would have a certain amount of confirmation in such submarine features as the trench trending south to north, known as the Bottomless Pit, off the Upper Guinea coast, and the Congo Trench.

Beneath the layer devoid of *G. menardii* encountered in various deep-sample probing tests, *G. menardii* is again found. In general, the fauna of the second layer with abundant *G. menardii* at the different stations is quite similar to its distribution on the sea floor at the present time.

[1] R. Brinkmann, "Über die Schichtung und ihre Bedingungen," *Fortschr. Geol. Palaeontol. 11* (1932), 189, 203.

It can be assumed, therefore, that the physical and chemical properties of surface water, and hence the living conditions for the pelagic Foraminifera, in the examination area were at that time about the same as today. It is most probable, therefore, that these layers were formed in the interglacial period and that the second faunistic *G. menardii* zone also represents a climatic stratum. At Stations 284 and 285 and at a depth of about 35 cm at Stations 279 and 280, the fauna of the second layer with abundant *G. menardii* contains many specimens of *Globorotalia tumida,* similar to the modern assemblage, whereas at Stations 307 and 258 very few representatives of that species are present. Whether this conspicuous increase and decrease of *Globorotalia tumida* which is chiefly found at great depths on the modern ocean floor was a result of rise and fall of the ocean floor cannot be judged with certainty from this limited material. Inasmuch as four stations show a fauna similar to that of today in the two layers with abundant *G. menardii,* no significant bottom changes seem to have occurred in the interim. Lithologically, the second faunistic *G. menardii* zone at Station 217 is marked by a clay layer; at Station 256 by a thin dark-striped layer; and at Station 257 by a red-brown stratum which probably is an immersion layer. At Stations 217 and 256 the upper faunistic limit coincides with the lithologic change (Globigerina ooze/red clay). In all other stations where the upper faunistic limit is not lithologically significant, the second faunistic limit is similarly not marked by a lithologic change.

After the attempt to give an interpretation of the stratigraphic layers according to the foraminiferal fauna in the ocean sediments, a few regional considerations should be added about the conditions which prevailed in the examined parts of the Atlantic Ocean during the last Ice Age, while the layer devoid of *Globorotalia menardii* was being deposited, insofar as these conditions can be deduced from the individual profiles.

A comparison of the spatial distribution of *Globigerina bulloides* and *Globigerina inflata* in sea-floor sediments of the present time with that in the layer devoid of *Globorotalia menardii* indicates that the South Equatorial Current and the outer margin of the Canary Current in the vicinity of the Cape Verde Islands, and hence also the Canary Current itself, were already present during the Ice Age. In consequence the change in ocean currents, assumed by Köppen and Wegener to have occurred during the diluvial period as a result of a shift of the equator, cannot be supported for the last Ice Age. The frequent and more abundant occurrence of *Globigerina bulloides* and *Globigerina inflata* in these areas is connected with the decline in temperature of the surface water; a stronger flow of these ocean currents cannot be accepted as an explanation. On the contrary, the disappearance of warmth-preferring *Globoro-*

*talia menardii* in the entire area of examination, during the diluvial period, points definitely to a decline in temperature. *G. menardii* seems to have withdrawn to a region west of the Cape Verde Islands during the last Ice Age; several stations in that region show some traces of that species in the zone elsewhere devoid of it.

It can be assumed with certainty that during the last Ice Age the Atlantic Ridge already protruded as a swelling from the ocean floor in the examined area. The isopleths showing the numbers of Foraminifera in one-gram samples from the layer devoid of *G. menardii* trace the area of the Atlantic Ridge in the same way that such isopleths outline it today. Regions with less than 100 Foraminifera in a gram sample were, however, more widespread in the diluvial period than they are at the present time. This is largely a result of the more widespread distribution of clay sediments, poor in Foraminifera. Moreover, the number of Foraminifera in a gram of dry sample was generally smaller during the Ice Age, presumably as a result of poorer living conditions at that time; also, the number of different species shows a general decline, relative to the present.

·  ·  ·  ·  ·

The approximate rate of sedimentation of recent ocean deposits can be computed from the thickness of the upper layer with abundant *Glo-*

Table 1

Thickness and sedimentation rates of recent sediments since the end of the diluvial period in the Equatorial Atlantic Ocean

| Kind of sediment: | Blue clay | Globigerina ooze | Red clay |
|---|---|---|---|
| Average thickness in centimeters | 35.5 | 24.06 | 17.14 |
| Maximum observed thickness in centimeters | 66.0 | 42.5 | 26.5 |
| Minimum observed thickness in centimeters | 18.0 | 10.5 | < 10.0 |
| Average sedimentation rate in cm per 1000 yrs | 1.78 | 1.2 | < 0.86 |
| Maximum sedimentation rate in cm per 1000 yrs | 3.3 | 2.13 | 1.33 |
| Minimum sedimentation rate in cm per 1000 yrs | 0.9 | 0.53 | < 0.5 |
| Number of samples used | 6 | 48 | 7 |

*borotalia menardii*, deposited since the start of the post-glacial period. According to various authors (Penck, Bruecker, Brooks, Soergel) the post-glacial period in the northern hemisphere started about 20,000 years ago. The results of computations, using that figure, are shown in Table 1.

· · · · ·

According to the sedimentation rates [given in the table above] . . . the layer devoid of *Globorotalia menardii* would seem to correspond to the very last ice age, the Baltic Advance.[2] The material of the second layer with abundant *G. menardii* would presumably have been deposited in the interglacial period prior to the Baltic Advance.

# HESS
Harry Hammond Hess (1906–    ), American geologist, graduated from Yale in 1927, received his Ph.D. degree from Princeton in 1932, became a member of the Princeton faculty in 1934, and since 1950 has been chairman of the department of geology there. His interest in submarine geology stems in part from his service as geologist on gravity measuring cruises of U. S. submarines during the 1930's and as an officer on ships of the U. S. Navy in the Pacific Ocean during the Second World War.

## DROWNED ANCIENT ISLANDS OF THE PACIFIC BASIN*

A large number of curious, flat-topped peaks have been discovered scattered over millions of square miles in the Pacific basin. These peaks are roughly oval in plan and their slopes suggest volcanic cones. The remarkable feature about them is that they are truncated by a level surface which now stands approximately 750 fathoms (4500 feet) below sea level. For convenience in discussing these submerged flat-topped peaks which rise from the normal ocean floor, the writer will henceforth call them "guyots" after the 19th century geographer, Arnold Guyot.

· · · · ·

When the writer first discovered guyots, he supposed that they were drowned atolls. However, this hypothesis proved untenable upon further study. A profile of an atoll should show a rise along the outer margin representing the area of active reef growth and should be dished in the middle, the lagoon, unless it were filled in with younger sediments. On

[2]W. Soergel, "Die Gliederung und absolute Zeitrechnung des Eiszeitalters," *Fortschr. Geol. Palaeontol. 4,* no. 13 (1925).
*From *American Journal of Science* 244 (1946), 772–791.

an atoll, the profile breaks abruptly outside of the living reef and descends in slopes averaging about 25°. There is no feature comparable to the gently sloping shelf found around the flat tops of nearly all guyots. In fact there seems to be no way of accounting for these shelves unless the guyots had developed in a sea which did not support reef-building organisms.

It may reasonably be assumed that guyots were originally volcanic peaks. After a long period of time they became stabilized and were eroded down to low relief. At this time they developed gently sloping shelves around them as might be expected in the case of a maturely dissected island. This was followed by a long period of marine planation, unhampered by reef growth, ultimately forming the flat upper surfaces. If marine planation cut the island down to about 30 fathoms below sea level then the outer margin of the gently sloping shelves, normally some 70 fathoms deeper, would have originally represented approximately a 100-fathom-curve around the island.

Possibilities of accounting for the reef-free surface of the guyots by some connection with a glacial epoch were considered and rejected. If reef growth had been inhibited by a glacial epoch, the guyots would have had to have suffered marine planation followed by sudden subsidence to below the level at which reef growth would recommence at the end of the glacial epoch—a coincidence which makes the hypothesis very unlikely. The glacial epoch would have had to be a very long one to permit complete planation of the larger guyots. It cannot possibly be referred to the Pleistocene epoch since the Marshall Islands atolls are younger than the guyots and there could obviously not have been time for marine planation, subsidence and upbuilding of the atolls all in this short epoch aside from the inconsistency that the cold water was called upon to keep the guyot surface reef-free but later on permitted the upbuilding of the atolls.

·　·　·　·　·

## Hypothetical Development of the History of the Pacific Basin and the Origin of Guyots

Most discussions of Pacific historical geology jam all the known history into the late Tertiary, Pleistocene and Recent ages. To be sure, the rocks visible on the surface of volcanic islands are mostly very young, predominantly Recent plus some Pleistocene and very rarely rocks that can be demonstrated to be as old as Tertiary. Many writers seem inclined to place Pacific atoll formation in the Pleistocene though others extend it back into the Tertiary.[1] On the other hand the Pacific Basin is generally considered to be very old, probably dating from early Pre-Cambrian time.[2] It seems reasonable to suppose that volcanic activity in the Pacific Basin and hence island formation has gone on sporadically since early Pre-Cambrian. Where then are the Pre-Cambrian, Paleozoic and Mesozoic islands? In order to answer this it is necessary to digress along several other channels.

Any island formed in the Basin can be assumed to have begun as a volcano or group of volcanoes. After vulcanism ceased and the island had become stabilized, the following sequence of events would necessarily take place. The island would be eroded to low relief, and after a long period of time (providing growth of reef-forming organisms did not interfere) the island would completely disappear as a result of marine planation. Such must have been the fate of all Pre-Cambrian islands before reef-forming organisms existed.

Kuenen[2] has concluded that there has been little change of sea level since early Pre-Cambrian time. He estimated that the rate of sedimentation in the deep sea is approximately 1 cm in 10,000 years for red clay, since the end of the Pre-Cambrian, and 1 cm in 5000 years for globigerina ooze. Since most of the material deposited on the ocean floor has ultimately come from the continents, isostatic adjustment of the load on the sea floor and the loss of weight from the continents has resulted in the sinking of the former and rise of the latter so that relative sea level with respect to the continents has not changed very much. One obviously cannot put a layer of several thousand feet of sediments into the oceans without causing the water to rise by an equivalent amount (less the water included in pore space in the sediments). Thus, quite apart from the discussion of isostatic adjustment mentioned above, every centimeter of sediment put into the ocean causes sea level to rise with respect to an oceanic island by just a little less than a centimeter (less by the amount of water in pore space of the sediment). Even though the figure cited for the rate of sedimentation may be inaccurate it nevertheless follows that oceanic islands are and have always been slowly sinking relative to sea level.

It stands to reason that once lime-secreting organisms appeared in the oceans, presumably in Cambrian time, they would grow upon any available shallow, wave-cut platform and both tend to protect it from further wave action and build it up to sea level. These reef-forming organisms need not have been very efficient reef builders to keep pace with a settling rate of 1 cm in perhaps 5000 years. So that beginning

[1] H. T. Stearns, *Am. J. Sci.* 244 (1946), 245–262.
[2] Ph. H. Kuenen, *Am. J. Sci.* [5] 43 (1937), 457–468; *ibid.* 239 (1941), 161–190.

in Cambrian time every island in warm seas which at that time had not been submerged below the level at which these organisms could live, would be built up to sea level or nearly to sea level and could henceforth maintain its growth. In other words all Paleozoic, Mesozoic and Tertiary islands which were eroded to low relief and submerged in warm seas must inevitably become banks or atolls and be maintained as such throughout the remainder of geologic time except for the interference of some rare diastrophic accident. Epochs of glaciation might inhibit growth of reef-forming organisms temporarily. But these epochs are too short to permit the islands to sink to such a level that growth would not recommence with the return of warmer water.

We may now turn to the ultimate objective of this long series of digressions, the guyots. It is proposed that they represent the relics of Pre-Cambrian islands formed by the processes suggested above. The group of guyots with which we have been mainly concerned range from 520 to 960 fathoms (3120 to 5760 feet) below sea level. Accepting Kuenen's figures for accumulation of sediments, at least 2000 feet of sediments (solid) would have been deposited in the deep sea since Pre-Cambrian time. The great bulk of sediments, however, are deposited along continental margins, on the shelves, slopes and shallow epeiric seas. It is almost impossible to estimate the amount of water displaced by these inasmuch as a thickness of tens of thousands of feet may displace only a relatively small amount of water since the bottom of such basins of sediments tend to sink isostatically under the load. These thick prisms of sediments may at a later time be deformed and welded to the continents, thereby enlarging the continents at the expense of the oceans. Certainly these processes have decreased the areal extent of the oceans a considerable if unpredictable amount since the end of the Pre-Cambrian. If sediments deposited in shallow waters around the continents displaced only half as much water as deep-sea sediments, an estimate which seems to the writer to be on the conservative side, then one could account for a rise of sea level relative to an oceanic island of 3000 feet (500 fathoms) since the end of the Pre-Cambrian which is comparable to the present depth of the shallowest guyots. Thus we might attribute most guyots to a Proterozoic episode of vulcanism. The occasional, less well-preserved surfaces mentioned in the text, having depths between 1100 and 1900 fathoms, might be older and well back in the Pre-Cambrian in age.

# BELOUSOV Vladimir Vladimirovich Belousov (1907–    ), Russian geologist, completed his formal training in geology at the University of Moscow in 1930. For the next eleven years he lived and worked in Lenin-

grad. Since 1942 he has been living in Moscow where he is Director of the Department of Geodynamics in the Institute of Earth Physics, Academy of Sciences of the USSR, as well as a professor at the State University. His principal research has been in tectonics, and his field studies have involved widely separated areas in the Soviet Union as well as the Eastern and French Alps and parts of China. He is largely responsible for the present status of geotectonic theory in the Soviet Union, the validity of which is now (1965) being appraised by geologists of other nations as well as by his compatriots.

## MECHANICS OF THE FORMATION OF FOLDS *

Study of folding deformations in the crust allows us to establish the presence of two main types of folding. The first type is characteristic of folded zones (geosynclines) and is expressed as an alternation of linearly elongated folds that more or less uniformly cover the area. This folding can be called complete or linear. The second type is found mainly on the platforms. It is represented by domelike or wavelike uplifts of the layers; these uplifts are often discontinuous throughout the area. Such folding can be called discontinuous or domelike folding.

Complete folding is characterized by the following features:
(a) continuity of development within the folded zone;
(b) uniform development of anticlines and synclines;
(c) linearity;
(d) horizontal movement of material, expressed in the regular dip of the folds.

In its typical manifestation, discontinuous folding is characterized by:
(a) discontinuity (local character) of the folds;
(b) nonuniform development of anticlines and synclines—along with clearly expressed anticlines, synclines are often absent, being replaced by residual depressions with almost horizontal beds;
(c) absence of linearity—domelike forms predominate;
(d) absence of horizontal movement of material—the dip of the folds is not regular, and changes even within a single fold.

The problem of the conditions of formation of local folds offers less difficulty than that of the mechanics of complete folding. The principal morphologic features of local folds attest that such folds are formed by vertical, upwardly directed tectonic forces; hence, their local character and the sharp predominance of anticlines, with wide development of flexures and vertical faults.

Local folds (domes) commonly flatten out upward; this is connected with the decreasing thickness of deposits from the flanks of the dome

* From "Mekhanizm obrazovaniia skladchatosti," *Compt. Rend., XIX Congres Géologique International,* Algeria, sec. 3, pt. 3 (1953), 183–190. Translated by John B. Southard.

toward the crest. Some layers completely wedge out toward the crest. Such a change in thickness is often connected with facies changes: the deposits become coarser and shallower-water toward the crest. These features of discontinuous folds attest that they are uplifted gradually over a long time, concurrently with deposition of the sediments. Because deposition requires subsidence, the entire process must be thought of as a gradual uprising of folds on a background of more general subsidence of the crust. However, we find nonuniformity in the uplift of discontinuous folds: from time to time the uplift slowed down and perhaps ceased altogether, and from time to time was broken by sharp "jumps," which led to uplift of the crest above sea level and to erosion of part of the sediments.

Discontinuous folding is developed primarily on the platforms. But there it is restricted mainly to regions of relative subsidence of the crust—syneclises. In this, however, discontinuous folding is more intense in syneclises located in relatively younger parts of a platform, principally along the platform margins.

There is a connection between discontinuous folds and the configuration of the syneclises to which they are restricted; wavelike, elongated discontinuous folds are parallel to the margins of the syneclises, or, more precisely, are parallel to the isopachs.

The forms of individual discontinuous folds are exceedingly diverse, determined by the intensity of the vertical forces in one place or another, their areal distribution, and the mechanical properties of this part of the crust.

In a number of cases we can establish a change in the form of continous folds with depth. A fold expressed at the surface by a plastic flexure of layers may be expressed at depth by a block uplift of the basement. In gentle discontinuous folds we often observe, with depth, a displacement of the crest, a breaking apart of the crest into several partial uplifts, and even a replacement of uplifts by depressions. In many cases such changes attest to migration of the place of maximum uplift through time, and change in the configuration of uplift through time. Some discontinuous folds grow at the site of previous local downwarp of the crust.

On the flanks of some domelike discontinous folds have been noted very small linear folds (with dimensions of the order of meters and tens of meters) expressed as sharp flexures of beds and arranged concentrically with respect to the dome. To explain them we can make the following hypothesis. Upwardly directed forces causing uplift of the fold meet a strong resistance from the layers that are being flexed and extended; in these conditions the layers on the crest of the dome are compressed, and some of them, the most plastic, are spread out vertically and their material is pressed out in layers on the flanks of the dome, where they are crowded together to form small disharmonic folds.

The problem of the mechanics and conditions of formation of complete folding is much more complex. This type of folding causes great divergences of opinion among geologists.

These divergences of opinion already appear in the question of the development of complete folding with time; is it formed, as with discontinuous folding, slowly and gradually, concurrently with sedimentation, or is it formed by "jumps," or short phases? Analysis of the existing factual material shows that to a considerable degree these divergences of opinion are caused by misunderstandings; the presence of two different types of folding is not always taken into account, and observations made on discontinuous folding are automatically transferred to continuous folding. Such a misunderstanding is possible especially because discontinuous folding, besides being distributed principally on the platforms, is developed partially also in parts of the geosynclines where the intensity of tectonic movements is relatively weak and the conditions approximate those of platforms. In discontinuous geosynclinal folding, as in platform discontinuous folding, we actually observe changes in thickness and facies within each fold, attesting to the slow uplift of the folds. But in typical complete folding, such changes of thickness and facies are not observed, and the history of their development is recorded by angular unconformities. Because angular unconformities are often connected with very brief stratigraphic breaks, the conclusion that complete folding was formed as a result of sharp, short phases of tectonic movements becomes inescapable. . . .

Complete folding develops in the closest relationship with oscillatory (epeirogenic) movements of the crust.

This relationship is expressed by the fact that each stage in the development of oscillatory movements in geosynclines corresponds to a definite stage in the development of folded structures. Each geosyncline is divided into zones of interior uplifts and depressions that are formed by slow, vertically directed movements of the crust. An important stage in the development of these movements in geosynclines is the appearance of new uplifts at the sites of previous depressions, with complete or partial transformation of original uplift (massifs) into regions of subsidence (intermontane depressions). Such development often leads to a complete transformation (inversion) of distribution of uplifts and depressions in the geosyncline, and it turns out to be possible to divide the history of the geosyncline into a stage before inversion and a stage after inversion.

In the first stage, before inversion, crustal subsidence generally predominates in the geosyncline; folding is weak, and its phases are restricted to the uplifts—geanticlines. The principal, strongest phases of folding are closely related to inversion and appear in the new, intensely developing uplifts that are formed at the site of the original depressions. As these new uplifts grow and expand, folding extends from the axes of the uplifts toward their margins, and the closing phases appear even in the marginal and intermontane depressions. Each folding phase is accompanied by brief uplift of the crust, some erosion, and subsequent partial subsidence, which leads to the formation of an angular unconformity.

In general we can state the connection between complete folding and crustal uplift in this way: as has been noted, prior to inversion the folding phases appear in the geanticlines, and after inversion they appear in the new uplifts, extending areally as the uplifts grow and expand.

At the same time, intensity of folding is connected with intensity of crustal uplift; the intensity of post-inversion folding, restricted to new uplifts that are growing energetically, is much greater than the intensity of the pre-inversion folding, localized in the original geanticlines, which rose relatively weakly. Folding is stronger closer to the axes of the uplifts and weakens toward the depressions, where it is finally replaced by discontinuous folding. The relationship between folding and uplift is so close that we often observe a local replacement of the former by the latter; a phase of movements expressed in one place as folding is manifested as uplift without folding in other parts of the same geosyncline.

Because the strong post-inversion uplift takes place where previously there were large depressions, we can say that the intensity of complete folding is directly related to the intensity and amplitude of the oscillatory movements of the crust.

To these regularities we should further add three forms of connection between folding movements and oscillatory movements.

Horizontal movement of material, determining the dip of the folds, is directed from regions of greater subsidence toward areas of lesser subsidence or of uplift, if we base ourselves on the distribution of areas of uplift and subsidence within geosynclines before inversion. For the distribution of the same areas after inversion the relationships are naturally the reverse (the folds dip from the post-inversion, i.e. final, uplifts toward the marginal and intermontane depressions).

Furthermore, the folds are distributed parallel to the isopachs. This explains many folds that are strange at first glance and the appearance of transverse folds in some places on plunging parts of anticlinoria, because the isopachs of the sequence that was deposited there are, roughly speaking, concentric with the anticlinorium, having longitudinal direction on its long flanks and transverse directions on its periclinal terminations.

An extremely important regularity is that the intensity of complete folding is determined by the gradient of thickness. It is stronger where the gradient is greater. The original depressions within the geosyncline are rarely symmetrical. Usually the axis of their maximum subsidence is displaced to one side or the other, and in connection with this the transition from depression to neighboring uplift has different contrast with different gradient of thickness, i.e. with different rate of change of the thickness from depression to uplift. Observations show that more intense folding is developed where the original geosynclinal depression adjoins an uplift of greater contrast, and becomes more gentle and simple where the transition to uplift is more gradual.

The latter regularity allows us to assert that folding in the geosyncline is developed not so much in connection with the occurrence of great subsidence and great accumulation of sediments, as in connection with the circumstance that in the geosyncline there is an alternation, over small areas, of zones with sediments having sharply different thicknesses with those having large gradient of thickness. The absence of complete folding on the platforms is connected with the low contrast of thicknesses, with the small gradient of oscillatory movements. This regularity is connected with what was said above about the restriction of intense folding to areas of large range of vertical movements of the crust. Large depressions are accompanied by a series of just as large uplifts; consequently, where the range of movements is greater, their contrast will be greater, and also the gradient of thickness.

How are the original tectonic forces that form complete folding directed? Is complete folding formed by horizontal compressive forces or vertical forces of uplift? Are there forces applied from outside the geosyncline, or do they arise within the geosyncline itself?

That complete folding is formed directly in the process of horizontal movement of crustal masses and their piling up in the form of waves follows from the overall morphology of folding. But can such movement be explained by horizontal compression applied from outside the geosyncline? Despite the popularity of ideas of external horizontal compression of the geosyncline, the following considerations categorically contradict it:

(a) *The complex form of folded zones.* The Alpine fold belt in Europe, for example, has a very complex outline, forming a number of sharp arcs, which, so to speak, are broken up into individual ovals. It is easy to conclude that such arcs and ovals could not at all have been formed by the approach of neighboring platform blocks, because individual segments of a single monolithic platform would have had to move in different directions.

(b) *Transverse folds.* The transverse folds that are developed in some places in geosynclines (especially on plunging anticlinoria) are incompatible with external horizontal compression.

(c) *History of development of folded zones.* We know that folding proceeds from the inner parts of a geosynclinal depression toward the margin, whereas with horizontal compression from outside we should expect, on the contrary, growth of folds from the margins into the geosyncline. The dying out of folding toward the platform also implies that external forces were not acting.

These points force us to consider that horizontal compression of layers that become crumpled into folds takes place not by the approach of rigid platforms that crush into the plastic geosynclinal zone, but by some processes that act within the geosyncline itself. These processes cause displacement of material within the geosyncline that in some segments leads to horizontal compression and the formation of complete folding. If we assume that within the geosyncline there is plastic flow of rocks toward certain axes, then in the zones of these axes there should be outflow of material and thinning of the sedimentary sequence; in other places, where this flow meets with resistance and is brought to a halt, we should observe crowding together of material and contortion of the layers into folds. With the presence of many centers of outflow in the geosyncline, the flow directions can be different, which makes possible the formation of ovals, arcs, and transverse folds.

Such a mechanism should basically predetermine a genetic relation between folding and vertical movements of the crust. Only if we assume that vertical movements within the geosyncline somehow cause, as a derivative process, flow of material and contortion of layers into folds, can we understand the above regular relationships between folding and oscillatory movements.

At first sight the requirements set forth here correspond to the idea of gravity folding, because it supposes outflow of material from the axes of uplifts and piling up on the flanks. However, opposed to this idea is the circumstance that in many cases folding in the crust is formed by movement of material not downward but upward, i.e. up the slope of the geosynclinal depression. Before the new uplifts that form after inversion on the sites of the original depressions have developed enough so that the depression is completely transformed into an uplift, the folds forming in the deep, most downwarped layers are, so to speak, pressed out upward, creeping from the base of the depression toward the uplift.

A different point of view on the origin of complete folding is set forth below.

It is well known that disharmonic folding is widespread in folded sequences. It is easy to establish that disharmonic folding, i.e. varying intensity of simultaneous folding in individual parts of layers, is related to nonuniform secondary variations in the thickness of the layers; only by combination of local thickening and thinning of various parts can the layers be folded into similar folds. Such thickening and thinning can form only by nonuniform compression of layers in the direction normal to the bedding. In this way, segments of thinning arise in the layers, from which material flows, and segments of thickening, into which material flows. In places of thinning the beds are flattened and extended, whereas in zones of thickening the total thickness increases primarily by contortion into folds.

The phenomenon of contortion of layers into folds in connection with laminar squeezing is observed on various scales, from small crimping in metamorphic sequences to large disharmonic folds, hundreds of meters in width.

The writer is inclined to consider that this process of mechanical squeezing of layered material of the crust from some places and its crowding into folds in other places leads into the mechanism of complete folding. The vertical stresses that are caused in the crust during vertical oscillatory movements give rise to this process. . . .

If we accept this point of view, then it becomes clear that all the regularities enumerated above that connect folding movements with oscillatory movements become not only comprehensible but necessary. For this it should only be assumed that the isopachs that characterize the regime of oscillatory movements can be considered as isopleths of the vertical stresses acting in the crust that cause crushing of layers and horizontal outflow of their material.

Indeed, if, where great thicknesses of pre-inversion series are observed, large countering vertical crushing forces also act, and, correspondingly, in places of smaller thickness of the same rock types, smaller forces, then flow of material should be directed from the region of greater thickness toward the region of smaller thickness, i.e. the dip of the folds should be precisely the same as is established by observation. This flow should be directed perpendicular to the isopachs, along the direction of maximum gradient of force, and consequently the folds should be parallel to the same isopachs; this also is in accord with observation. And, finally, the intensity of horizontal outflow will increase with increasing gradient of thickness and force.

By making the above assumption we see that all the regularities established above are tied together and become comprehensible. The assumption itself about the coincidence of the isopachs and the isopleths of vertical crushing forces is quite likely, because in zones of maximum subsidence prior to inversion there is, as a rule, also maximum uplift after inversion. From this it follows that the crust undergoes maximum vertical mechanical stresses in zones of greatest thickness, whereas regions of small thickness and amplitude of vertical movements should not experience such large stresses.

It is difficult, of course, to assert categorically at present that future study will lead to precisely the same interpretation of the mechanics of complete folding that has been set forth above. The important role of other factors, e.g. the weight of the rocks, which during vertical movements of the crust can undergo considerable redistribution, might be brought to light. . . . But in any case it is certain that complete folding is in no way connected with contraction of the surface of the crust, either on a planetary scale or within individual geosynclines. The development of complete folding is caused by horizontal plastic redistribution of material within the crust, with outflow from some places and accumulation in other places, under the influence of vertical stresses arising in the process of strongly differentiated oscillatory movements.

# KING
Lester Charles King (1907–    ), South African geologist, was born in London, England, emigrated to New Zealand at an early age, and secured his training as a geologist at Victoria University in Wellington. In 1935 he moved to South Africa and began lecturing at the old Natal University College in Pietermaritzburg, but transferred to Durban in 1948, where he has continued as head of the Department of Geology in the University of Natal. The paper excerpted here is based upon extensive field studies in diverse regions and is a perceptive analysis of the state of geomorphology at mid-century.

## THE EVOLUTION OF LANDSCAPES *

### STATEMENT OF THE PROBLEM

Davis' original conception of landscape evolution under the subaerial processes of rainfall, running water, and weathering has often been summed up in a series of progressive sections in which an uplifted landscape is depicted as first dissected under stream incision with the production of narrow valleys. After the streams have attained grade (defined as the

*From "Canons of landscape evolution," *Geological Society of America Bulletin 64* (1953), 721–752.

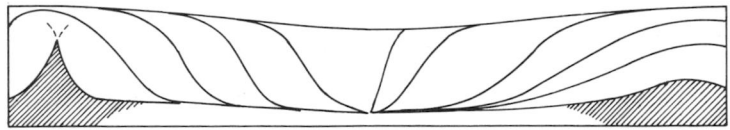

Fig. 1. Contrasted slope profiles. Widening of valleys and change in slope profile during the cycle. Right, youth to old age, according to W. M. Davis; left, with parallel scarp retreat, according to W. Penck. (From Davis, 1930.)

condition in which all major irregularities have been eliminated from the thalweg), the rate of river incision is reduced to negligible proportions, so that the valley bottoms are lowered very little during the remainder of the cycle. According to Davis, the valley sides are then reduced under weathering and surface creep, and perhaps wash, to ever flatter and flatter angles, until they meet upon the interfluves and destroy the last remnants of the initial surface. As the slopes continue to flatten, the interfluves are lowered more rapidly than the river beds until only "a lowland of faint relief remains." To this ultimate landform Davis assigned the title of *peneplain*. The concept is illustrated by Davis' own diagram which is here reproduced (Fig. 1). The progressive lowering of the interfluves under weathering is a vital concept in the "Normal Cycle" as visualized by Powell, by Davis, and by Cotton.

The Davisian concept has not passed without challenge, notably in his own Harvard University, where the strong school of Kirk Bryan accepted parallel retreat of scarps. Some authorities have indeed rejected the cyclic concept altogether[1]; others, with whom we align ourselves, have accepted the general concept of a cycle of landforms developed under erosion, while considering that the detailed forms and sequences depart considerably from those visualized and adduced by Davis. The essential differences of viewpoint lie in the interpretation of slope forms and the manner of hillslope development.

In summary, this opinion, after beginning the cycle of erosion with stream incision into an uplifted land surface exactly as in the Davisian model, would place limits to the amount of hillslope flattening, regarding the slopes as attaining a stable gradient (defined for local conditions) after which the upper parts of the slopes retreat parallel to themselves. A well-known example is due to Kirk Bryan.[2] At the foot of the slope is left a *pediment* sloping gently down to the river. This pediment is concave in profile, so that, when the interfluves are consumed by parallel

[1] W. Penck, *Die morphologische Analyse* (Stuttgart, 1924). See also pp. 227–234 of this volume.

[2] K. Bryan, *Erosion and Sedimentation in the Papago Country, Arizona*, U. S. Geol. Survey Bull. 730 (1922), pp. 19–90. See also pp. 209–212 of this volume.

383

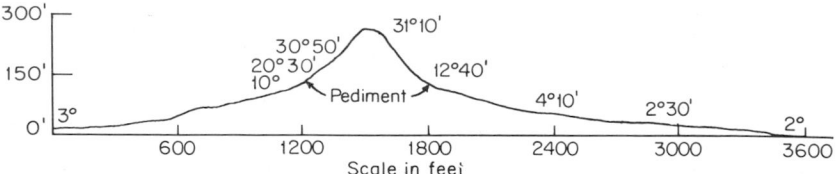

Fig. 2. Slopes of a Natal monadnock. Surveyed by T. J. D. Fair. On either side is a broad concave pediment, and the hillsides are steep (30°). Summit convexity is small. This type of monadnock agrees much better with Penck's doctrine of parallel scarp retreat than with Davis's flattening slope profiles and widespread convexity (Fig. 1).

scarp retreat, the opposing pediments from adjacent valleys would meet without forming a broad convexity across the interfluve (Figs. 1, 2).

The ultimate landscape under this philosophy, being composed of many coalescing pediments, is termed a *pediplain,* and it is distinguishable at sight from the Davisian peneplain by the multi-concave instead of multi-convex nature of its surface and the presence of steep-sided rather than gentle residuals. The fundamental difference between the two is, of course, not merely a difference of surface form—which indeed may be dubious, for concavities might occur in relation to peneplains—but of different history and mode of development.

The two concepts of an erosion cycle are largely exclusive. Over any given area, one can be true, but not the other. In the viewpoint of many geologists, the so-called "Normal Cycle of Erosion" appears under humid climates, and the Pediplanation cycle under semiarid and arid climates. The viewpoint is not without absurdity. One can understand that a characteristic cycle and set of landforms should be generated in frigid zones where water is frozen into ice and the whole mechanism of abrasion alters, where cirques are formed by thaw and freeze under specific conditions (D. W. Johnson), and where roches moutonnées are overridden by masses of solid ice; but that mere differences in amount and incidence of rainfall, evaporation, and like factors should have such far-reaching effects as to result in two entirely distinct cycles requires further investigation. The primary agent moulding the landscape in both humid and arid cases is water flow, and this should produce comparable results in both types of region.

· · · · ·

### PENEPLAIN VERSUS PEDIPLAIN

The distinction between the two types of landscape shows best in tough granitic terrains and is least marked in regions of weak shales and limestones.

Let there be no compounding upon this point: Though both landscapes may conform to the loose definition of "a landscape of low relief resulting from prolonged subaerial erosion" they are not, nor at any stage ever were, the same thing.

If the prime agents in each case, slope flattening or scarp retreat and pedimentation, operate almost exclusively, then one form is valid and the other is not. If both are regionally operative as, for instance, slope flattening in humid-temperate regions and parallel scarp retreat in semi-arid regions, then peneplains may be expected in the former and pediplains in the latter environment.[3] What has Nature to say on this? Do we find both forms, or either exclusively?

Before answering this question we shall consider an opinion of Walther Penck whose concept of senile landforms agrees with the pediplain. This form he called an *Endrumpf.* But Penck recognized also landscapes in which convex slopes appeared owing to gentle uplift and weak incision of the rivers. This landscape type he deemed to be initial in a new phase of erosion and termed it a *Primärrumpf.* He related both landforms to land movement, either slower or more rapid than the rate of erosion; I have preferred to think of them in terms of the erosion cycle as a pediplain and a redissected pediplain (two-cycle) respectively —that is, as landforms pure and simple, the former is an end-product of the erosion cycle, the latter, after rejuvenation of the rivers, is the initial stage in a new, second cycle of erosion. . . .

. . . All the truly old-age surfaces I have seen, and I have studied and mapped quite a few, were multi-concave in form, and bore residuals that were steep-sided and concave in profile themselves. The topographic boundaries of such residuals often do not coincide with geological boundaries between resistant and weak rocks. Even if the residuals are of resistant rocks, the topographic discontinuity between the residual and the adjacent plain had almost invariably transgressed from the weak onto the resistant formation. The landforms were pediplains or *Endrumpfe.*

Convexity occasionally appeared along the crests of some of the divides especially in areas of weak rocks such as Karroo shales, but it is clearly a feature induced only as senility advances, and was subordinate to concavity in the landscape observed as a whole. It was always summit convexity only.

Convexity in the neighborhood of the streams upon an old-age land surface, however slight, was found to be an infallible token of incision

[3] Dr. T. J. D. Fair comments: "Davis's peneplains were described mainly from humid temperate climates where, with heavy vegetation and deep soil, creep probably operates more obviously than in semi-arid climates. Thus, just as the pediplain of semi-arid regions probably displays greater summit convexities in humid-temperate regions, so probably do Davis's peneplains of humid-temperate regions display smaller summit convexities in semi-arid areas."

controlled by the arrival of a new cycle of erosion, and if the observer follows downstream, the amount of incision generally increases, and the second cycle becomes obvious. Below the region of maximum incision, youthful convexity of course decreases again in the second cycle, and concavity appears at the bases of hillslopes.

Judged on these criteria, observed in nature, I must declare that I have seen pediplains and diagnosed dissected pediplains. *i.e.* features akin to Penck's *Endrumpf* and *Primärrumpf* but I have never seen a peneplain. To arrive at this conclusion, I have scrupulously rejected from consideration numerous planed landscapes in the history of which doubt existed (*e.g.,* of resurrection), or where the second cycle had advanced much beyond the incipient stage. I have also neglected many with essentially straight hillslopes where stream incision and hillslope development appear in a delicate state of balance. They do not seem to afford exceptions to the theory. Fair has measured several slopes of this type.

Slow uplift is not essential, in my opinion, to the generation of a *Primärrumpf* from an *Endrumpf,* but slow incision of the streams, from any cause—*e.g.,* gentle tilting toward a basin—brings out the relation.

．　　．　　．　　．　　．

### Canons of Landscape Evolution

(1) Landscape is a function of process, stage, and structure. The relative importance of these is indicated by their order.

(2) The word *epigene* as applied to landscapes means "at the surface" or "subaerial." It does not include landscapes moulded beneath a solid cover of ice, and certain modifications are understood to be necessary in regions of permafrost.

(3) There is a general homology between all epigene landscapes. The differences between landforms of humid-temperate, semiarid, and arid environments are differences only of degree. Thus, for instance, monadnocks and inselbergs are homologous.

(4) Four elements may occur in a hillside slope. From the top, these are: the waxing slope, the free face, the detrital slope, the waning slope (usually pediment). Each or any element may be suppressed on a given hillslope.

(5) Each of the four elements of hillslope may evolve more or less independently, although each affects the others in some degree.

(6) The most active elements of hillslope evolution are the free face and the debris slope. If these are actively eroded, the hillside will retreat parallel to itself.

(7) In planed landscapes, pediments are the most important features.

In stable regions like Southern Africa, pediments may occupy more than half the whole landscape, and locally may exceed nine tenths of the landscape.

(8) The waxing slope is developed under weathering and soil creep.

(9) When the free face and debris slope are inactive, the waxing slope becomes strongly developed and may extend down to meet the waning slope. Such concavo-convex slopes are degenerate.[4]

(10) Parallel retreat of slopes is aided by (a) high relief, tending to maintain a clear free face and a debris slope; (b) resistant formations, tending to make cliffs (a good free face); (c) horizontal structure in sedimentary rocks; (d) generation originally as a tectonic scarp (*e.g.,* fault or monoclinal scarp).

(11) Erosion of the free face and the debris slope is accomplished chiefly by rill wash forming gully heads.

(12) Whereas the transport of debris upon the waxing slope, free face, and detrital slope is governed by both gravity and water work, that upon the pediment is solely accomplished by water work.

(13) Davis' old deduction of continuous lowering of hillside gradients, a feature also of Strahler's "Equilibrium Theory", is incorrect, and never existed as a general process of landscape development apart from terrains of rocks so weak that they cannot maintain a free face and detrital slope.

(14) Rock floors in epigene landscapes appear commonly between the base of hillslopes and stream channels. These rock floors, which are found under all three climatic regimens, originate by retreat of the hillslopes behind them and are subsequently modified by the passage of water across them which confers upon them a concave profile. Such rock floors should, in all cases, be called *pediments.*

(15) Stream spacing is closer in humid than in nonhumid regions so that an evenly distributed rainfall is largely discharged by channel flow. Wider spacing of streams and heavier incidence of rainfall favor sheet flow and also allow room for wider pediments.

(16) Pediments are normally veneered with detrital material which is in process of transport across them. But pediments themselves are essentially cut-rock surfaces.

(17) Pediments which have ceased to evolve may show weathering of the bedrock.

(18) A pediment is the ideal landform for the rapid dispersal of surface water, encouraging sheet flow and [having] a proper hydraulic pro-

---

[4]Dr. Fair demurs: "Rather does the waning slope extend *upwards* to meet the waxing slope and so give the pediment its predominantly concave form." He is thinking chiefly of African conditions, I of European. Both statements may be true.

file. Pediments are, indeed, moulded under sheet flow.

(19) The pediment is the fundamental landform to which epigene landscapes tend to be reduced the world over.

(20) Gullying may appear upon pediments where laminar flow of water is changed to linear flow.

(21) The break in profile between pediment and hillside may be abrupt if little detritus is supplied from above.

(22) Quantitative study of both slopes and processes provides a sequence of landscape forms different from those propounded by W. M. Davis.

(23) The early studies in the erosion cycle were conducted in Europe and northeastern North America, both of which regions were previously subjected to a glacial or periglacial climate. These areas and landscapes came to be cited as "normal" for the globe, a misconception that should no longer be tolerated.

(24) The standard or "normal" type of landscape, both now and in the geological past, is the semiarid type with broad pediments and parallel scarp retreat.

(25) Processes of erosion and evolution of landforms can, as a consequence of the above, be best observed in semiarid regions.

(26) Semiarid landscapes are the most efficiently developed. Deviation from the semiarid norm results in less efficient transport of waste, seen on the one hand in the broad, alluviated valley floors and smothered hillslopes of humid regions culminating in moraine and till under glaciation; and the abundant fans and bahadas, or even desert dunes of extremely arid regions.

(27) Water may flow across landscapes either in threads or in sheets. In thin sheets, water may flow in laminae. Such laminar flow is nonturbulent and nonerosive.

(28) In storms of moderate intensity, the manner of water flow appears to best advantage. Rill flow on the steep hillsides is powerfully erosive; in the upper pediment thin laminar flow (nonerosive) may occur, with deeper sheet flood lower down accompanied by turbulence and erosiveness.

(29) Laminar flow past an obstacle shows a depressed water surface, linear flow banks up the water surface against the obstacle.

(30) Only in late Tertiary time have smooth concavo-convex slopes become common. This is a result of retardation of surface wash by a carpet of grass, and consequent enhancement of soil creep.

(31) Before mid-Tertiary time, landscapes generally were of the semiarid (scarp and pediment) type.

(32) Stream work affects the nature of adjacent hillslopes directly

only during the early stages of the landscape cycle. After the streams are graded the dominant agencies are the processes acting directly upon the hillslopes, which evolve in an appropriate manner. The streams are, however, affected by the evolution of hillslopes through the nature of the detritus which these supply for transport by the streams.

(33) New cycles may penetrate inland either by nickpoints and incision of the rivers followed by retreat of the valley sides producing "flanking pediments," or by the retreat of wall-like scarps which are independent of the drainage lines [producing] "mountain pediments."

(34) On the whole, a landscape is dissected and reduced in a new cycle more rapidly following widespread river incision than by retreat of cyclic scarps originating tectonically. Conversely, the history of a landscape may be deciphered more readily where cyclic surfaces rise step-like between major cyclic scarps than where the landscape has been gutted by stream dissection.

(35) The ultimate cyclic landform is the *pediplain,* consisting dominantly of broad coalescing pediments. Residuals are steep-sided and have concave slopes. Flood plains may or may not be extensive.

(36) A pediplain is multi-concave upward. When the streams begin to incise themselves due to tilting, uplift, or climatic change, convexity enters the landscape adjacent to the stream channels. The interfluves then become transversely convex, and a landform morphologically different from the pediplain is produced. It is an initial stage of the cycle of erosion; the pediplain represents a senile stage. This expresses Penck's *Endrumpf–Primärrumpf* concept insofar as land form is concerned. We do not necessarily follow his further argument relating these differences to decreasing or increasing rates of land movement.

(37) A peneplain in the Davisian sense, resulting from slope reduction and downwearing, does not exist in nature. It should be redefined as "an imaginary landform."

(38) Davis has quoted low granitic domes of arid regions as though their form resulted specifically from long-continued erosion. Observations in Southern Africa show, however, that these forms are normally functions of structure; that, where the vertical systems of jointing are strong, bornhardts and castle koppies (large and small inselbergs) appear, and where flat or gently dipping joint systems are paramount "ruwares," or flat domes of granite, appear in the landscape. That such flat domes do not result from the erosion of bornhardts is, for this region, certain; they follow the broadly convex joints formed apparently in plutonic rocks by "unloading" as superincumbent rock systems were removed under erosion.

(39) Monadnocks are concave in profile as a rule (including Mt.

Monadnock itself) and have originated by surface wash rather than by downweathering and soil creep. They are not necessarily sited upon outcrops of more resistant rocks.

(40) Inherent in the pediplanation cycle, with scarp retreat, are *two* cyclic land surfaces, the older above a retreating scarp, the younger below.

(41) Many of the major cyclic erosion scarps originate tectonically as fault or monoclinal scarps, especially along outwardly tilted coast lines.

(42) Major cyclic erosion scarps retreat almost as fast as the nickpoints which travel up the rivers transversely to the scarp. Such scarps therefore remain essentially linear and do not have very pronounced re-entrants where they cross the rivers.

(43) Major continental erosion scarps in many lands retreat at a rate of about a foot in 150 years to a foot in 300 years.

(44) A landscape once reduced to a pediplain may remain in that state for an indefinite time with only minor alteration, until some change, tectonic or climatic, is introduced.

(45) Notwithstanding the above, small changes continually take place by regrading and conflict of pediments. These changes, insignificant in the landscape as a whole, perhaps amounting to the removal of only a few inches or feet of material, produce great differences in the superficial deposits of the pediments.

(46) Land surfaces may be dated by the deposits upon them. "Actual" ages are local ages fixed by directly dating the deposits in any given locality. "Comparative" ages refer to the dates at which land surfaces were originally bevelled, and are obtained from the oldest superficial deposits.

(47) Land surfaces may bear deposits of any age from the oldest, used for "comparative" dating, to the present day.

(48) A tentative approach, using "comparative" datings, has been made toward the correlation of major cyclic landscapes from continent to continent.

(49) More use of quantitative methods is necessary in landscape study; especially needed is more morphological mapping.

(50) When more suitable data are available statistical analysis may become a useful tool in landscape study.

# LIBBY Willard Frank Libby (1908– ), American chemist, received

the B.S. degree in 1931 and the Ph.D. degree in 1933 from the University of California. He was a member of the faculty of his Alma Mater from 1933 to

1945 and Professor of Chemistry in the Institute for Nuclear Studies at the University of Chicago from 1945 to 1954. For the next five years he was a member of the U.S. Atomic Energy Commission, and since 1959 he has been Professor of Chemistry and Director of the Institute of Geophysics and Planetary Physics in the University of California at Los Angeles. His discovery of the usefulness of $C^{14}$ as a radioactive timekeeper added an important new tool to the implements of geochronology.

## RADIOCARBON DATING *

The discovery of cosmic radiation by V.F. Hess in 1911 led to repeated conjectures as to possible permanent effects this radiation might have on the surface of the earth. The energy received by the earth in the form of cosmic radiation is commensurate with that received as starlight. It is therefore really quite small in terms of the solar energy. The specific energy, that is, the energy per constituent particle, is very much higher than for any other type of radiation, averaging several billions of electron volts (1 electron volt is $1.6 \times 10^{-12}$ ergs, which is the average energy of motion of a gas molecule at $10,000°$ C.). It is conceivable, therefore, that the cosmic radiation will alter the earth's atmosphere in detectable ways.

It was discovered shortly after the neutron itself had been discovered that neutrons were present in the higher layers of the atmosphere probably as secondary radiations produced by the primary cosmic rays. Measurements by cosmic-ray physicists have clearly established that the population in the atmosphere rises with altitude to a maximum somewhat above 40,000 feet and then falls. This proves the secondary character of the radiation—that it is not incident on the earth from interstellar space but is a product of the impact of the true primary radiation on the earth's atmosphere. A corroborating point in this connection is the recent demonstration that the neutron is truly radioactive with a lifetime of about 12 minutes, which of course removes any possibility of the neutrons having time to travel any considerable distance in interstellar space, though the trip from the sun could be made without complete decay to hydrogen.

Consideration of possible nuclear transmutations which the cosmic rays might effect leads one immediately to consider what the neutrons known to be produced by the cosmic rays might be expected to do to the earth's atmosphere. In the laboratory many studies have been made of the effects of neutrons of various energies on all the ordinary elements and especially on nitrogen and oxygen, the constituents of the air. In

*Reprinted from *Radiocarbon Dating*, University of Chicago Press, 1952, pp. 1–10. Reprinted by permission. Copyright 1952 by The University of Chicago.

LIBBY

general, the results are that oxygen is extraordinarily inert but that nitrogen is reactive. It appears certain that, of the two nitrogen isotopes, $N^{14}$, of 99.62 per cent abundance, and $N^{15}$, of 0.038 per cent abundance, $N^{14}$ is the more reactive. With neutrons of thermal velocity the reaction

$$N^{14} + n = C^{14} + H^1 \qquad (1)$$

is dominant, the cross-section of the $N^{14}$ atom for a room temperature thermal neutron being in the vicinity of $1.7 \times 10^{-24}$ cm.$^2$, whereas the thermal neutron cross-section for reaction with $O^{16}$ is of the order of 0.1 per cent of this. It is therefore quite certain that thermal neutrons introduced into ordinary air will react according to Equation (1) to form the radiocarbon isotope of mass 14 and half-life of $5568 \pm 30$ years.

The neutrons in the air being formed by the energetic cosmic rays possess energy themselves, probably of the order of 5–10 mev (million electron volts) on the average when first formed. After birth they then collide with the air molecules and lose their energy by collision, either elastic or inelastic, either reacting on one of these collisions and so being absorbed or finally attaining thermal energies where they are quite certain to be absorbed to form radiocarbon by Reaction (1). Laboratory studies of the effects of energetic neutrons on air again indicate that the nitrogen is the more reactive constituent. Reaction (1) is still dominant, though a second reaction,

$$N^{14} + n = B^{11} + He^4, \qquad (2)$$

occurs.[1] The latter reaction becomes dominant at energies above 1 mev but even at the most favored energies attains cross-sections of only 10 per cent of that of nitrogen for thermal energies. Reaction (1), on the other hand, goes with considerable probability in the region of 0.4–1.6 mev.

A third type of reaction of high-energy neutrons with nitrogen,

$$N^{14} + n = C^{12} + H^3, \qquad (3)$$

has been reported in the laboratory.[2] The nature of the laboratory experiment was such that it was difficult to estimate the cross-section for the reaction, but the reported value was $10^{-26}$ cm$^2$, to an accuracy of about a factor of 5. It is certain from the masses of the atoms involved in Reaction (3) that neutrons of not less than 4 mev are involved, since the reaction is endothermic to this extent. The hydrogen isotope in Reaction (3) is the radioactive hydrogen called tritium, of 12.46 years' half-life, which decays to form the stable isotope of helium, $He^3$, which occurs

[1] C. H. Johnson and H. H. Barschall, *Phys. Rev. 80* (1950), 819.
[2] R. Cornog and W. F. Libby, *Phys. Rev. 59* (1941), 1046.

2192

392

in atmospheric helium in an abundance of $1.2 \times 10^{-6}$ parts $He^3$ per ordinary helium in atmospheric air.[3] It is thought that this value is accurate to about 30 per cent. The abundance of $He^3$ in ordinary helium from terrestrial sources varies widely from undetectably small values in uranium ores, where an excessively large amount of $He^4$ is found, to the values of $12 \times 10^{-6}$ parts for certain Canadian rocks. In general, however, the $He^3$ content of helium from the earth's crust is not over one tenth as large as that of atmospheric helium. Since tritium produced by Reaction (3) lasts such a short time, one knows that any tritium produced by Reaction (3) will introduce an equivalent amount of $He^3$ into the earth's atmosphere, so that one possible effect of the cosmic-ray bombardment of the earth's atmosphere could be the introduction of $He^3$ into the atmospheric helium. It is seen that this may be the case, since it is observed that atmospheric helium is richer in $He^3$ than terrestrial helium.

Summarizing the three most probable reactions, only the first and third lead to radioactive isotopes. It is therefore to be expected that the neutrons produced by the cosmic radiation may produce these radioactive materials in the earth's atmosphere. After these points were made,[4] a search in nature for both radioactivities was instituted. Both have since been found[5] in amounts and concentrations corresponding roughly to those expected.

Therefore, we now have more confidence in the basic postulates made in the arguments outlined above—that the behavior of the cosmic-ray neutrons in the air is predictable from the observed behavior of laboratory neutrons on nitrogen and oxygen and that the possibility of the neutrons having higher energy than laboratory neutrons appears not to confuse the issue appreciably.

The prediction of the expected amounts of radiocarbon and tritium can be made only on the basis of some information about the relative probabilities of Reactions (1), (2), and (3). Reaction (1) is so much more probable, however, that it is clear that the yield of radiocarbon will be nearly equal to the total number of neutrons generated by the cosmic rays, a number which we shall call $Q$ in units of number per square centimeter per second. The tritium yield, due to Reaction (3) only, is taken to be of the order of the ratio of these cross-sections, or about 1 per cent of $Q$. The latter will be considerably more uncertain than the yield of radiocarbon, since the cross-section for Reaction (3) is much

[3] L. T. Aldrich and A. O. Nier, *Phys. Rev. 74* (1948), 1590.

[4] W. F. Libby, *Phys. Rev. 69* (1946), 671.

[5] E. C. Anderson, W. F. Libby, S. Weinhouse, A. F. Reid, A. D. Kirshenbaum, and A. V. Grosse, *Science 105* (1947), 576; E. C. Anderson, W. F. Libby, S. Weinhouse, A. F. Reid, A. D. Kirshenbaum, and A. V. Grosse, *Phys. Rev. 72* (1947), 931; A. V. Grosse, W. H. Johnston, R. L. Wolfgang, and W. F. Libby, *Science 113* (1951), 1.

more uncertain than that for Reaction (1) and more specifically than the dominance of Reaction (1). If we integrate the data for the neutron intensity as a function of altitude from sea-level to the top of the atmosphere, to obtain the total number of neutrons, $Q$, produced per square centimeter per second, and average this over the earth's surface according to the observed variation of neutron intensity with latitude,[6] we obtain a figure for $Q$, the average number of neutrons generated per square centimeter of the earth's surface per second by the incidence of cosmic radiation. If we further assume that the cosmic-ray production of radiocarbon is an ancient phenomenon in terms of the 5600-year half-life of radiocarbon (i.e., the cosmic rays have remained at essentially their present intensity over the last 10,000 or 20,000 years), we can conclude that there is some place on earth enough radiocarbon to guarantee that its rate of distintegration is just equal to its rate of formation. Evaluation of $Q$ from the experimental data available gives 2.6 as a most likely value. Since the earth's surface has $5.1 \times 10^{18}$ cm$^2$, the radiocarbon inventory must be such that $1.3 \times 10^{19}$ beta disintegrations occur per second.

$$C^{14} = \beta^- + N^{14+}. \tag{4}$$

Since laboratory measurement of the specific disintegration rate of radiocarbon[7] gives $1.6 \times 10^{11}$ disintegrations per second per gram, dividing we obtain $8.1 \times 10^7$ grams, or 81 metric tons, as the predicted inventory for radiocarbon on earth. This is equivalent to 365 million curies (1 curie is that quantity of radioactivity which gives a disintegration rate of $3.7 \times 10^{10}$ per second). Reasoning similarly, we predict a tritium inventory of about 3 million curies in nature.

The question remains as to where the radiocarbon will occur. A moment's thought answers this, however. We consider the problem of the ultimate fate of a carbon atom introduced into the air at a height of some 5 or 6 miles. It seems certain that within a few minutes or hours the carbon atom will have been burned to carbon dioxide molecule. It is true that there are points of interest to discuss in the question of the kinetics of combustion of atomic carbon in the air, and research is necessary to supply definite answers for the many questions which would arise in such a discussion. It seems probable, however, that the carbon will not long remain in any condition other than carbon dioxide. Postu-

[6] J. A. Simpson, Jr., *Phys. Rev., 73* (1948), 1389; L. C. L. Yuan, *Phys. Rev. 76* (1949), 1267, 1268.

[7] A. G. Engelkemeir, W. H. Hamill, M. G. Inghram, and W. F. Libby, *Phys. Rev. 75* (1949), 1825; W. M. Jones, *Phys. Rev. 76* (1949), 885; W. W. Miller, R. Ballentine, W. Bernstein, L. Friedman, A. O. Nier, and R. D. Evans, *Phys. Rev. 77* (1950), 714; A. G. Engelkemeir and W. F. Libby, *Rev. Sci. Instr. 21* (1950), 550.

lating that this is so (i.e., the absorption of cosmic-ray neutrons by nitrogen of the air is equivalent to the production of radioactive carbon dioxide), we can proceed to an immediate answer to the question as to where natural radiocarbon should occur on earth. Radioactive carbon dioxide will certainly mix with considerable speed with the atmospheric carbon doxide, and so we conclude that all atmospheric carbon dioxide is rendered radioactive by the cosmic radiation. Since plants live off the carbon dioxide, all plants will be radioactive; since the animals on earth live off the plants, all animals will be radioactive. Thus we conclude that all living things will be rendered radioactive by the cosmic radiation. In addition, there is another carbon reservoir for the natural radiocarbon, and this is the inorganic carbon in the sea present as dissolved carbon dioxide, bicarbonate and carbonate, for it is known that an exchange reaction occurs between carbon dioxide and dissolved bicarbonate and carbonate ions. The time for radioactive carbon dioxide in the air to distribute itself through this reservoir probably is not in excess of 500 years. This is the so-called "turnover" time for the life-cycle which has been widely discussed by geochemists. The estimates vary quite widely, but it does seem that this time can hardly exceed 1000 years. Since this is a time short as compared to the lifetime of radiocarbon, we conclude that any given radiocarbon atom will make the round trip several times in its lifetime, and we therefore predict that the distribution of radiocarbon throughout the reservoir will be quite uniform, there being little vertical or latitudinal or longitudinal gradients left. One has some cause to suspect that there might be variations in intensity over the earth's surface, for the reason that it is known that the cosmic-ray neutron component varies by a factor of about 3.5[8] between equatorial and polar regions, the intensity being greater in the polar regions.

As expected, however, on the basis of the probable brevity of the turn-over time as compared to the lifetime of radiocarbon, it has been found that the distribution is uniform. Materials have been selected from various points on the earth's surface and from various altitudes, and the specific radioactivity has been found to be identical within the error of measurement, which amounts to some 3–5 per cent.

In order to predict the specific radioactivity of living carbon, the amount of carbon in the exchange reservoir must be estimated. Careful consideration of the complex biochemical questions involved leads us to the numbers given in Table 1.

The dominance of the inorganic material dissolved in the sea is obvious from these numbers. This has the immediate consequence that

[8] J. A. Simpson, Jr., *Phys. Rev.* 73 (1948), 1389; L. C. L. Yuan, *Phys. Rev.* 76 (1949), 1267, 1268.

TABLE 1.  Carbon inventory

| Source | Amount (gm/cm$^2$) |
|---|---|
| Ocean "carbonate" | 7.25 |
| Ocean, dissolved organic | 0.59 |
| Biosphere | 0.33 |
| Atmosphere | 0.12 |
| Total | 8.3 |

variations in living conditions which will lead to variations in the amount of living matter on earth will not appreciably affect the total carbon in the reservoir. Or, conceivably, the only possible significant variations of the quantity of carbon in the reservoir must involve changes in the volume, the temperature, or the acidity (pH) of the oceans. This probably means that the reservoir has not changed significantly in the last few tens of thousands of years, though there is the point to consider of the effect of the glaciation on both the volume and the mean temperature of the oceans. If the numbers in Table 1 are correct, there are some 8.3 grams of carbon in exchange equilibrium with the atmospheric carbon dioxide for each square centimeter of the earth's surface, on the average, and since there are some 2.6 neutrons incident per square centimeter per second, we must expect that these 8.3 grams of carbon will possess a specific radioactivity of 2.6/8.3 disintegrations per second per gram, or 2.6 × 60/8.3 disintegrations per minute per gram. This number, 18.8, is to be compared with the experimentally observed value of 16.1 ± 0.5.[9] The agreement seems to be sufficiently within the experimental errors involved, so that we have reason for confidence in the theoretical picture set forth above.

The agreement between these two numbers bears on another point of real importance—the constancy in intensity of the cosmic radiation over the past several thousand years. If one were to imagine that the cosmic radiation had been turned off until a short while ago, the enormous amount of radiocarbon necessary to the equilibrium state would not have been manufactured and the specific radioactivity of living matter would be much less than the rate of production calculated from the neutron intensity. Or, conversely, if one were to imagine that the intensity had been much higher in the past until very recently, the specific radioactivity would greatly exceed that calculated from the observed neutron intensity. Since 5568 ± 30 years will be required to bring the inventory

[9] E. C. Anderson, Ph.D. thesis, University of Chicago, 1949; E. C. Anderson and W. F. Libby, *Phys. Rev. 81* (1951), 64.

halfway to any new equilibrium state demanded by the change in cosmic-ray intensity, we find some evidence in the agreement between these numbers that the cosmic-ray intensity has remained essentially constant for the last 5000–10,000 years. This does not mean that it could not exhibit hourly, daily, or even annual fluctuations. It does mean, however, that the intensity averaged over 1000 years or so has not changed. There is the slight possibility that an approximately compensating change in the carbon inventory has occurred, but for the reasons mentioned above the buffering action of the great reservoir in the sea makes this very remote.

A further point of interest in connection with the inventory and the observed specific assay is that the carbon isotopes apparently are fractionated in being incorporated into the biosphere from the inorganic world. This effect was discovered some time ago for the isotope $C^{13}$, which has a mean abundance of 1.1 per cent in ordinary carbon. It was found that the ratio of the abundance of $C^{13}$ in inorganic carbon to that in biological carbon is 1.03. On the basis of this, one would expect a value of 1.06 for the analogous ratio for $C^{14}$, radio-carbon. Since the mass spectrographic measurements of the $C^{13}$ abundance are quite accurate and the theory on which one calculates the 1.06 ratio from the observed 1.03 ratio for $C^{13}$ is quite rigorous, we are inclined to multiply our assay of biological material by 1.06 rather than to take the mean value of the small number of measurements we have made on inorganic carbon. The mean of the biological assay is $15.3 \pm 0.1$. Multiplying by 1.06, we obtain 16.2 for inorganic carbon; then, averaging according to the weight factors given in Table 1, we derive the average 16.1 for the carbon inventory as a whole. One must remember, however, that wood or other biological material will present an assay of 15.3 and that modern seashell will present an assay of 16.2.

If the cosmic radiation has remained at its present intensity for 20,000 or 30,000 years, and if the carbon reservoir has not changed appreciably in this time, then there exists at the present time a complete balance between the rate of disintegration of radiocarbon atoms and the rate of assimilation of new radiocarbon atoms for all material in the life-cycle. For example, a tree, or any other living organism, is in a state of equilibrium between the cosmic radiation and the natural rate of disintegration of radiocarbon so long as it is alive. In other words, during the lifetime the radiocarbon assimilated from food will just balance the radiocarbon disintegrating in the tissues. When death occurs, however, the assimilation process is abruptly halted, and only the disintegration process remains.

It has been known for many years that the rate of disintegration of radioactive bodies is extraordinarily immutable, being independent of the nature of the chemical compound in which the radioactive body resides and of the temperature, pressure, and other physical characteristics of its environment. The reason for this is that the transformation is a nuclear phenomenon involving energies very much larger than those corresponding to the chemical bonds and to the various physical influences to which matter might conceivably be subjected. Therefore, we conclude that the rate of disappearance of radioactivity following death corresponds to the exponential decay law for radiocarbon as represented by the solid curve in Fig. 1, in which the world-wide assay of 15.3 for biological materials corresponds to zero time, and the predicted specific

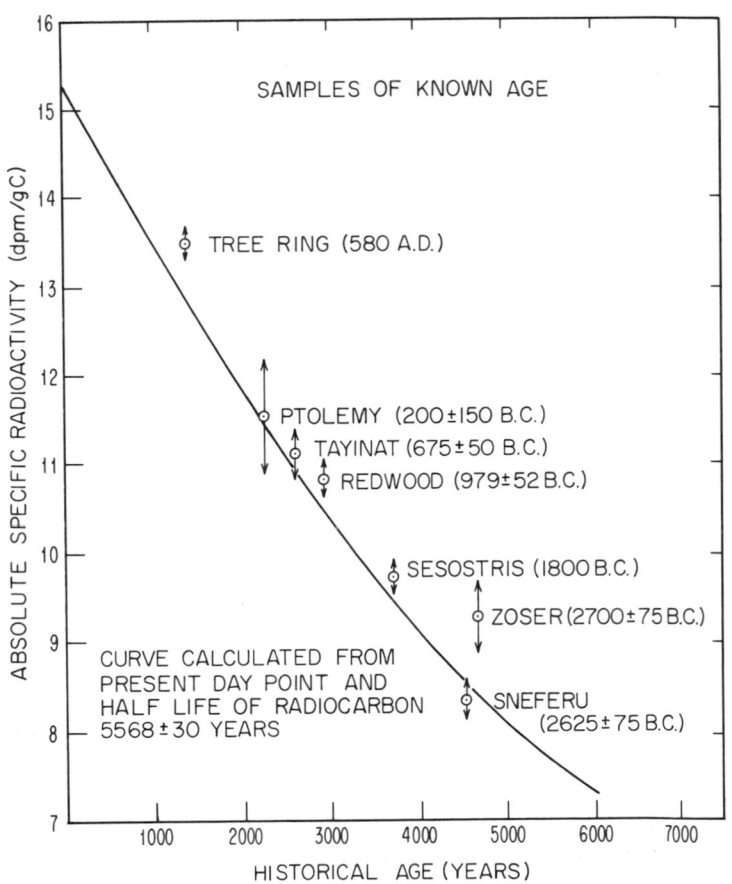

Fig. 1. Predicted versus observed radioactivities of samples of known age.

radioactivities for various times thereafter are given by the curve. The equation for the curve is

$$I = 15.3 \exp\left(-0.693\,\frac{t}{5568}\right), \tag{5}$$

or

$$I = 15.3\ 2^{(-t/5568)}, \tag{5'}$$

in which $t$ is the age of the organic material in years, age being defined as the time elapsed since death occurred. The experimental points shown in Fig. 1 are the observed assays for various samples of known age, discussed later. Insofar as the points fit the curve, we have reason to believe that the method is sound and gives the correct ages. The errors indicated on the experimental points are standard deviations, and it appears that the results are favorable as judged statistically.

It is obvious that we must be careful in selecting samples to choose materials that contain the original carbon atoms present at the time death occurred. In other words, samples must not have been preserved with organic materials containing carbon of age different from that of the sample. Care must also be taken that chemical changes have not led to replacement of the carbon atoms. In a general way, organic materials consisting mainly of large molecules, such as cellulose and charcoal, are favored. An example of questionable material is shell, for it is quite conceivable that shell which is powdery and chalky in appearance has had its carbonate atoms replaced.

# WILSON

John Tuzo Wilson (1908–    ), Canadian geologist, received his B.A. degree from the University of Toronto in 1930, and his Ph.D. degree from Princeton University in 1936. He served in the Canadian Army from 1939 to 1946 and has been Professor of Geophysics in the University of Toronto since his release from military duties. He has engaged in field studies for the Canadian Geological Survey at various times and is a member of the National Reserarch Council of Canada.

## THE PATTERN AND POSSIBLE CAUSE OF YOUNG MOUNTAIN RANGES AND ISLAND ARCS *

### INTRODUCTION

In an accompanying paper Scheidegger and Wilson[1] have examined those methods of failure which are theoretically to be expected in spher-

*From *Geological Association of Canada Proceedings 3* (1950), 141–166.

[1] A. E. Scheidegger and J. T. Wilson, "An investigation into possible methods of failure of the earth," *Proc. Geol. Assn. Canada* (1950).

ical shells under various conditions and with especial reference to the outermost shells of the earth.

They assumed that mountain ranges and island arcs represent those places where failure has occurred in the outer shells of the earth. A preliminary examination of some modern arcs suggested that they might be well approximated to by circular arcs. In some cases spiral curves fitted the ranges or arcs as well as parts of circles.

No system of forces acting upon a uniform spherical shell has been discovered which can explain a system of arcuate failures such as occur on the earth. On the other hand, a non-uniform spherical shell with points of weakness or zones of weakness along continental margins may be capable of failing so that there might be produced a series of arcuate failures near those margins. It seemed to Scheidegger and Wilson most likely that such a system of arcuate failures would arise as a result of sliding fractures due to cooling and tension occurring below the crust in the upper part of the mantle.

They pointed out that it had never been proved that the earth was heating up and that recent information has increased the probability that it is cooling in the manner long maintained by Jeffreys.[2] They also showed that the recent studies by Benioff[3] of some deep-focus earthquakes appeared to support the suggestion that such fractures do exist.

It is the object of this paper first to discuss why fractures due to tension at depth are the cause of mountains due to compression at the earth's surface and second to analyse the young orogenetic belts on the earth to see whether the theory can be applied to explain them [see Fig. 1].

### The Level of No Strain and Cause of Thrust-faulting in the Lithosphere

It is well known that mountains are due to compression. To fit the theory which has been advanced an explanation must be given of why fractures which are due to tension and hence which have acted as normal faults are overlain by mountains built by compression. Tension means less than normal pressure.

It has been pointed out by Jeffreys that if the earth is cooling and contracting, there must be a level of no strain above which the rocks are in compression and below which they are in tension. This is precisely the condition required. The depth of the level of no strain, which Jeffreys placed very approximately at 100 km, is gradually deepening as the earth

[2] H. Jeffreys, *The Earth, Its Origin, History and Physical Constitution*, 2nd ed., Cambridge University Press, 1929.

[3] H. Benioff, "Seismic evidence for the fault origin of oceanic deeps," *Bull. Geol. Soc. Am. 60* (1949), 1837–1856.

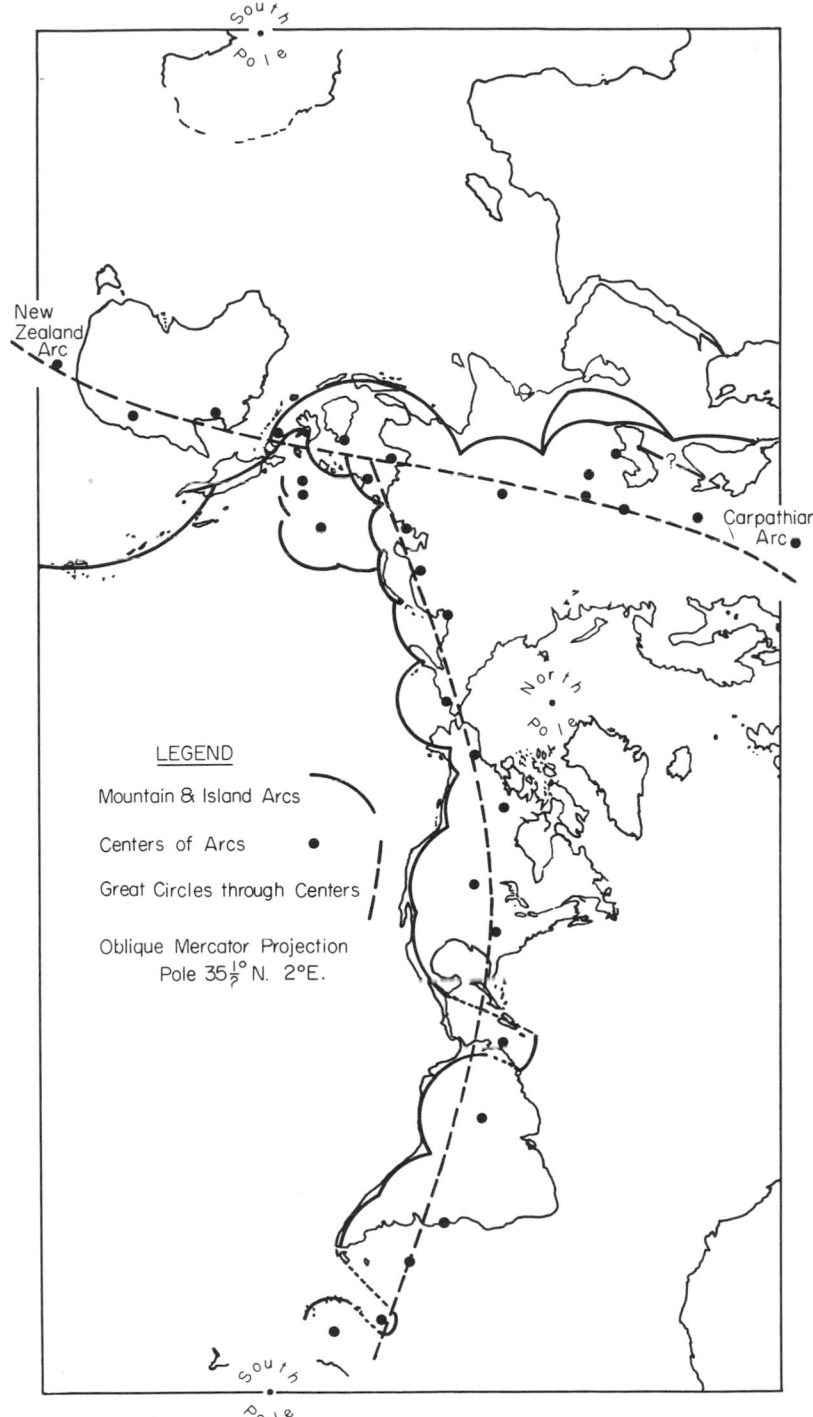

Fig. 1. Mesozoic–Cenozoic mountain and island arcs approximately indicated as circular arcs. Some of the less regular arcs lie outside of the map area. The projection displays the relation of the two belts.

cools and is not necessarily connected with any change in composition of the mantle. It is the direct result of thermal effects.[4]

Benioff suggested that the great faults which underlie the arcs reach the surface, cropping out as thrust faults.

Near surface faults ought to be thrusts, for the rocks are in compression above the level of no strain. At that level, the change from tension to compression theoretically results in a zone of discontinuity in which there is no movement. Above that level compression causes thrust faults, below it tension leads to normal faults.[5]

Benioff clearly recognized the existence of a discontinuity at about the required depth in both the great fault systems which he investigated. For the Tonga-Kermadec system he states: "Since the curve for the shallow sequence (of earthquakes) bears no relationship to that of the deep sequence it may be concluded that there is no effective mechanical coupling between the two layers in which these sequences have their origins. Thus the boundary which separates them at a depth of approximately 70 km must be a surface of profound discontinuity in the physical state or composition of the rock. The discontinuity in the seismic wave speed at this boundary appears to be quite small. . ."[6]

The absence of change in the seismic velocities suggests that there is no change in composition at that depth. Therefore, the discontinuity observed by Benioff may well be at the level of no strain, where a marked change in the type of earthquake would be expected. Japanese seismologists had already remarked on the scarcity of earthquake foci between 70 and 90 km deep.[7]

If the shallow and deep earthquakes are respectively due to thrust and normal faults the directions of first motion of shocks should differ. In most of 100 earthquakes investigated by Byerley and Evernden[8] this was found. It is hoped that the matter will be investigated further.

The absence of movement at the level of no strain perhaps makes it theoretically unnecessary for there to be any connection whatsoever between shallow and deep earthquakes surfaces,[9] but the theory neglects complexities. In view of them, it does not seem unreasonable that the crustal thrust faults should in a general way be connected with and should overlie the profound normal slip-surfaces, but the lack of me-

[4] H. Jeffreys (above, n. 2), p. 282.

[5] Scheidegger and Wilson (above, n. 1), Fig. 1.

[6] H. Benioff, (above, n. 3), p. 1844.

[7] K. Wadati, "Deep-focus earthquakes in Japan and its vicinity," *Proceedings of the Seventh Pacific Science Congress 1*, 142.

[8] P. Byerley and J. Evernden, "First motion from deep and shallow shocks," *Bull. Geol. Assn. Am. 60* (1949), 1953.

[9] H. Jeffreys (above, n. 2), p. 279.

chanical coupling may explain why the complexities of a mountain system may be only the surface expression of more uniform and simple movements at depth.

If these views are accepted it follows that the broad pattern and shape of arcs are due to deep-seated tension, but it has been shown that this may be co-existent with folding and thrusting caused by surface compression in the same region at the same time.

Many geologists, from Suess onwards, have observed this conflict of tension and compression, of plastic and brittle behaviour in the building of mountain and world structures. This puzzling interplay of forces has been thoroughly discussed by Bucher.[10] The proposed theory provides an explanation of how compression and tension features can both appear in the same orogenetic revolution at the same time.

Although the deep-seated slip-surfaces are regarded as the primary features and the cause of mountain building, they are generally hidden and not located precisely. Indeed, they are only known at all from theory and deep earthquakes. For that reason, the surface mountain and island arcs will be the features chiefly referred to in the ensuing discussion and a close connection in cause between fractures and arcs will be assumed. One of the most striking and permanent features of arcs are the chains of volcanoes. In this discussion it will also be assumed that these chains bear a constant relation to the causative faulting.

$$\bullet \quad \bullet \quad \bullet \quad \bullet \quad \bullet$$

### Six Types of Arcs

The Tonga-Kermadec Islands and the Andes Mountains present very different physiographic appearances. They have both been attributed by Benioff to a similar, simple cause. The great differences in appearance and structure were evidently considered by him to be due to secondary causes, the nature of which must now be examined. It appears convenient to divide all young arcs into six types, single, double and complex island arcs, and single, double and complex ranges. Several reasons for these differences have been exhaustively treated by Umbgrove, who has given one of his conclusions in these words:

"Different physiographic aspects presented by such mountain belts as the Alps, the Himalaya, the structural belts of Burma, and the island-festoon of the East Indies do not represent different evolutionary stages in a continuous process of mountain-making. The differences are mainly controlled by the thickness of the crust, the available quantity of waste-

[10] W. H. Bucher, *The Deformation of the Earth's Crust,* Princeton University Press, 1933.

products from the land and the palaeogeographic conditions that prevailed during the structural history of each region, more especially during the latest epochs of crustal compression."[11] The influence of the first of these is difficult to evaluate, for there are few data upon variations of the thickness of the crust, except for the major difference between continents and ocean basins. The great importance of the availability of sediments is clear from the fact that arcs of small islands form when failure occurs far from land whereas great mountain ranges are formed close to the hearts of great continents and there is a gradation between the two that appears to depend upon distance from land and proximity to the heart of the larger continents.

Another important consideration is whether crustal forces have acted uniformly in one direction or intermittently in two or more different directions.

The distinguishing feature[s] of the six types of arcs will be briefly summarized:

SINGLE ISLAND ARCS are uniformly curved chains of volcanoes with an oceanic foredeep. The Aleutian and South Sandwich Islands are examples. There are large negative, gravity anomalies over the foredeeps and a characteristic arrangement of earthquakes.

DOUBLE ISLAND ARCS develop where single island arcs approach continents. In them an outer chain of islands composed of folded sedimentary rocks replaces the foredeep. Examples of such islands are Kodiak, Timor and Trinidad. This development has been considered to be due to an increasing supply of sediments which first fill the deep and then, during orogenetic movement, get folded and squeezed up to the surface. The negative gravity anomalies are found over the outer arc of sedimentary islands.[12]

COMPLEX ISLAND ARCS may be either single or double but display an irregularity of shape and features which is considered to be due to interaction of forces from two directions. The island arcs from New Guinea to New Zealand provide several examples which will be discussed later.

SINGLE MOUNTAIN RANGES have the same essential features as a single island arc, that is a volcanic arc with an oceanic foredeep, but due to abundance of sediment supplied earlier in their history or in a different way from double island arcs it is the volcanic arc which has grown while the deep has remained. The Andes of northern Chile and of Peru are examples.

DOUBLE MOUNTAIN RANGES correspond to double island arcs in having a volcanic and predominantly igneous range on the concave side of a

[11]J. H. F. Umbgrove, *The Pulse of the Earth,* 2nd ed., The Hague, 1947.
[12]*Ibid.,* chap. vii.

parallel range which is predominantly sedimentary. The Sierra Nevada and the Coast Ranges of California provide an example of such a double range. Gravity anomalies are negative over the sedimentary range, which may also contain deep-water sediments which have been squeezed to the surface.

COMPLEX MOUNTAIN RANGES appear to be those in which the presence of older continental nuclei on each side has exerted a disturbing effect. This has probably been accomplished largely by excessive supply of sediments. The Alpine-Himalayan system contains many examples.

As is well known, belts of thick sediments are weak. Failure tends to follow them. Failure produces uplift, erosion and thus new and parallel belts of sediments in which further failure can occur. Abundant sedimentary material thus introduces an element of mobility into failure which produces complex patterns. Where there is less sediment available failure more often follows the simple lines of the mathematical theory.

It is an interesting fact that most arcs regardless of their nature are of a fairly uniform curvature and size. This common size is approximately that of the Aleutian arc which may be taken as the type arc. Few are as much as twice as big or as small as half this size. There are exceptions among the complex island arcs, but causes for this will be discussed. Such an approximation to uniformity strengthens the case for a mathematically simple origin of the arcs.

·    ·    ·    ·    ·

## CONCLUSIONS

It had previously been suggested on theoretical grounds that failure in the earth might be expected to occur as a series of arcuate fractures arising from weak zones in the earth's crust and formed initially by tension at depth. It had been shown that this appeared to be compatible with thermal and seismic evidence.[13]

In this paper an explanation has been given as to why tension failure at depth produces compression failure at the surface.

The mountain ranges and island arcs of the two young belts of failure of the earth have been examined. It has been suggested that these ranges and arcs are fairly uniform in size and can be generalized into simple patterns which could have arisen by failure of the type proposed occurring at continental margins.

It has been found that the mechanism propounded allows for there to be a broad similarity in history of each great system of belts, a closer contemporaneity in the events of each arc and between adjacent arcs,

[13] Scheidegger and Wilson (above, n. 1).

but that it does not demand any world-wide periodicity of diastrophism.

As Rutten concluded, "Instead of world-wide, synchronic, orogenetic revolutions, there thus have been periods of long duration, characterized by varying and fluctuating tectonic activity. The active periods are not world-wide. While part of the earth was in tectonic rest, elsewhere tectonic activity was found. The quiet regions may have already been folded during an earlier date, or they will be folded at a later date, or they may remain ultimately undisturbed. Differences in time of folding may be found not only in different continents, but also along one and the same orogenetic belt."[14]

It has been briefly suggested that the same mechanism might be applied to explain all earlier orogenetic belts also, but the details of these have not been deciphered. It may, however, be stated that it is considered that the continents are built up from the roots of former primary mountains. The idea that they have grown thus since Precambrian time is already widely accepted.[15] The principle of uniformitarianism suggests that the same processes went on during Precambrian time.[16] In three preliminary papers to this one, the writer has endeavoured to show that the concept that continents have entirely grown during geological time is compatible with the geological, cosmological and geophysical evidence in the Canadian Shield.[17] The old idea that the continental basement is an original sialic block finds no support from Precambrian geology.[18]

The full statement of such a theory must include not only a description of the location of previous mountain belts, but also a quantitative discussion of the origin, location and rate of accumulation of geosynclines and the effect of profound failure upon the origin of batholiths. For it must be supposed that profound faults allow solutions and magmas to rise which may serve to explain the association of intrusives with orogenetic revolutions. These discussions will be left to a separate paper because they require the introduction of additional ideas irrelevant to the structural analysis which has constituted the theme of this paper.

[14] L. M. R. Rutten, "Frequency and periodicity of orogenetic movements," *Bull. Geol. Soc. Am. 60* (1949), 1769.

[15] A. Holmes, *Principles of Physical Geology* (New York, 1946), p. 401.

[16] R. A. Sonder, "Discussion of 'Shear patterns of the earth's crust' by F. A. Vening Meinesz," *Trans. Am. Geophys. Union 28* (1947), 939–945.

[17] J. T. Wilson, "Some major structures of the Canadian Shield," *Trans. Canadian Inst. Min. and Metal. 52* (1949), 231–242; "The origin of continents and Precambrian History," *Trans. Royal Soc. Canada 43* [3], 157–184; "Recent applications of geophysical methods to the study of the Canadian Shield," *Trans. Am. Geophys. Union 31* (1950), 101–114.

[18] W. H. Bucher, "Megatectonics and geophysics," *Trans. Am. Geophys. Union 31* (1950), 495–507; "The crust of the earth," *Sci. Am. 182* (1950), 32–41.

# GRIGGS David Tressel Griggs (1911–    ), American geophysicist, received the degrees of A.B. in 1932 and A.M. in 1933 from Ohio State University and was a member of the Society of Fellows at Harvard University from 1934 to 1941. During the Second World War he served as a civilian consultant in the U.S. Army and since 1958 he has been Professor of Geophysics at the University of California in Los Angeles. Much of his research has pertained to the deformation of rocks under high pressure, and in the paper excerpted here he presented the results of one of his important pioneer studies of the behavior of crystalline rocks when stressed under confining pressures.

## EXPERIMENTAL FLOW OF ROCKS UNDER CONDITIONS FAVORING RECRYSTALLIZATION *

. . . The materials with which this paper is concerned are the compact crystalline rocks and not loosely consolidated sediments—crystalline aggregates in constitution, not weakly cemented discrete particles. The mechanisms of flow in crystalline aggregates may be classified in three general categories:

1. Cataclasis—deformation characterized by mechanical granulation.
2. Gliding—intragranular twin- or translation-gliding dominant, with secondary intergranular adjustment consequent on the change of grain shape resulting from intragranular motion.
3. Recrystallization—deformation by molecular rearrangement through the medium of solutions, local melting, or solid diffusion; intergranular motion dominant.

The relative importance of each of the three mechanisms of flow has been the subject of violent controversy for decades. The evidence presented for each viewpoint has been largely that of detailed study of rock fabrics—first megascopically, then with simple microanalysis, and more recently with the revolutionary statistical microscopic methods of Sander and Schmidt.

The controversy about mechanism of flow has hinged on the question of whether mineral orientation in rocks is developed by shearing, which aligns grains and glide-planes in the shear planes, or by recrystallization, forming flow cleavage by the growth of crystals perpendicular to the direction of maximum compression. In partial reconciliation of the various viewpoints, the concept of zones of fracture and flow was adopted, with the result that one could insure his preferred mechanism by proper choice of the hypothetical environment in which the deformation was supposed to have occurred.

Petrofabric analysis has brought a wealth of objective data bearing

*From *Geological Society of America Bulletin 51* (1940), 1001–1022.

on the problem. Interpretation has lagged far behind this accumulation of data, however, for the reason that the mechanism of rock deformation is largely unknown. In the last analysis, every interpretation of a fabric diagram depends upon hypotheses of mineral orientation in part analytical and in part developed from analogies with the fabrics of deformed metal aggregates.

Insofar as interpretation depends on observed geologic structures, it may be said conservatively that the field data are not wholly satisfactory. A large portion of the most detailed petrofabric analysis has been done in the Eastern Alps, where, to say the least, the major structure is uncertain. It is to be hoped that detailed analyses will be made in areas in which a simple geologic structure is well known in three dimensions—as, for example, in highly developed mining camps—to show the relation between the mineral orientations developed and the structure.

The analytical part of the interpretation rests largely on the assumption that rock cleavage is the result of shearing and that some crystal vectors will be oriented in the shear planes. It is possible to get a considerable amount of internal evidence by comparison of the fabrics of the various mineral constituents of the rock, and this method has been used to derive several hypothetical mechanisms of crystal deformation— twin- and translation-glide planes which have yet to be demonstrated in the laboratory. Because of the complexity of the structures and the geological history of the areas in which these studies have been made, all these interpretations rest on assumptions which are difficult to verify.

Insofar as the interpretation of fabrics is based on analogy with the behavior of crystalline metal aggregates, one must consider the justification of such analogies. Rock deformation superficially seems to have much in common with the deformation of metals. They both exhibit twin- and translation-gliding; they both deform by recrystallization. Other analogous physical properties are work-hardening, elastic flow, and creep. On the other hand, the atomic bonding of the metal crystals is very different from that of the rock-forming minerals, and the rules relating atomic structure to deformation developed for some metals do not hold for rock minerals. Metals readily recrystallize in the dry state when a certain critical temperature is exceeded, but similar recrystallization has not been produced on an observable scale in the rock-forming minerals with which the writer has experimented. It seems necessary that the latter be in contact with solutions.

It is to be hoped that laboratory experimentation on the deformation of rocks will show how far the analogies with metal behavior are applicable to the interpretation of rock fabrics and in what respects it is necessary to develop new laws of flow. The experiments described in the present paper strongly indicate that, unlike the deformation of metals, solution and recrystallization play an important role in rock deformation. Goranson suggests, however, that similar thermodynamic equations describe the dry flow of metals and the recrystallization flow of rocks. . . .

* * * * *

One of the characteristics of the behavior of alabaster under these conditions of creep [the slow deformation under small stresses acting over long periods of time] which has important applications to geology is the tendency of the specimen to fracture under a small stress that has been acting for a long period of time. This behavior was contrary to the writer's expectations, which were that the effect of solution and recrystallization under stress would be to dissolve material at the points of stress concentration and thus relieve the localized stresses inevitable in any crystalline aggregate. This would have the effect of rendering the stress distribution more homogeneous throughout the specimen, and consequently it was expected that under these conditions the material would be able to support a higher differential stress than in the dry state, instead of being much weaker.

As creep passes into the third stage and the creep rate increases, it appears that there is gradual loss of cohesion in the specimen, until finally complete separation occurs, producing sudden rupture very similar to normal breaking tests in the testing machine. It would seem that the increase in creep rate reflects the first stage in rupture, namely the beginning of localization of deformation along the surfaces which later develop into the surfaces of rupture, so we may say that incipient fracture occurs at the point of inflection where the creep rate begins to increase. Curiously enough, incipient fracture so defined is observed to occur at approximately the same amount of shortening, regardless of the stress or rate of creep. . . . It may be an important factor in the development of fracture cleavage simultaneously with flow cleavage. Thus it may be possible to get both flow cleavage and fracture cleavage in the same region by developing flow cleavage in those layers where the amount of deformation is below the critical value for fracture, and fracture cleavage where the deformation exceeds the critical value.

Another application of the principles illustrated in this flow may be made to rock fracture in earthquakes or in mine bursts. It might be expected, if deformation preceding rock fracture in these instances could be observed by geodetic or strain gage measurements, that the velocity of deformation would follow some such relationship as that shown in these creep experiments, namely an initial decrease in rate of deformation, followed by a period of more or less constant velocity and finally a period of increasing velocity. If such were the case, then it might be possible to develop criteria by which rock fracture could be predicted and some of the disastrous consequences avoided. Such prediction is possible in the case of laboratory creep experiments, and it does not seem beyond the realm of possibility that it may be developed for these other types of delayed fracture.

·  ·  ·  ·  ·

We have seen that high confining pressures may cause some rocks to flow with the production of textures resembling some of those found in nature. Pressure alone, however, does not reproduce all the conditions of rock flow in nature. It causes the strength to increase to values which seem too high to be attained by differential forces within the earth's crust. Moreover, it does not produce flow in quartz, as we have reason to believe occurs in nature. Because pressure alone has been insufficient, we must excerise great caution in applying the principles of deformation derived from high-pressure experiments to the deformation of rocks in the earth's crust. This is particularly true of the field of structural petrology, where one might conclude that mineral orientation produced under high pressure in the laboratory must be developed by processes similar to those which produce mineral orientation in nature.

Preliminary experiments indicate that temperature alone produces unimportant effects on deformation of rocks, unlike the metals, which change their properties markedly as the temperature is raised.

Creep tests show that the flow of limestone loaded to 1400 kg/cm$^2$ is so slow that the deformation would be negligible even if continued at this rate for millions of years.

When, however, conditions of testing are such that solution and recrystallization may occur, the observed characteristics of rock flow are entirely different. In marble, it is possible to produce deformation without the high development of mechanical twinning which seems to provide the mechanism of plastic deformation when the marble is deformed dry. In alabaster, where an inconsequential amount of deformation may be produced when the specimen is dry, the same specimen wet will flow at a relatively rapid rate.

It has been possible in the tests on alabaster to establish two principles of flow which may be of general application: (1) Fracture occurs after a certain amount of deformation, over a wide range of stress. (2) The rate of flow depends on the stress in a manner entirely different from ordinary viscosity. Thus, the logarithm of the velocity of deformation is proportional to the stress, so that as the stress is increased, the rate of flow increases exponentially.

The goal of experimental investigation of rock deformation is the simultaneous attainment of all the conditions of environment which prevail in nature. The method of the experimenter is to investigate the effects of each variable separately and then their joint effect. Previous work has dealt with the effects of high confining pressure, high temperature, and varying velocities, together with some combinations of these variables. The present paper adds experiments which illustrate the effects of solutions, combined with varying differential stresses, consequently varying velocities, and with confining pressure. The step remaining before we may say that the field has been covered in a reconnaissance way is the addition of high temperature to these systems. . . .

# FAIRBRIDGE Rhodes Whitmore Fairbridge (1914–    ),
Australian-American geologist, received the degrees of B.A. from Queen's University (Australia) in 1936, B.S. from Oxford University in 1940, and D.Sc. from the University of Western Australia in 1944. From 1938 to 1941 he was a field geologist with the Iraq Petroleum Company, and after serving in the Royal Australian Air Force from 1942 to 1946 he was Lecturer on Geology at the University of Western Australia until 1953. For two academic years, 1953–55, he was Associate Professor of Geology at the University of Illinois, and since 1955 he has been Professor of Geology at Columbia University. His principal interests are in the areas of sedimentation, tectonics, and geomorphology. Fully aware of the importance of fossil coral reefs as potential reservoir rocks for petroleum, he presented in the paper excerpted here the results of a thorough investigation of modern Australian reefs.

## RECENT AND PLEISTOCENE
## CORAL REEFS OF AUSTRALIA*

### ABSTRACT

The contemporary and Pleistocene coral reefs of the Australian shelf regions illustrate reef development in a relatively stable epicontinental environment—the most common facies in geology. All reef forms—fringing, barrier, atoll, and platform reefs—and five varieties of coral island are found here. The vertical distribution of corals is controlled mainly

*From *Journal of Geology* 58 (1950), 330–401.

by light, a function of turbidity, and the areal distribution mainly by temperature (minimum is about 18° C average for the coldest month). The shape of coral reefs is generally controlled by wind, wave, and current, although complex forms due to old geomorphologic or structural controls later modified by wind, etc., are also common. Normally, a small reef patch, in a region of a single dominant wind and current, will grow into a horseshoe form, then to an atoll, and will eventually fill up to become a large platform. Coral islands are due either to accumulation of sand or shingle, in which case they tend to have an oval or streamlined shape, or to a Recent eustatic drop in sea level, leading to emerged coral limestones that tend to be eroded into irregular scalloped patterns. "Negroheads" may be formed by such erosion and by jetsam-like accretion on the reef margin.

Reef borings and structural and geomorphologic features show that ecologic, tectonic, and eustatic factors may all play a part in reef development. The reality of Pleistocene-Recent eustatic oscillations is proved on geological and physiographic grounds, regardless of coral reefs. Most of the reefs in the Australian area are believed to have grown up from initial coastal fringing reefs during eustatic lows, but the foundations of many of the deeper reefs (in the Great Barrier Reef and on the outer Sahul Shelf) must have subsided tectonically. Physiographic evidence shows that an antecedent platform (a continental shelf) existed prior to the main development of the reefs.

Sedimentation is extremely rapid in the enclosed Great Barrier Reef lagoon but is slow on the exposed northern and western shelves. In both living and ancient reefs the proportion of actual colonial corals grown *in situ* is extremely small in relation to the enormous quantities of "coralline" sedimentary debris. The ratio of reef structures to areas of "normal" shelf sedimentation, even in the most prolific coral areas, is also very small. The thickness of reef structures in the Great Barrier Reef lagoon has been proved by boring not to exceed 500 feet. Physiographic evidence shows that most of the near-shore reefs are not more than 60 feet thick. Similar evidence shows that in extreme marginal areas (which probably underwent Quaternary subsidence) certain reefs may exceed 1,500 feet in thickness (e.g., on the outer Sahul Shelf).

The Great Barrier Reef borings and those of Funafuti, Bikini, etc., show that tectonic subsidence was fairly rapid in all of them. Concentrations of $MgCO_3$ of about 5–16 per cent are evidence of stillstands; lower percentages are evidence of rapid submergence. Submarine dolomite formation requires reducing conditions—an environment in the closed atoll ring of Funafuti but absent in the Barrier Reef. Lack of dolomite in Queensland borings is thus not surprising.

412

## Conclusions

1. Reefs of the shelf have been divided into four principal types based on form: fringing, barrier, atoll, and platform. These terms have no genetic implication.

2. Five main types of coral island are distinguished: unvegetated sand cay; stable, vegetated sand cay; shingle cay; sand cay with shingle ridges or "ramparts" on the reef platform; coral islands with partly eroded core of older emergent coral limestone (see also conclusions 5 and 6).

3. The shape of reefs is controlled principally by winds, waves, and currents. Several stages of reef evolution are recognized. Stage 1 is the initial reef patch; stage 2, crescentic or horseshoe patch. Following these stages the larger and smaller types develop differently. Stage 3A (larger) is the semiatoll; stage 3B (smaller) is a horsehoof-shaped reef. Stage 4A of the larger reef is a complete atoll, which is followed by stage 5A, an infilled platform reef. Stage 4B, or end-stage of the smaller reef, is a small, oval, reef platform.

The reef shape is influenced also by old geomorphologic and structural features. A fringing reef, for example, may be initiated along a shore line when the sea level is lower than today. Reefs may follow a submerged fault scarp or ranges of drowned hills. The Outer Barrier Reef (in the northern sector) exhibits both structural and geomorphological controls, but the curving wings at the extremities of each ribbon-like section of the reef are due to wind and current control.

4. Coral islands on the Australian shelves may be explained in either of two ways: (a) By accumulation of sand or coral shingle under wave action, to form cays. The lighter sand forms a bank at the leeward extremity of the reef-flat and eventually a sand cay, whereas coral shingle is thrown up only a short distance by waves on the windward side to form shingle beach ridges, ramparts, or in a group, a shingle cay. (b) By a eustatic drop in sea level, exposing older coral reefs. Since the mid-Recent high sea level, about 10 feet above the present level, some four thousand years ago, there have been three successive drops in sea level, the first to 5 feet, the second to 2 feet, and the third to the present stand. Coral reefs formed during each of these stable periods now form the nucleus of many coral islands. Still older coral limestones (Pleistocene) are found in the cores of the Abrolhos Islands.

5. Coral islands due to accumulation are generally rounded or oval in shape, "streamlined," even though they periodically undergo erosion. Those produced by a eustatic drop in sea level possess a scalloped, irregular outline and generally undergo rapid erosion except where they are protected by new shingle ridges, etc.

6. "Negroheads," isolated coral boulders of large dimensions on reef margins have been thrown up in some places from the reef margin by storms, and in others they are due to erosion *in situ* of emerged coral limestone terraces and islets.

7. The distribution of the coral reefs around the Australian continental shelves cannot be explained by ecologic factors alone. Except in shallow, favored areas, coral reefs are not growing up from the floor of the shelf today. The platform, atoll, and barrier types of reefs, therefore, require some change of sea level. The changes may have been the eustatic swing that occurred during the Pleistocene and Recent epochs; but those reefs rising from depths exceeding 300 feet must be related to tectonic movements of the shelf itself. An adequate account of reef distribution and evolution requires consideration of ecologic factors, eustatic factors, and tectonic factors—altogether and *not* singly.

8. Fringing reefs can be explained in ecologic terms. They are common on northern shores but are rare elsewhere; on the southern part of the Queensland Shelf this is probably due to the excessive rainfall and sediment, around the Gulf of Carpentaria because of rivers and sediment, along the Eighty Mile Beach and many sections of the western coast because of sandy bottom, lee shore, and poor nutrients. Most fringing reefs show an inner, raised platform, a mid-Recent eustatic terrace, commonly covered with sediment and in part with mangroves.

9. The inner reefs (small patch reefs, island reefs, platform reefs, and the few shelf atolls of the Great Barrier Reef lagoon) rise from a shelf terrace submerged 15 or 25 fathoms and therefore possess a linear arrangement. Broad open channels are found in the Barrier Reef lagoon where there are no inner reefs. The latter probably evolved from former discontinuous fringing reefs during the postglacial eustatic rises of sea level, because the water is generally too deep in the central part of the shelf for reefs to have grown up from the floor under present ecologic conditions. It is unlikely that the Great Barrier Reef lagoon will be blocked by coral growth unless sedimentation considerably reduces its depth.

10. The outer-barrier reefs of Queensland (northern sector) rise from depths of over 100 fathoms. Because this exceeds the sum of the present ecologic limits of reef growth (here about 20 fathoms) and the 50 fathoms allowed for maximum Pleistocene eustatic lowering, tectonic subsidence must have occurred. The central sector (Cairns-Townsville) shows a drowned outer barrier which suggests very rapid subsidence locally because the postglacial rise elsewhere failed to drown long sections of reef. The southern sector rises inside the 100-fathom line in all places. No coral growth may have occurred here during much of the Pleistocene because of the adverse climate. Only in the last warm stages of the Pleistocene was coral growth initiated.

11. The great atoll reefs of the Coral Sea Platform, which adjoin the outer barrier, show evidence of tectonic subsidence to as much as 6,000 feet.

12. On the Sahul and North-West shelves, several large atolls occur near the shelf margins in 200–300 fathoms of water. This depth greatly exceeds the usual estimates for eustatic rise of sea level. This fact plus the atoll forms, regional low level of the shelf edge, and various structural evidence suggest tectonic subsidence.

13. The complex atoll groups of the Houtman Abrolhos Islands on the west-coast shelf rise only from a 25-fathom shelf and require no hypothesis of subsidence. They disclose a core of old coral reef and lagoon limestones, which was heavily dissected by karst erosion during the late Pleistocene and veneered by reefs and coral shingle of the various mid-Recent stillstands and of the present day.

14. In the Great Barrier Reef lagoon, sedimentation is extremely rapid. The deposits are mainly terrigenous, although big lenses of coral and coral debris are intercalated in them. In the borings at Michaelmas Cay and Heron Island, "Recent" reef corals (with other "Recent" fossils) go down over 400 and 500 feet, respectively. Because the present shelf floor is only 90–150 feet below the surface, an accumulation of 300–400 feet of sediment during the last hundred thousand years seems probable. The absence of submarine valleys across the shelf is another indication of rapid filling by postglacial sediments. The rapid accumulation is attributed to the retaining effects of the outer-reef barrier.

15. Slow or even suspended terrigenous sedimentation characterizes the open-shelf areas (Arafura, Sahul, North-West, and West Coast shelves). Glauconites are common; coral materials are rare. The small outcrop of the granite basement on the Aroe Islands, near the outer edge of the Arafura shelf, suggests only a thin covering of Tertiary and Quaternary sediments.

16. Even in the regions of most vigorous reef growth, the proportion of reef sediments to terrigenous material is small. In the reefs proper, the proportion of true coral grown *in situ* to coraligenous sedimentary debris and other associated organogenic material is small. The so-called "coral" sands generally contain less than one-third coral debris.

17. The calcium carbonate muds in the borings of both lagoons are in part fine clastics and in part true precipitates.

18. The massive coral growths are a rough framework in and around which loose and uncompacted clastic calcareous sediments accumulate. In fringing reefs this material accumulates on the seaward side, in barrier reefs mainly on the inner side; and in atolls it fills the interior and accumulates in a cone to leeward of the reef. Most platform reefs probably originated in the same way as barriers and atolls did during pro-

gressive submergence. The circular or ovoid ones exhibit what appears to be a filled-in lagoonal core.

19. Sedimentation, modern or Pleistocene, influences the distribution and growth of reefs in only a secondary way. Reef growth is greatest in the Great Barrier Reef lagoon, where sedimentation is greatest, whereas in areas of minimum sedimentation, like the Sahul Shelf, coral reefs are comparatively rare.

20. Great Barrier Reef borings show not less than 200 feet of loose glauconitic quartz sands (Pleistocene) beneath the 400–500 feet of "Recent" coral material.

21. Calcareous beach rock, an intertidal deposit, occurs in the deepest boring, some 700 feet below sea level. Foraminifera and Mollusca in these sands are all of living types and cannot be older than Pleistocene.

22. Tectonic subsidence in the Great Barrier Reef area is probable. If the beach rock at 700 feet (Heron Island boring) was formed during a Pleistocene low sea level (minimum generally taken as 300 feet), then 400 feet of subsidence has taken place since. If the 400–450-foot level in the Michaelmas Cay boring corresponds to the 450–500-foot level in the Heron Island hole, then subsidence has been 50–100 feet greater in the latter.

23. The borings of Florida and other continental shelves also show terrigenous (mainly quartz) sands, likewise overlain by several hundred feet of reef rock, loose coralline debris, and foraminiferal sands. The borings on Funafuti, Bikini, and other oceanic atolls show less similarity. Little or no terrigenous material and thicker Quaternary coral deposits suggest more rapid subsidence.

24. No dolomite is found in any Australian reef borings or emerged coral reefs. Submarine dolomite formation is now thought to take place in closed lagoons under reducing conditions and increased $CO_2$ pressure, an environment almost totally absent from the Australian region. The only dolomite in the Quaternary rocks of Australia consists of blocks enclosed in volcanics on Murray Island (Haddon, 1894). Perhaps the northern section of the Great Barrier Reef may rest on a basement older than, or different from, that of the southern sector.

25. Magnesium carbonate enrichment, organic and inorganic, takes place in the intertidal belt. In borings on the Barrier Reef and at Bikini, Funafuti, etc., a sharp rise in $MgCO_3$ from a normal of about 1–5 per cent to 5–16 per cent is marked by beach-rock layers, indicating stillstands, either tectonic or eustatic. Low $MgCO_3$ indicates rapid change of sea level, whereas higher figures suggest relative stability.

26. Aragonite is found in the Great Barrier Reef borings, as in Funafuti, in the upper 50–100 feet, below which it is almost completely leached

out and converted to calcite. This leaching is attributed to subaerial exposure during the Pleistocene lowering of sea level. At 400 feet in Michaelmas Cay and 500 feet in the Heron Island boring, the aragonite appears, suggesting that the sections below these levels were not exposed to late Pleistocene subaerial erosion. The failure of aragonite to reappear in the Funafuti boring implies that, in this rapidly subsiding atoll, the whole section was exposed progressively to repeated exposures during the Pleistocene lows.

27. Neither Great Barrier Reef boring reached hard basement. An antecedent platform is probable. Its character is revealed on various continental islands, where granite and metamorphic rocks of Paleozoic or greater age are exposed. The basement is generally deeply buried by sediment, not less than 700 feet at Heron Island, and is not well known.

28. Existence of a submerged plane of erosion is demonstrated by cliffed and steep coasts, drowned drainage systems, etc. Borings in the alluvial coastal plain of the mainland show the hard floor over 100 feet below sea level in Queensland and as much as 250 feet below in New South Wales. The cutting of this erosion plane in hard rocks required a considerable period of time and could not have been done during the short periods of low sea level at the Pleistocene glacial epochs. It is correlated with the great Tertiary peneplanation of eastern Australia, which was terminated by epeirogenic warping and fracturing in late Tertiary times. During this "Kosciusko" phase (of Andrews), the eastern highlands were elevated *en bloc,* and the adjacent areas to the east subsided along major normal faults.

29. The outer margin of the continental shelf is apparently downfaulted along the entire eastern seaboard of Australia. This is demonstrated by the abruptness of the slope, by the almost rectilinear pattern, and by such structural and paleogeographic evidence as the truncation of former geosynclines, fresh-water basins, and the total absence of marine Tertiary sediment.

30. The subsided land mass ("Tasmantis" of Sussmilch and David) is partly represented by the floor of the Tasman Sea (in the south), but in the north, opposite the Queensland Shelf, it is marked by a northward-tilted block, the Coral Sea Platform, separated from the shelf by a deep graben, the Queensland Trench, while on the north it is cut off from the New Guinea–New Hebrides orogenic belt by a 2,000-fathom-deep extension of the Papuan Geosyncline, the Papuan Trough.

31. Because the continental shelf of Queensland is structurally identical with that of New South Wales, where there are no corals, the Queensland reefs cannot be thicker than the depth below sea level of the shelf basement—not that of the superficial sediments, which the borings have

shown may exceed 600 feet in thickness. Borings have not shown reefs here to exceed 500 feet in thickness.

32. The glauconitic quartz sands of the lower 200 feet of the Great Barrier Reef borings are probably Pleistocene, formed in a period of coral depopulation. This conclusion is supported by living species throughout the fossil record in the borings.

33. The thickness and character of the Pleistocene coral reefs, if any, in the more tropical belts of Australia are unknown.

34. The hard basement of the northern shelf areas is thought to be fairly shallow in places (e.g., small outcrop of granite in Aroe Islands) but is probably deeper off the basins of the mainland. Subsidence seems to be in progress opposite the mobile East Indian arcs, resulting in atolls and a drowned barrier reef which may exceed 1,500 feet in thickness.

35. The hard basement of the western shelf also appears to be shallow. The Abrolhos Islands apparently stand on the margin of an uptilted fault block of pre-Cambrian rocks.

36. From the stratigraphic viewpoint, it is seen that coral reefs may grow even in so-called "stable" shelf environments. Shallow, thin-bedded reefs develop laterally along immense stretches of coastline under conditions of tectonic and eustatic stability, whereas poorly bedded and massive reefs, of limited lateral extent but of considerable thickness, develop under unstable tectonic and eustatic conditions.

37. The Australian shelf reefs require the utilization, at least of some parts, of (a) the subsidence theory promulgated by Darwin, Dana, and Davis, (b) the antecedent-platform theory as set forth by Wharton, Agassiz, Andrews, Vaughan, Hoffmeister and Ladd, and (c) the glacial-control theory of Penck, Daly, and others.

# GRAHAM John Warren Graham (1918    ), American geologist
and geophysicist, received his Ph.D. degree from Johns Hopkins University in 1949 and was a member of the staff of the Department of Terrestrial Magnetism, Carnegie Institution, from 1947 to 1958. Since then he has been associated with the Woods Hole Oceanographic Institution. His study of remanent magnetism in sedimentary rocks, excerpted here, established a firm foundation for the burgeoning research of later years in that sector of geophysics and gave structural geologists a new tool with which to do their work.

## THE STABILITY AND SIGNIFICANCE OF MAGNETISM IN SEDIMENTARY ROCKS*

. . . Laboratory studies, and observations of the direction of magnetization (often referred to hereafter as the polarization or magnetization)

*From *Journal of Geophysical Research* 54 (1949), 131–167.

of modern sediments, have led to the conclusion that a fine-grained sediment bearing finely divided magnetic particles may receive a polarization at the time of deposition. In addition to factors that normally control the positions assumed by all particles on coming to rest on the bottom (hydrodynamic forces, bottom character, Brownian movement, colloidal phenomena, etc.), magnetic particles in an appropriate size-range are preferentially oriented by the earth's magnetic field to an extent necessary to give to the sediment a measurable polarization that is substantially coincident with the magnetic field prevailing at the site of deposition. It is thought probable that . . . at least some (possibly many) sedimentary rocks received their initial magnetizations in this manner. . . .

It was recognized that if this pattern of primary magnetization could be shown to be permanent, a property of considerable interest would be at hand. It should be possible then to determine how the direction of the earth's magnetic field has varied during geologic time and, if the pattern were not obliterated by folding and thrusting, the property could be useful in the solution of structural problems.

. . . . . .

This study was undertaken to investigate whether sedimentary rocks can retain without change their directions of remanent magnetization through long periods of geologic time. . . .

Investigations of stability were carried out in field work extending over large areas and on rocks extending back to the Silurian. A discovery was made of new evidence which is considered satisfactory proof that the magnetizations in certain rocks have remained permanent over periods ranging from 15,000 years to over 200,000,000 years. Conflicting evidence and views on this point have appeared in the literature over the past fifty years, but these have been based on inadequate technical methods.

Indications have been found of a regional similarity in the magnetization of a Silurian formation over a moderate distance (of the order of 50 miles before the folding). This uniformity cannot be reasonably accounted for by remagnetization processes arising from electrical current systems or by any process except the growth of magnetic minerals in a regionally uniform magnetic field (earth's magnetic field) prior to the folding, or by the original deposition of magnetic particles in the earth's magnetic field.

One method of determination has been to observe the magnetization in a bed that long ago was deformed in such a way that the polarizations at various points in the bed became oriented in different directions relative to one another and to the direction of the earth's field. If the polarizations in such a bed are magnetically unstable, they will shift toward parallelism with one another throughout the deformed bed. If the polarizations are stable, and are not shifted by plastic-flow processes, they will maintain a constant relationship to the bedding, during and after deformation, such that when the bed is reconstructed to its original flat condition the polarizations will once again become parallel.

An alternate procedure has been to look for random polarizations in beds that were laid down in a random manner. The premise is that, if in a conglomerate, for example, all the pebbles have the same direction of magnetization, then these polarizations must be regarded as ones that were acquired after the pebbles became imbedded; but if the polarizations in the pebbles are dispersed, stability of the magnetization of each pebble is indicated.

Studies in Pleistocene clays that were folded shortly after their deposition show, within limits of error which appear reasonable for disturbed beds, that for each degree the beds were tilted in the deformation, the polarizations on the average were tilted correspondingly. This fact indicates that the polarizations have remained largely unchanged, and that in the deformation, shearing of the beds was not appreciable. On restoring the beds to the flat condition, the polarizations did not become perfectly parallel because of irregularities in the folding and the initial magnetization. . . .

Pebbles of a Miocene lake-deposited sediment imbedded in a conglomerate were found to have scattered polarizations. On the other hand, the polarizations in the undisturbed source beds of these pebbles were found to cluster together on the projection plot. The conclusions are reached that the polarizations of the pebbles and the lake beds have remained stable since the time of deposition, and that the cluster of directions of magnetization represents the approximate direction of the earth's magnetic field in Miocene time. A coarse-grained Eocene sandstone was found to have scattered polarizations. Tests demonstrate that this distribution of the polarizations could be the result of disturbing conditions during deposition. The conclusion is reached that, although the polarizations have no relation to the earth's field in Eocene time, they nevertheless have remained stable.

The polarizations in a Silurian bed, folded near the end of the Paleozoic era, are found to maintain systematic angular relationships to the bedding throughout a severe fold. When the bed is reconstructed to its flat condition, the polarizations all become approximately parallel, indicating that they have not changed since the folding 200 million years ago. This behavior of the polarizations and field evidence show that shearing in these beds during folding was slight.

At a distance of 32 miles from the exposure where stability in the Silurian beds was demonstrated, folds in the same formation give comparable results, except in the uppermost layers.

Studies in a closely folded Silurian limestone were inconclusive. The pattern of polarizations does not conform to the folding, and the cause has not been determined. The possibilities are considered that either true magnetic instability or shearing and extruding processes during deformation were responsible for the observed pattern.

The chief contribution here presented is evidence of a new kind for accepting the conclusion that the direction of the earth's magnetic field, as it existed in remote geologic time, is preserved in certain [sedimentary] rocks which can be identified as satisfactory for this purpose. . . .

This demonstration may provide a basis for geological studies of folding and deformation processes, as well as other new evidence bearing on the history of the earth.

# GUIDE TO SUBJECT MATTER
# INDEX

# GUIDE TO SUBJECT MATTER

The more significant contributions to certain important phases of geological science are here listed in the chronological order of the dates of publication.

# INDEX